Laboratory Exercises in
General Biology

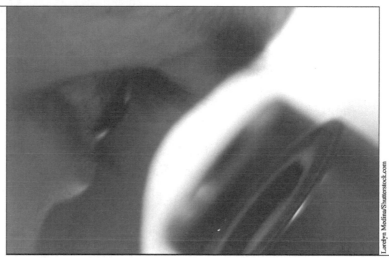

Biology Department Faculty

MACOMB COMMUNITY COLLEGE

Eleventh Edition

macmillan learning
curriculum solutions

Printed in the United States of America

10 9 8 7 6 5 4 3 2 1

ISBN 978-1-5339-2338-7

Macmillan Learning Curriculum Solutions
14903 Pilot Drive
Plymouth, MI 48170
www.macmillanlearning.com

MCC-BIO 2338-7 F20

Sustainability
Hayden-McNeil/Macmillan Learning Curriculum Solutions is proud to be a part of the larger sustainability initiative of Macmillan, our parent company. Macmillan has a goal to reduce its carbon emissions by 65% by 2020 from our 2010 baseline. Additionally, paper purchased must adhere to the Macmillan USA Paper Sourcing and Use Policy.

Hayden-McNeil partners with printers that use paper that is consistent with the environmental goals and values of Macmillan USA. This includes using paper certified by the Forest Stewardship Council (FSC), Sustainable Forestry Initiative (SFI), and/or the Programme for the Endorsement of Forest Certification (PEFC). We also offer paper with varying percentages of post-consumer waste as well as a 100% recycled stock. Additionally, Hayden-McNeil Custom Digital provides authors with the opportunity to convert print products to a digital format to use no paper at all. Visit http://sustainability.macmillan.com to learn more.

Table of Contents

BIOLOGY 1000

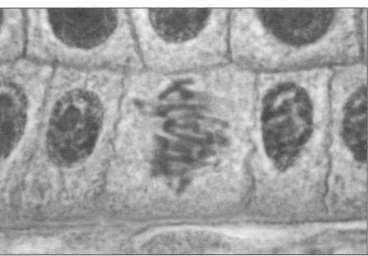

PREFACE

The exercises contained in this manual are intended to fulfill several functions. First, they are designed to develop basic laboratory skills that will be of service to you in the future. Secondly, these exercises will illustrate as well as amplify certain basic principles that form the foundation of this course. These experiments are designed to develop your science awareness based upon observation and experimentation. Lastly, experiments have been designed to increase your enjoyment of the laboratory experience while still learning the skills and principles.

Laboratory Preparation

Your chances of meeting these goals will be greatly enhanced if you follow these suggestions. **Carefully read through each exercise prior to class**. Listen attentively to your laboratory instructor's directions. Carefully carry out your work, and neatly record your observations. Attend each and every scheduled laboratory session.

Laboratory Review

Throughout most laboratory exercises, there are questions that will help determine if you have understood the experiment and achieved the objectives for that exercise. Always complete these questions, and ask your instructor for assistance if necessary.

INSTRUCTIONS FOR COMPLETING DATA SHEETS

Always

1. Use a pencil to fill out data sheets.
2. Print all information.
3. Write your name and the date that the experiment was carried out.
4. Record all required data.
5. Be accurate with drawings.
6. *Label* drawings:
   a. Use a ruler to make labeling lines.
   b. Keep labeling lines parallel to the top or bottom of the page.
   c. Never cross labeling lines.
   d. Write legibly.
7. Double-check numerical data.
8. BE NEAT!

Never

1. Record extraneous information.
2. Doodle, take notes, or otherwise deface the data sheets.
3. Tear, fold, crease, etc., data sheets.
4. Color drawings or graphs unless specifically told to do so.

STUDENT LABORATORY POLICIES AND PROCEDURES

1. *Never work alone* in the laboratory.

   Students should select lab partners who can help them in case of an emergency.

2. Eye protection:

   a. Chemical operations should be carried out, when possible, below the eye level.

   b. It is recommended that students wear safety goggles in the laboratory, especially when handling chemicals.

   c. Eyewash bottles are located at the rear of the laboratory. If chemicals are splashed in eye(s)—*do not rub eyes*—immediately rinse the eye. Place eye directly in the stream from the bottle with the affected eye below the unaffected eye; a partner or instructor should hold the injured eye(s) open. Flush eye(s) for at least 15 minutes.

   d. Tampering with safety equipment is strictly prohibited.

3. Protective clothing:

   a. It is recommended that students wear a lab coat, but they are not required.

   b. Students must wear shoes that cover the whole foot.

   c. It is recommended that shorts not be worn in any laboratory. Arms and legs should be covered.

   d. Long and/or loose flowing hair should be secured behind the head and shoulders.

   e. Avoid fuzzy sweaters, highly flammable clothing (shirt, blouse, or sweaters), loose ribbons, and neckties (use clasps to hold in place).

4. Emergency safety measures:

   a. Personal injuries:

      Report all injuries or illnesses immediately to your instructor and/or Campus Police at **911**.

   b. Chemical spills:

      Report all spills to your instructor. Spill cleanup kits are located in B 309. The laboratory supervisor or instructor should clean up spills whenever possible, provided that the spill is minor. Campus Police must be contacted in case of a major chemical spill.

   c. Fire:

      i. In case of fire, leave the laboratory area and sound the alarm (pull box).

      ii. Students who catch on fire should STOP moving, DROP on the floor, and ROLL until the fire has been put out. Remember: **STOP, DROP, and ROLL. Do *not* run.**

      iii. Fire extinguishers:

         Do *not* operate fire extinguishers unless you are absolutely sure of the proper operating procedures.

         Know the location of the fire extinguishers.

         If the fire is large enough to require a fire extinguisher, students should leave the laboratory in an orderly fashion and exit the building.

5. General safety measures:

   a. **Eating and drinking are prohibited in all biology laboratories.** Absolutely no food or beverages are to be brought into laboratories unless sealed and left inside book bags. Under no circumstances is any piece of lab equipment to be placed in the mouth. Do not put on any lipstick or chapstick in the lab. Do not put pens or pencils that have been on the lab bench in your mouth.

   b. Plan your lab work ahead, noting any special instructions and possible danger. Work carefully and cooperatively to assist fellow students.

   c. Do not remove equipment, media, models, chemicals, or glassware from the lab. The performance of unauthorized experiments is strictly forbidden.

   d. Clothes (coats, jackets, sweaters, hats, etc.) and bags must not be placed on laboratory tables or the floor. Use coat racks and shelves.

   e. Materials and equipment taken out of cabinets, tables, or carts must have all parts intact when returned to the same location from which they were taken.

   f. Use only wood pointers or rulers to point out parts on models, bones, and microscopes—never pen or pencil.

   g. Always disinfect tables before and after use.

   h. Close all cabinets and drawers after use. Chairs and stools should be pushed under the bench. Wind cords around equipment before putting it away. (No cords should be sticking out of cupboards when equipment is put away.)

   i. Wash hands thoroughly before leaving the lab.

6. Note special instructions for the following:

   a. **Housekeeping**: In order to keep unsafe chemicals and/or microbes from contaminating your clothes, body, or experiment, proper housekeeping in work areas (including cleaning of balances, supply areas, and benchtops) is mandatory. Immediate clean up of spills is imperative.

   b. **Chemicals**: Read chemical labels very carefully. Read them three times—when you pick it up, just before use, and after you have finished. Never return unused reagents to the reagent bottle. Take only what you actually need, and do not contaminate reagents. Always replace covers on all chemicals. Tighten all caps to avoid spills or injury.

   c. **Disposal of material**: Labeled containers are available for waste material. Your instructor will point out the necessary containers for each lab.

   d. To avoid injury, all broken glassware must be swept up immediately and placed in the Broken Glass Container. These are located at the front of every laboratory. Do *not* put broken glass in the waste paper baskets. Conversely, do not put trash (including paper towels) in the Broken Glass Container.

   e. Turn off Bunsen burners or other heat sources when not in use.

f. Slides: Prepared slides must be put back on the correct tray. *Use lens-cleaning paper only to wipe prepared slides.* Clean, dry, and return blank slides to slide box. Dispose of used coverslips in Broken Glass Container.

g. Women who are pregnant or may become pregnant should discuss the potential risk of dissection and exposure to preservatives or chemicals with their obstetricians. Material Safety Data Sheets (MSDS) are available.

h. When removing a plug from an electrical outlet, grasp and pull the plug, *not* the wire.

i. Microscopes: Proper use and care of the microscope is an integral part of every biology lab. You will be assigned a microscope for use throughout the semester. It is imperative that you take proper care of your microscope by following the rules listed below.

    i.   Always wrap the power cord around the arm of the microscope.

    ii.   Clean lenses. **Use *only* lens cleaning paper.**

    iii. Clean and lower the stage. *Never* leave slides on the stage.

    iv.   The **scanning objective** (4×) must be in working position.

    v.   The light (illuminator) must be turned off before unplugging the microscope.

    vi.   The microscope must be put back in its assigned cabinet with the arm facing out.

    vii. Microscopes must be put away such that the cabinet can be closed (that is, no wires hanging out, etc.).

7. Emergency telephone numbers:

    Telephones are located in all laboratories. Telephone numbers are posted by the telephones as well as below:

EMERGENCY	
Campus Police	911
	7135 (non-emergency)
Laboratory Supervisor	3449
Arts and Sciences Office	7106

LAB SAFETY AGREEMENT

Whenever I am in the laboratory, I will use good safety practices and behave in an orderly manner. I agree to follow all of the safety precautions listed below while participating in laboratory activities. If I do not comply with these requirements, I will not be allowed to participate in the laboratory.

1. I will wear proper clothing and footwear in the laboratory as specified by the department. I will also wear approved safety goggles or safety glasses at times and places specified by the department.

2. I know the exact location of the fume hoods, eyewash stations, fire extinguisher, fire blanket, shower, first aid kit, and telephone. I know how and when to use them.

3. I will not work in the laboratory when the instructor is not present. I will not perform any unauthorized experiments or procedures.

4. I will not eat, drink, or smoke in the laboratory or use any laboratory containers for food or drink. I will not taste, touch, or directly smell any chemical. If I need to leave the lab, I will shut down my experiment, wash my hands, and notify my instructor.

5. I will remove any materials, equipment, and personal belongings not essential to conducting the experiment from the laboratory work surface.

6. I will avoid touching hot objects. I will not use broken or cracked glassware. I will always check the label on each chemical dispensing container <u>twice</u> before using it.

7. I will dispose of all materials used in each experiment as directed by my instructor.

8. I will immediately notify my instructor of any accident or injury that occurs, no matter how minor. I will seek additional first aid or medical care at my expense if my injury requires it.

9. I will immediately notify my instructor of any spills or glassware breakage and will consult with my instructor for the appropriate method of clean-up and disposal.

10. At the end of the laboratory period, I will clean up any equipment I have used, wash my work area, help clean up the common areas, and wash my hands. *I will then follow the departmental procedure established for finishing laboratory activities.*

RELEASE OF LIABILITY

<u>Students under the age of 18 must also obtain parental agreement and release.</u>

In consideration for being allowed to participate in laboratory activities at Macomb Community College, I hereby release Macomb Community College, its trustees, and employees from all liability for any damages or costs I may incur as a consequence of bodily injury or property damage suffered as a result of participating in laboratory activities at Macomb Community College.

By signing below, I certify that I have read and understand the above Agreement and Release.

STUDENT SIGNATURE: _____ NAME (PRINT): _____

COURSE: _____ SECTION NO.: _____ DATE: _____

LABORATORY INSTRUCTOR: _____

PARENT SIGNATURE: _____ NAME (PRINT): _____

LAB SAFETY AGREEMENT

Whenever I am in the laboratory, I will use good safety practices and behave in an orderly manner. I agree to follow all of the safety precautions listed below while participating in laboratory activities. If I do not comply with these requirements, I will not be allowed to participate in the laboratory.

1. I will wear proper clothing and footwear in the laboratory as specified by the department. I will also wear approved safety goggles or safety glasses at times and places specified by the department.

2. I know the exact location of the fume hoods, eyewash stations, fire extinguisher, fire blanket, shower, first aid kit, and telephone. I know how and when to use them.

3. I will not work in the laboratory when the instructor is not present. I will not perform any unauthorized experiments or procedures.

4. I will not eat, drink, or smoke in the laboratory or use any laboratory containers for food or drink. I will not taste, touch, or directly smell any chemical. If I need to leave the lab, I will shut down my experiment, wash my hands, and notify my instructor.

5. I will remove any materials, equipment, and personal belongings not essential to conducting the experiment from the laboratory work surface.

6. I will avoid touching hot objects. I will not use broken or cracked glassware. I will always check the label on each chemical dispensing container <u>twice</u> before using it.

7. I will dispose of all materials used in each experiment as directed by my instructor.

8. I will immediately notify my instructor of any accident or injury that occurs, no matter how minor. I will seek additional first aid or medical care at my expense if my injury requires it.

9. I will immediately notify my instructor of any spills or glassware breakage and will consult with my instructor for the appropriate method of clean-up and disposal.

10. At the end of the laboratory period, I will clean up any equipment I have used, wash my work area, help clean up the common areas, and wash my hands. *I will then follow the departmental procedure established for finishing laboratory activities.*

RELEASE OF LIABILITY

<u>Students under the age of 18 must also obtain parental agreement and release.</u>

In consideration for being allowed to participate in laboratory activities at Macomb Community College, I hereby release Macomb Community College, its trustees, and employees from all liability for any damages or costs I may incur as a consequence of bodily injury or property damage suffered as a result of participating in laboratory activities at Macomb Community College.

By signing below, I certify that I have read and understand the above Agreement and Release.

STUDENT SIGNATURE: _____ NAME (PRINT): _____

COURSE: _____ SECTION NO.: _____ DATE: _____

LABORATORY INSTRUCTOR: _____

PARENT SIGNATURE: _____ NAME (PRINT): _____

The Metric System

Exercise 1

Objectives

1. List the fundamental units of length or distance, weight or mass, volume, and temperature.

2. Measure accurately using rulers, balances, graduated cylinders, and thermometers.

3. List the conversion factors, and be able to perform unit conversions between metric units.

Introduction

The metric system is the standard system of units and measurements used in all sciences, including biology, chemistry, and physics, and throughout the world.

The basic unit of length in the metric system is the meter (m) (approximately 39.37 inches), as determined by the International System of Units (SI). The gram (g) is the basic unit of mass. The basic unit of volume in the metric system is the liter (l) (equal to 1.056 quarts); 1 liter (l) is 1000 milliliters (ml).

All multiple units or subunits of the three fundamental dimensions are based on ten. Table 1.1 lists the prefix as well as the symbol and the factor for the multiple units and subunits you will be using.

Table 1.1. Metric Units of Measurement

Prefix	Symbol	Value/Factor
Kilo-	k	1×10^3 or 1000
Hecto-	h	1×10^2 or 100
Deca-	D	1×10 or 10
Unit (meter, liter, gram)		1
Deci-	d	1×10^{-1} or $1/10$
Centi-	c	1×10^{-2} or $1/100$
Milli-	m	1×10^{-3} or $1/1000$
Micro-	µ	1×10^{-6} or millionth
Nano-	n	1×10^{-9} or billionth

Part A: Measurement of Length

Materials

1. Meter sticks

2. Small metric ruler

3. Plastic pipettes

Method

1. Using a small metric ruler, measure the following line _____ to the nearest millimeter. Record the length to the nearest millimeter and make the necessary conversions to complete the data sheet.

2. Measure the length of a meter stick. Record on your data sheet.

3. Measure the length of a pipette and record on your data sheet.

4. Make the necessary conversions to complete the data sheet.

Part B: Measurement of Weight

Materials

1. Electronic balances

2. Rocks

3. Plastic box or wooden block

4. Bag of sand

5. Weigh paper or weigh boat

Method

1. Practice weighing various objects with an electronic balance.

2. You will be instructed how to use the balances and how to weigh objects with them. *Never* weigh any object directly on the metal pan or surface; instead, place the object on the available weigh paper or weigh boat.

3. Weigh objects to the nearest tenth of a gram and record on your data sheet.

4. Convert to the units indicated on the data sheet.

Part C: Measurement of Volume

Materials

1. Plastic box or wooden box

2. 10 ml graduated cylinder

3. Small beaker

4. Plastic pipette

5. Display cylinders

Method

1. Volume of a container can be calculated if the length, width, and height are measured. Measure the length, width, and height of the box.

2. Calculate the volume of the box. What is the unit of volume?

3. Obtain a 10-milliliter (ml) graduated cylinder, which has an accuracy to the nearest 0.1 ml indicated by the numbers.

4. Fill a small beaker with tap water.

5. To practice measuring volumes with the metric system, measure out 2, 4, and 7 ml of water into a graduated cylinder using a disposable pipette and water from the small beaker. When measuring with a graduated cylinder, always read the volume at the bottom of the **meniscus**.

6. Observe the graduated cylinders on display. Determine and record the volumes in milliliters and liters on the data sheet.

Part D: Measurement of Temperature

The SI unit of temperature is Kelvin (K). However, temperature is measured using either the Celsius or Fahrenheit scales. At one atmosphere of pressure, pure water freezes at 0 degrees Celsius (0 °C), which corresponds to 32 degrees Fahrenheit (32 °F) or 273 K. It boils at 100 degrees Celsius (100 °C), 212 degrees Fahrenheit (212 °F), or 373 K.

Materials

1. Temperature demonstrations

Method

1. Take the temperature of a sample of water using a thermometer, and record that temperature in degrees Celsius or degrees Fahrenheit on the data sheet.

2. Use the following formula to convert Celsius to Fahrenheit and vice versa:

$$°C = 5/9 \, (°F - 32) \text{ or } (°F - 32) ÷ 1.8$$

$$°F = (9/5 × °C) + 32 \text{ or } (1.8 × °C) + 32$$

3. Use the following formula to convert Celsius °C to Kelvin (K)

$$K = 273 + °C$$

Part E: Practice Metric System Conversions

Method

1. Complete table and temperature conversions on the data sheet. (Note: Conversions on the lab practical must be completed without a calculator or conversion table.)

The Metric System

Data Sheet 1

Name Paulina Dadura

Section

Date 1/12/21

Part A: Measurement of Length

Line		Meter Stick		Pipette	
small		*medium*		*large*	
2.3	cm	3.6	cm	6.6	cm
0.023	m	0.036	m	0.066	m
23	mm	36	mm	66	mm

Part B: Measurement of Weight

Rock		Box or Block		Bag of Sand	
0.00545	kg		kg		kg
5.45	g		g		g
5450	mg		mg		mg

Part C: Measurement of Volume

1. Volume of Plastic Box or Wooden Block

Length =	cm
Width =	cm
Height =	cm
Volume = L × W × H=	cm³

If 1 cm³ = 1 ml

Volume = _____ ml

20 drops = 0.05 mL   avg drop size

avg drop size = 1 mL / # of drops

2. Volume of Fluid in Graduated Cylinders

Unknown I	Unknown II	Unknown III	
0.03			Liters (l)
30			milliliters (ml)

Part D: Measurement of Temperature

Water Samples	°F	°C	K
1. Hot	131	55	404
2. Cold	35.6	2	308.6
3. Room temp.	73.4	23	346.4

Part E: Practice Metric System Conversions

243.5 cm	mm	
1000 g	kg	
750 ml	l	
6400 g	kg	
34 g	kg	
10 ml	µl	
0.25 ml	l	
1.6 mm	µm	
0.27 mm	µm	
55 nm	µm	
4.5 µm	nm	
8.2 l	ml	
1500 mm	cm	dm
1.00 l	ml	µl
7.9 l	ml	µl
80.8 g	mg	µg
0.33 kg	g	mg
2.5 cm	mm	µm
45 km	m	cm
95.6 km	cm	mm
4000 nm	µm	mm
1000 mm	cm	dm

Show all calculations for the following questions

Convert the following temperatures to Celsius (°C) and Kelvin (K):

a.   0 °F

b.   248 °F

c.   104 °F

Show all calculations for the following questions

d.   −14 °F

Convert the following temperatures into Fahrenheit (°F):

a.   100 °C

b.   13 K

Show all calculations for the following questions

c.   22 °C

d.   303 K

Diversity of Life

Exercise 2

Objectives

1. Define heterotroph and autotroph.

2. List distinguishing characteristics of organisms from domain Bacteria and kingdoms Protista, Fungi, Plantae, and Animalia.

3. Identify representative organisms from the Phyla Porifera, Cnidaria, Platyhelminthes, Annelida, Mollusca, Nematoda, Arthropoda, Echinodermata, and Chordata.

4. Distinguish between basic bacterial cell shapes.

5. State the importance of bacteria, protists, fungi, and plants.

Introduction

The vast collection of organisms on earth has been divided into three domains of life: Bacteria, Archaea (the prokaryotes), and the Eukarya (the eukaryotes). The Eukarya include the kingdoms: Protista, Fungi, Plantae, and Animalia.

This exercise is intended to acquaint you with the major groups of living organisms on earth. In the kingdom Animalia, which currently is subdivided into more than 30 phyla, you will be presented with nine. The means by which this will be done will involve work done in the laboratory and with the use of displays in the hall cabinets. As you conduct your lab work and view the displays, you should consult your textbook for additional material on the groups presented. Although the displays will not illustrate all of the phyla of the living world, they will draw your attention to the major phyla that you are most likely to encounter in your life.

Part A: Kingdom Eubacteria (Domain Bacteria)

This kingdom includes the bacteria and cyanobacteria. Bacteria are often classified based on their mode of nutrition and morphology. Based on nutrition, bacteria may be **heterotrophic**, meaning they rely on an outside source of nutrition. *Escherichia coli* are an example of heterotrophic bacteria. **Autotrophic** bacteria are capable of making their own nutrients using an external source of energy, like light. The cyanobacteria *Oscillatoria* are photosynthetic autotrophs. Ancient cyanobacteria are thought to have contributed the oxygen we have in our atmosphere today. Morphological classification includes the three basic bacterial shapes: bacilli or rod-shaped, cocci or round-shaped, and spirilli or spiral-shaped bacteria.

Materials

1. Demonstration microscopes showing bacterial cell types

2. Demonstration microscope of *Oscillatoria*

Method

1. Examine the slides showing the bacterial types. **Note:** These microscopes are equipped with a special objective called an oil-immersion lens that allows for higher magnification. *rod spherical basilli*

2. Draw a few representative bacterial types on your data sheet.

3. Examine the slide of *Oscillatoria*. Sketch a filament on your data sheet.

Part B: Kingdom Protista (Domain Eukarya)

The protists are a diverse group of eukaryotes that includes algae, protozoa, and slime molds. Some are autotrophic, while many are heterotrophic. The autotrophic algae form the base of the food chains in many aquatic environments. Kelp, for instance, form forests in the seas, providing food and shelter.

Materials

1. Demonstration microscope of *Spirogyra* and *Volvox*

2. Demonstration microscope of diatoms

3. Demonstration microscope of *Amoeba proteus*, *Paramecium caudatum*, *Euglena* spp.

4. Culture plate of *Physarum polycephalum*

Method

1. Examine the slides showing *Spirogyra, Volvox,* and diatoms. These are all algae.

2. Draw each species in the space provided in your data sheet.

3. Examine the slides of *Amoeba proteus, Paramecium caudatum,* and *Euglena* spp. These are all protozoa.

4. Draw each species of protozoa in the space provided in your data sheet.

5. Examine the culture plate of *Physarum polycephalum*. This is a slime mold.

6. Draw this species in your data sheet.

Part C: Kingdom Fungi (Domain Eukarya)

All fungi are heterotrophic, have cell walls of chitin, and perform extracellular digestion. Most are **saprobes**, meaning they live on dead or decaying organic matter. So, along with bacteria, they are major decomposers. They are also a source of food (mushrooms and morels) and necessary for making bread, cheese, beer, and wine.

The body of a fungus is called the **mycelium** and is composed of numerous individual threads called **hyphae** or **stolons**. Atop vertical stalks called **sporangiophores** may be found spore-containing **sporangia**.

Materials

1. Demonstration microscope of *Rhizopus nigricans*

2. Culture plate of *Rhizopus nigricans*

3. Demonstration microscope of *Peziza*

4. Specimens of mushrooms, puff balls, shelf fungi

Method

1. Examine the slide of *Rhizopus nigricans* and *Peziza*.

2. Draw each species in the space provided in your data sheet.

3. Examine the culture plate of *Rhizopus nigricans*. Observe little black sporangia.

4. Examine and draw various other fungi in your data sheet.

Part D: Kingdom Plantae (Domain Eukarya)

Plants are multicellular, photosynthetic autotrophs with cell walls of cellulose. This very familiar group includes seedless, nonvascular plants like liverworts and mosses; seedless, vascular plants like ferns and club mosses; and the nonflowering and flowering seed plants, gymnosperms and angiosperms. The angiosperms are traditionally subdivided into dicotyledons and monocotyledons. Plants are descendants of green algae.

Plants: Kingdom Plantae				
Nonvascular	**Vascular**			
Mosses & Liverworts	Have xylem and phloem			
	Seedless	**Seeded**		
	Ferns	**Gymnosperms**	**Angiosperms**	
		Naked Seeds *Conifers*	Fruits (ovaries) & Flowers	
			Monocotyledons *Corn, Grasses, Lilies*	**Dicotyledons** *Roses, Apples, Peas, Beans, Sunflower*

Materials

1. Moss specimen

2. Fern specimen

3. Gymnosperm specimens: needles, cones, leaves

4. Angiosperm specimens: fruits, leaves, seeds

Method

1. Examine the various plant specimens.

2. Draw structures from various species in your data sheet.

Part E: Kingdom Animalia (Domain Eukarya)

Animals are multicellular, heterotrophic organisms. They lack cell walls and are capable of movement. Over the course of this semester, the display cabinets will house the following nine phyla of animals: Porifera, Cnidaria, Platyhelminthes, Annelida, Mollusca, Nematoda, Arthropoda, Echinodermata, and Chordata.

Materials

1. Displays of phyla of the Animal Kingdom in hallway cabinets (Diversity of Life showcase)

Method

1. Observe the displays. These will change every two weeks according to the schedule that was given at the beginning of the semester.

2. Gather information as directed by your instructor.

Diversity of Life

Data Sheet 2

Name _____

Section _____ Date _____

Part A: Kingdom Eubacteria

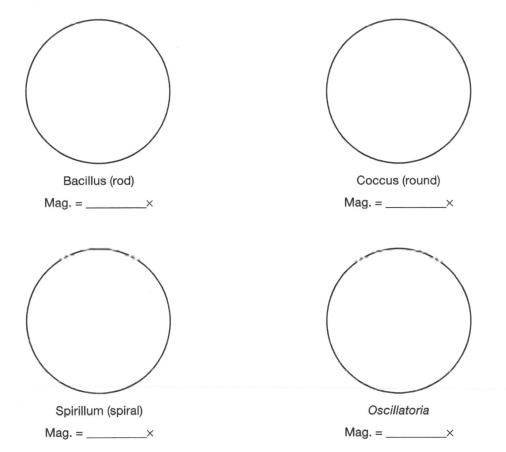

Bacillus (rod)

Mag. = _____×

Coccus (round)

Mag. = _____×

Spirillum (spiral)

Mag. = _____×

Oscillatoria

Mag. = _____×

Part B: Kingdom Protista

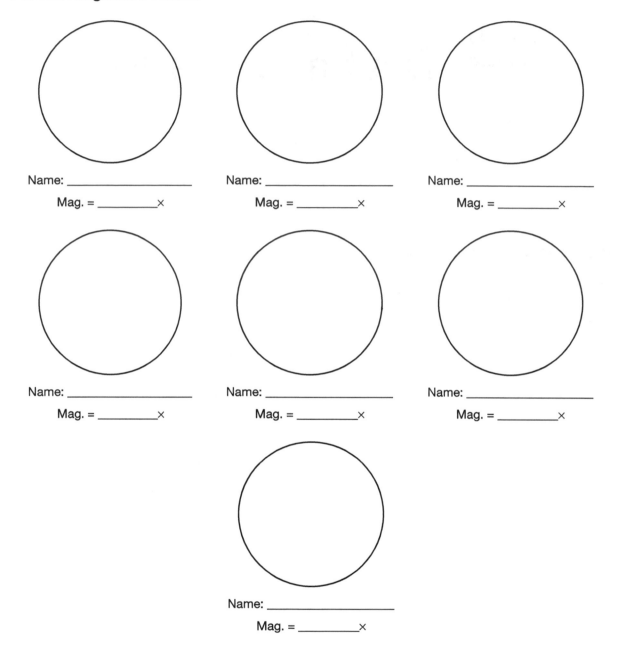

Name: _____

Mag. = _____×

Name: _____

Mag. = _____×

Name: _____

Mag. = _____×

Name: _____

Mag. = _____×

Name: _____

Mag. = _____×

Name: _____

Mag. = _____×

Name: _____

Mag. = _____×

Part C: Kingdom Fungi

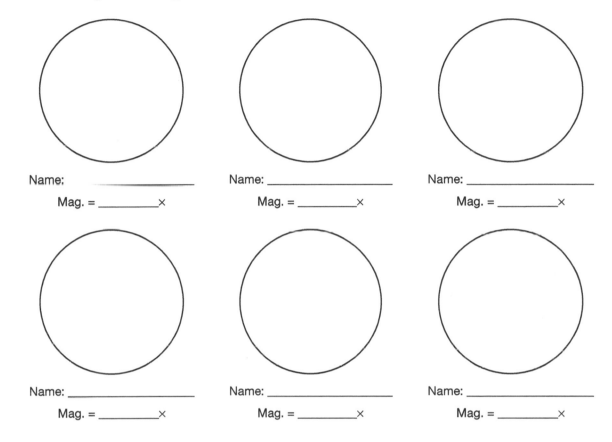

Name: _____

Mag. = _____×

Name: _____

Mag. = _____×

Name: _____

Mag. = _____×

Name: _____

Mag. = _____×

Name: _____

Mag. = _____×

Name: _____

Mag. = _____×

Part D: Kingdom Plantae

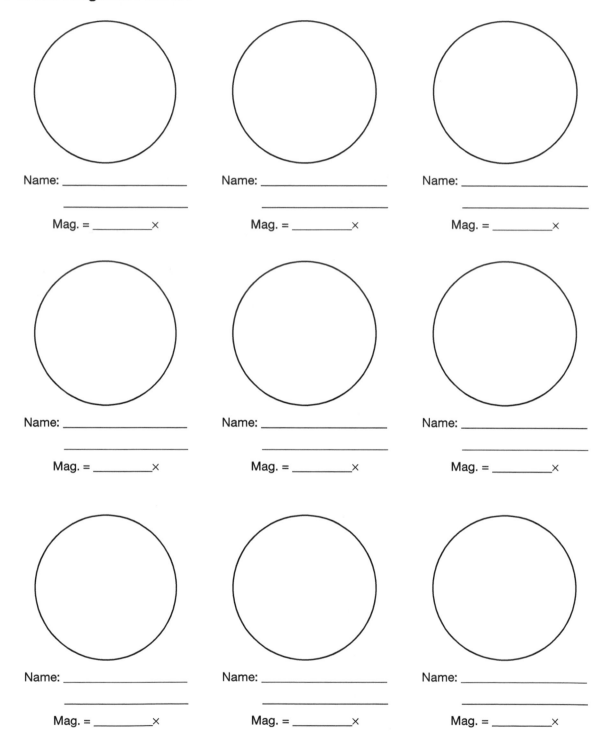

Name: _____
_____
Mag. = _____ ×

Name: _____
_____
Mag. = _____ ×

Name: _____
_____
Mag. = _____ ×

Name: _____
_____
Mag. = _____ ×

Name: _____
_____
Mag. = _____ ×

Name: _____
_____
Mag. = _____ ×

Name: _____
_____
Mag. = _____ ×

Name: _____
_____
Mag. = _____ ×

Name: _____
_____
Mag. = _____ ×

Taxonomy

Exercise 3

Objectives

1. Define taxonomy, dichotomous key, and binomial nomenclature.
2. Explain the importance of scientific names, and be able to write scientific names in the proper format.
3. Identify the genus and species epithet given a scientific binomial.
4. List the common taxa in order of hierarchy.
5. Use a dichotomous key.

Introduction

Taxonomy is the branch of biology that classifies and names organisms. Classification is necessary for unambiguous communication, which can be a problem if using common names. For instance, basswood and linden are common names for the tree that scientists call *Tilia americana*. The scientific name refers only to one kind of organism and is used throughout the world. Thus, classification and nomenclature simplifies scientific study.

As impossible as it may seem, taxonomy attempts to place all known species into categories or groups called **taxa** (singular: taxon). Commonly used taxa from the most inclusive to the least inclusive are: **Domain**, **Kingdom**, **Phylum**, **Class**, **Order**, **Family**, **Genus**, and **Species**. Currently, all organisms have been broadly divided into three domains and six kingdoms:

Domain Bacteria: Kingdom Eubacteria

Domain Archaea: Kingdom Archaea

Domain Eukarya: Kingdom Protista

Kingdom Fungi

Kingdom Plantae

Kingdom Animalia

As new information becomes available, classification of organisms in various taxa may change.

The current **binomial system** of nomenclature was set down over 200 years ago by the Swedish taxonomist, **Carl Linnaeus**. According to this system, an organism's scientific name consists of its **Genus name** plus its **species epithet**, for example: *Homo sapiens* (humans) or *Zea mays* (corn). Note that the genus name is always capitalized, while the species epithet is not. Also, scientific names are written in *italics* (since these are Latin names) or underlined.

When a modern day biologist is confronted with an unfamiliar organism, he usually refers to a taxonomic tool called a **dichotomous key**, which helps attribute a genus and species name to his "unknown." Dichotomous keys are constructed by professional taxonomists and are based on choices between two alternatives. In this lab, you will learn to use this important tool in order to classify trees.

Part A: Use of a Dichotomous Key

Materials

1. Metric ruler

2. Tree biodiversity handout, with dichotomous key

3. Herbarium specimen cards

Method

1. Your instructor will select a leaf and key it out, demonstrating the use of the dichotomous key.

2. Once you have keyed out your samples, you will be shown how to fill out herbarium specimen cards.

Microscopy

Exercise 4

Objectives

1. Identify the parts of the binocular compound microscope and describe their functions.

2. Be able to focus a binocular microscope.

3. Describe the correct procedures for handling, storing, and cleaning microscopes.

4. Be able to calculate magnification.

5. Prepare and view a wet mount.

Introduction

Of all the optical devices man has invented, none has made a greater contribution to the understanding of the living world than the microscope. The microscope you will use is similar to the one illustrated in Figure 4.1. The term compound refers to the use of multiple lenses to magnify an object. A light microscope uses visible or white light to illuminate an object. Your microscopes are binocular, meaning each eye has its own viewing lens.

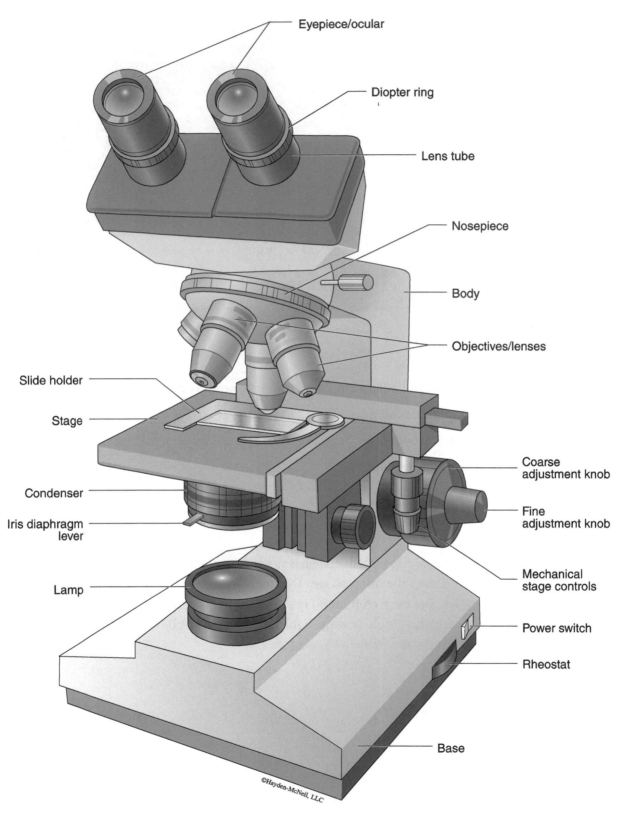

Eyepiece/ocular

Diopter ring

Lens tube

Nosepiece

Body

Objectives/lenses

Slide holder

Stage

Coarse adjustment knob

Condenser

Fine adjustment knob

Iris diaphragm lever

Lamp

Mechanical stage controls

Power switch

Rheostat

Base

©Hayden-McNeil, LLC

Figure 4.1. Parts of a binocular compound microscope

Part A: Parts of the Microscope and Important Terms

Refer to Figure 4.1 when reviewing the following terms.

1. **Base**

2. **Body**

3. **Eyepiece (ocular):** The lens mounted at the top of the microscope, through which you look. These have a magnification (10×) stamped on them.

4. **Nosepiece:** Site of attachment for objectives.

5. **Objectives:** The lenses attached to the revolving nosepiece. Your microscope has a scanning (4×), a low-power (10×), and a high-power (40×) lens. Some microscopes may also have an oil-immersion (100×) lens.

6. **Mechanical stage:** The device mounted on the microscope stage to hold and move slides.

    a. **Stage:** The black platform on which the slides are placed.

    b. **Mechanical stage control knobs:** Knobs used to move the slides left to right, and forward and backward.

7. **Coarse adjustment (focus) knob**

8. **Fine adjustment (focus) knob**

9. **Condenser:** Focuses light onto the stage.

10. **Pointer:** A black needle-like line extending out from the edge of the field of view. Used to direct a viewer to any detail.

11. **Lamp (illuminator):** Source of light.

12. **Rheostat:** Controls the brightness of the lamp.

13. **Field of view:** The circular area you view when looking through the lenses of the microscope, usually illuminated with an artificial light.

14. **Iris diaphragm lever:** The device beneath the stage that controls the light intensity of the field of view.

15. **Parfocal:** When you can change objectives without making significant adjustments to the focus, your scope is said to be parfocal.

16. **Resolving power:** A measurement that describes the degree of clarity in the image formed by your microscope.

17. **Magnification:** The measure by which an image is enlarged.

18. **Diopter ring**

19. **Lens tube**

Your instructor may provide you with additional terms.

Part B: Care of the Microscope

The microscope is a delicate and expensive instrument. It is also the most utilized piece of equipment in this lab. Thus, proper handling is imperative! Improper handling leading to damage of the microscope may result in the loss of your laboratory privileges. The following simple guidelines will ensure longevity of our microscopes.

1. When transporting the microscope, always use the correct two-handed technique: one hand holding the arm, and the other the base.
2. Clean lenses before and after use. Use only lens paper to clean the oculars and objectives.
3. Keep the stage clear of any liquids.
4. Use only the mechanical stage controls to position a slide.
5. Never force any of the adjustments or remove any parts of the microscope.
6. Never slide the microscope across lab tables.
7. Do *not* use the coarse adjustment with the 40× (or 100×) objective. Use the coarse adjustment knob to lower the stage completely before and after use!
8. The 4× (scanning) objective should be in place prior to returning the microscope to its proper place.
9. Turn the rheostat down and turn off the lamp using the power switch when finished.
10. Never unplug by pulling on the cord.
11. Wrap the cord securely around the base of the microscope.
12. Return the microscope to the benchtop where it was found.

Part C: Microscope Operation

We will learn to focus the microscope using a very familiar specimen, the **letter** *e* slide.

1. Focusing:
    a. Make sure the microscope is plugged in and the power switch is on.
    b. Place a prepared slide of the letter *e* on the stage, and secure it with the mechanical stage clip.
    c. Next, center the slide over the stage aperture using the mechanical stage controls.
    d. Look into the oculars using *both* eyes and adjust the light intensity using the iris diaphragm lever. Notice how the light changes as you move the lever from side to side. Always start with the diaphragm closed and the light at highest intensity. **Caution:** Most students generally use too high of a light intensity.
    e. Adjust the interocular distance to match your interpupillary distance by moving the lens tube.
    f. Begin to focus by raising the stage with the coarse adjustment knob.

g. Once you find the specimen, use the fine adjustment knob to get a crisp (clear, sharp) image.

h. With the specimen in focus, move the slide around slowly, again using the mechanical stage controls. *You will note the microscope reverses movement and inverts images.*

i. Before shifting to low power (10× objective), center the specimen in the field of view.

j. Rotate the nosepiece until the 10× lens clicks into place over the specimen.

k. Use the fine adjustment knob to get a crisp image. Your microscope is parfocal, meaning a specimen in focus at low magnification will be nearly so at the higher magnifications. Thus, it is not necessary to use the coarse adjustment.

l. As you went from a scanning field to a low power field, what happened to the light intensity? You may need to adjust the diaphragm to compensate for the decrease in light intensity.

m. Shifting from low power to high power will reduce the field of view, so be certain to center in the field of view the portion of the specimen you wish to examine under high power. Shifting to high power changes the depth of the field. By careful use of the fine adjustment, you will be able to clarify the interior of thick specimens.

n. Rotate the nosepiece and click your high-power objective into position.

o. Use *only* the fine adjustment knob when focusing the high-power objective.

p. You probably noticed a reduction in light intensity again when shifting from low power to high power. Correct the light intensity by using the diaphragm lever. What happened to the field of view as magnification increased?

q. In summary, tips for quickly achieving good focus are:

1. Light bright, diaphragm closed.

2. Stage down, 4× objective in place.

3. Place slide in stage clip, bring stage all the way up.

4. Focus will be slightly down.

5. Adjust diaphragm and focus when changing powers.

2. Determining magnification:

The eyepieces of your microscope have a magnification (10×) stamped on them. The objectives have their magnification stamped on them as well. The scanning power is 4×, the low-power is 10×, and the high-power objective is 40×.

a. To obtain the magnification of the field of view, simply multiply the magnification of the eyepiece (10×) by the magnification of the scanning objective (4×), the low-power objective (10×), or the high-power objective (40×). Record your results on the data sheet.

b. A microscope may also be equipped with an oil-immersion objective (100×). On the data sheet, record the magnification of the field of view if an oil-immersion objective is being used.

Part D: Observing Biological Specimens

Having successfully learned to use the microscope using the letter *e*, you are now ready to examine more interesting and challenging biological specimens.

1. Observe prepared specimens.

    a. Follow the focusing procedure that was outlined in Part C.

    b. Observe specimens under each magnification.

    c. Draw what you observe in the field of view. Use the magnification that is appropriate for each specimen, as indicated by your instructor.

    d. Label your drawing with the following:

        i.   specimen name

        ii.   total magnification

        iii. any structures indicated by your instructor

2. Prepare a wet mount.

    a. Prepare a wet mount of a sample of pond water. Place one drop of pond water on a clean slide. Place a coverslip over the specimen. Note: It may be necessary to add a drop of Detain when making a wet mount.

    b. Follow the focusing procedure that was outlined in Part C. Observe and record the various organisms in a drop of pond water.

Part E: Depth of Field

1. Obtain a prepared slide of colored threads.

2. Center the slide over the stage aperture.

3. Using the scanning lens, find the point where the three colored threads cross. Center this point.

4. Gradually increase magnification to the high power. At this point, take note of the depth of field.

5. Using the fine adjustment, determine which of the threads is uppermost, middle, and lowermost in the field of view. Keep in mind that as the stage moves up (or the lens moves down), threads on top will come into focus first.

6. Record your observations on the data sheet.

Part F: Optional—The Stereozoom Microscope

Your instructor may require the use of the stereozoom microscope, also called a dissecting microscope. If so, you will be given directions for its operation. See the illustration of the stereozoom microscope in this exercise (Figure 4.2).

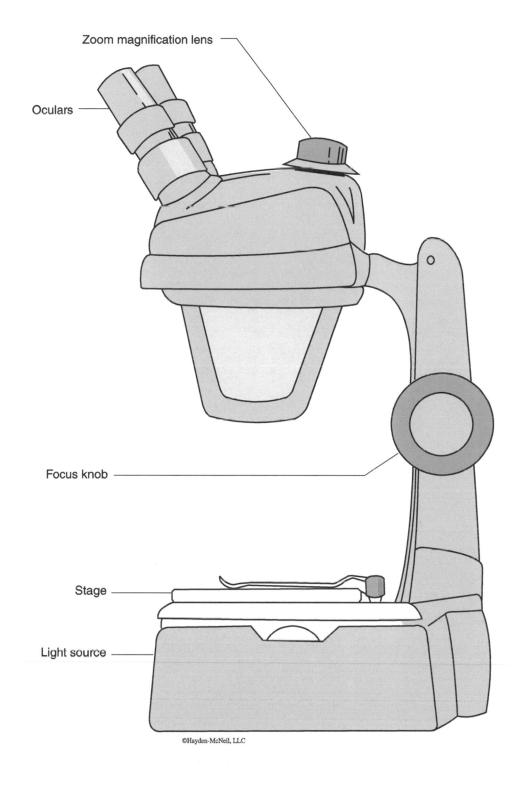

Zoom magnification lens

Oculars

Focus knob

Stage

Light source

©Hayden-McNeil, LLC

Figure 4.2. Parts of a stereozoom (dissecting) microscope

Microscopy

Data Sheet 4

Name _____

Section _____ Date _____

Part C: Microscope Operation

1. Letter *e*

Letter *e* as viewed on slide   Letter *e* as viewed through a microscope

a. How has the image of the letter *e* changed when viewed through the microscope? _____

_____

b. What happened to the field of view as magnification increased? _____

_____

2. Determining magnification

   a. eyepiece 10× scanning objective 4×   = _____ ×

   b. eyepiece 10× low-power objective 10×   = _____ ×

   c. eyepiece 10× high-power objective 40×   = _____ ×

   d. eyepiece 10× oil-immersion objective 100× = _____ ×

Part D: Observing Biological Specimens

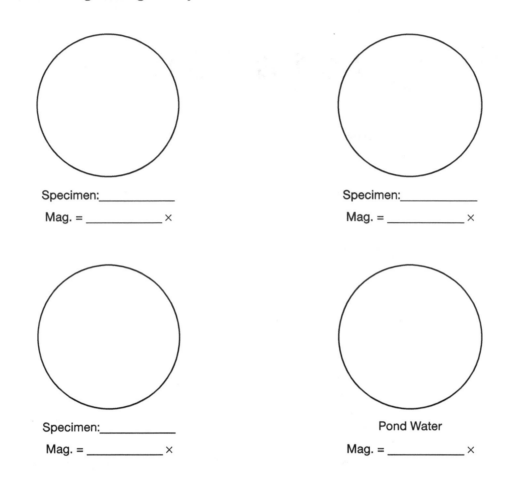

Specimen:_____

Mag. = _____ ×

Specimen:_____

Mag. = _____ ×

Specimen:_____

Mag. = _____ ×

Pond Water

Mag. = _____ ×

Part E: Depth of Field

Indicate the color of the upper, middle, and lower threads.

_____ Upper thread

_____ Middle thread

_____ Lower thread

Cells

Exercise 5

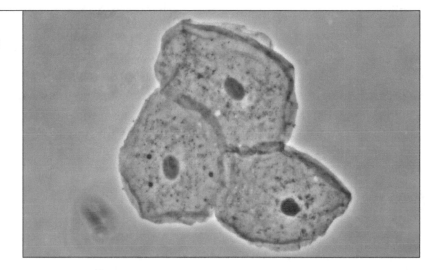

Objectives

1. Recognize cells and basic cellular structures.

2. Relate the functions of the major organelles of cells.

3. Identify common unicellular and colonial organisms: *Amoeba, Paramecium, Euglena, Spirogyra.*

4. Distinguish between plant and animal cells.

Introduction

This exercise is intended to introduce you to cells. The English scientist, Robert Hooke, first reported cells in the middle 1600s while examining cork under the microscope. By the 1840s, the cell was recognized as the basic unit of structure and function of living organisms. This idea was summarized by biologists Matthias Schleiden, Theodor Schwann, and Rudolf Virchow in the now famous **cell theory**, which states:

+ A cell is the basic unit of life.

+ All cells come from pre-existing cells.

+ All organisms are made up of cells.

There are two basic types of cells: **prokaryotic cells** and **eukaryotic cells**. Prokaryotic cells lack a nucleus and other organelles. Eukaryotic cells have a nucleus and other organelles. An **organelle** is a subcellular membrane-bounded structure that performs specific function(s) for the cell.

Cells can be used to construct living organisms in one of three basic ways. Living organisms can be "built" of a single cell. These are called single or **unicellular** organisms. At the other end of the spectrum we find living organisms constructed from large numbers of highly interdependent cells. These forms of life are called **multicellular**. Occupying the middle ground are organisms formed from numerous cells, though the cells lead a highly independent existence. Biologists describe these forms of life as **colonial** organisms. This exercise will introduce you to cells from all three different forms of life.

Materials

1. Microslide 58: "Cell Structure"
2. Microslide viewer
3. Animal cell model
4. Plant cell model
5. *Amoeba, Paramecium, Euglena* models
6. Living cultures: *Amoeba, Paramecium, Euglena, Spirogyra*, aquatic plant
7. Prepared slides: *Amoeba, Paramecium, Euglena, Spirogyra*
8. Toothpicks
9. Detain
10. Stain
11. Onion epidermal tissue
12. Human epidermal tissue

Part A: Animal and Plant Cell Structure

1. View the Cell Structure microslide, and complete Part A of your data sheet.

2. Identify the following structures/organelles on the plant and/or animal cell models. Then label Figures 5.1 and 5.2.

Plasma or cell membrane
Ribosome
Golgi apparatus
Mitochondrion
Vesicle (lysosome, peroxisome, vacuole, etc.)
Chloroplast
Cell wall
Centrioles

Nucleus
    Nuclear pores
    Nuclear envelope
    Chromatin
    Nucleolus
Endoplasmic reticulum
    Rough endoplasmic reticulum
    Smooth endoplasmic reticulum
Central vacuole

Your instructor may point out additional structures.

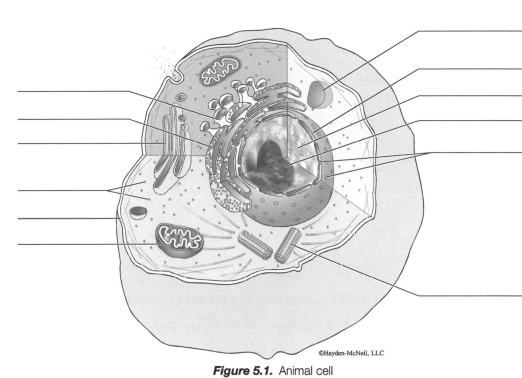

Figure 5.1. Animal cell

Label all the parts on this figure of a typical animal cell.

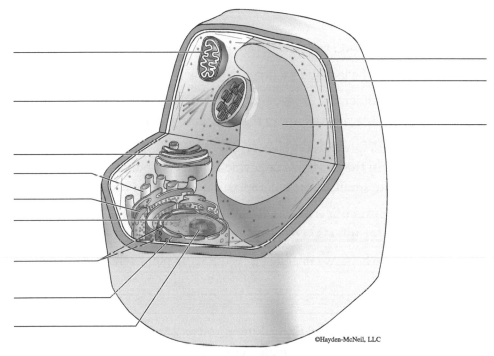

Figure 5.2. Plant cell

Label all the parts on this figure of a typical plant cell.

Human Cheek Cells

The human cheek cell is a good example of a typical animal cell.

1. Prepare a wet mount of cheek cells: Place a drop of stain on a clean slide. Gently scrape the inside of your cheek using a toothpick. Dissolve the cheek cell culture in the stain. *Immediately dispose of the toothpick.*

2. Using the low-power (10×) objective of your microscope, locate a specimen.

3. Draw and label a representative specimen on your data sheet using the high-power (40×) objective. Indicate the **nucleus, cell membrane**, and **cytoplasm**. **Note**: Clean your own slide of the cheek cell preparation.

Onion Cells

The onion cell is an example of a simple plant cell.

1. Following the procedure just outlined, prepare a wet mount (in iodine solution) of onion cells.

2. Use the low-power (10×) objective of your microscope to locate the cells.

3. Draw and label a representative specimen on your data sheet using the high-power (40×) objective. Indicate the **cell wall** and **nucleus**.

4. In the future, you will be held responsible for identifying the onion cell as well as the structures mentioned.

Aquatic Plant Leaf

The aquatic plant leaf cells that you will observe are part of a multicellular organism.

1. Secure a small fragment of a leaf and mount it in the form of a wet mount.

2. Examine this fragment under the low-power (10×) objective of your microscope. Locate an individual cell. Now, examine this cell under the high-power (40×) objective of your microscope.

3. Observe the small, green, football-like objects within the cell. These are the chloroplasts. **Note**: Unlike the chloroplasts in the *Spirogyra* cell, which are few in number and quite large, these are very numerous and quite small. These chloroplasts are typical of plants.

4. Sketch one cell as it appears under the high-power (40×) objective of your microscope, in your date sheet. Label the **chloroplasts** and the **cell wall** of this cell.

5. In the future, you will be held responsible for recognizing plant cells and identifying the structures mentioned.

Your instructor may have you view additional microslides: Microslide 51: "Animal Tissues" and Microslide 66: "The Ultra-Structure of Animals Cells."

Part B: Cells

Amoeba

The *Amoeba* is a good example of a **unicellular** organism. *Amoeba* is a common inhabitant of fresh-water lakes and ponds, found at the bottom of ponds or near vegetation in search of food. These organisms have a constantly changing body shape and are relatively large protozoa. Review the following structures on Figure 5.3, photograph, models, and textbook:

Nucleus   **Pseudopodia**

Contractile vacuole   **Food vacuole**

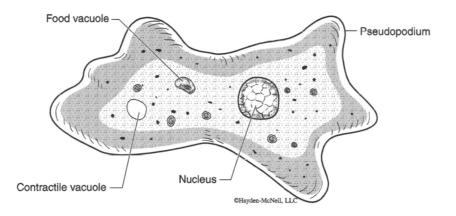

Figure 5.3. *Amoeba*

1. Observe a prepared slide of *Amoeba*. Locate the structures listed above.

2. Draw and label a representative specimen on your data sheet.

3. Prepare a wet mount using the live culture of *Amoeba*. Remember to take your sample from the bottom of the jar, and be sure to include some of the white, fuzz-like debris in the sample.

4. Using the low-power (10×) objective of your microscope, locate a specimen. Identify the nucleus, pseudopodia and observe **cytoplasmic streaming**. You may have to utilize the high-power (40×) objective of your microscope. **Note**: Most students use too high of a light intensity; adjust the diaphragm!

5. In the future, you will be held responsible for identifying the *Amoeba* as well as the structures listed above.

Paramecium

The *Paramecium* is another common **unicellular** freshwater protozoan. This organism is capable of rapid motion due to the coordinated beating of thousands of hairlike cilia that cover its surface. Review the following structures on Figure 5.4, photograph, models, and textbook:

Nucleus   **Cilia**

Contractile vacuole   **Food vacuole**

Oral groove

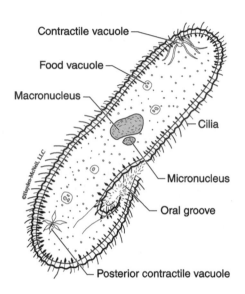

Figure 5.4. *Paramecium*

1. Observe a prepared slide of *Paramecium*. Locate the structures listed above.

2. Draw and label a specimen on your data sheet.

3. Prepare a wet mount using the live culture of *Paramecium*. Add a drop of culture to a drop of Detain. Detain retards activity of mobile organisms.

4. Using the low-power (10×) objective of your microscope, locate a specimen. You may have to use the high-power (40×) objective of your microscope to see some of the structures. Observe the coordinated movement of cilia that propels the *Paramecium*.

5. In the future, you will be held responsible for identifying the *Paramecium* as well as the structures listed above.

Spirogyra

Spirogyra is an example of **colonial, green algae**. This colony consists of a series of rectangular cells arranged in a long chain or **filament**. The algae are normal inhabitants of freshwater lakes and ponds and are commonly found in Michigan. Review the following structures on Figure 5.5, photograph, and textbook:

Nucleus   **Chloroplast**

Cell wall   **Pyrenoid**

Cytoplasm

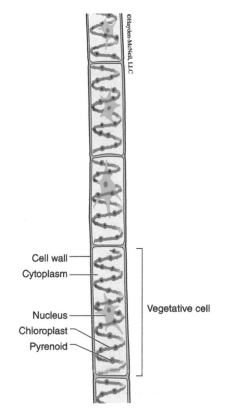

Cell wall
Cytoplasm
Nucleus
Chloroplast
Pyrenoid
Vegetative cell

©Hayden-McNeil, LLC

Figure 5.5. *Spirogyra*

1. Observe a prepared slide of *Spirogyra*. Locate the structures listed above.

2. Draw and label a single *Spirogyra* cell on your data sheet.

3. Prepare a wet mount using the live culture of *Spirogyra*.

4. Using the scanning-power (4×) objective of your microscope, locate a specimen. You may have to use the low-power (10×) objective of your microscope to see some of the structures.

5. Make a sketch of a short section of *Spirogyra* filament on the data sheets.

6. In the future, you will be held responsible for identifying *Spirogyra* as well as the structures listed above.

Euglena

Euglena is an example of a **unicellular**, motile, algal organism. This organism is also commonly found in freshwater environments in Michigan. Review the following structures on Figure 5.6, photograph, model, and textbook:

Nucleus   **Pyrenoid**

Flagellum   **Eyespot**

Cytoplasm   **Contractile vacuole**

Chloroplast

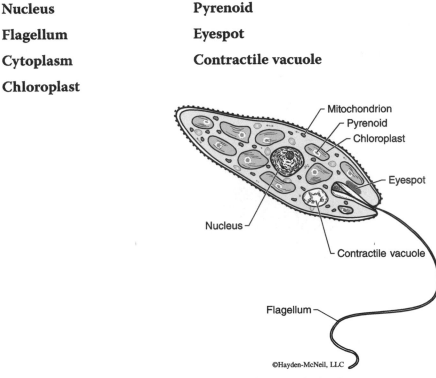

Figure 5.6. *Euglena*

1. Prepare a wet mount using the live culture of *Euglena*. Add a drop of culture to a drop of Detain.

2. Using the low-power (10×) objective of your microscope, locate a specimen. You may have to use the high-power (40×) objective of your microscope to see some of the structures. You may be able to observe the beating of the flagellum that propels the *Euglena*.

3. Draw and label a representative specimen on your data sheet.

4. In the future, you will be held responsible for identifying the *Euglena*, as well as the structures listed above.

Data Sheet

5

Name _____

Section _____ Date _____

Part A: Animal and Plant Cell Structure

Microslide 58: Cell Structure

Photograph Number 1

1. What type of cells are shown in the photograph? _____

2. Who viewed these cells for the first time? _____

3. In what century were these cells first viewed? _____

4. Sketch several of these cells as they appear under the viewer in the space provided.

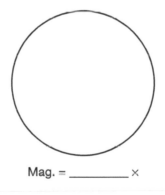

Mag. = _____ ×

Photograph Number 2

1. What type of cell is shown in the photograph? _____

2. How many nuclei are there per cell? _____

3. Sketch one of these cells as it appears under the viewer in the space provided below. Indicate the **cell wall**, **nucleus**, and **cytoplasm**.

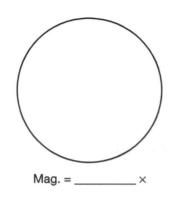

Mag. = _____ ×

Photograph Number 4

1. What type of cell is shown in the photograph? _____

2. What is indicated by the arrow? _____

3. Sketch one of these cells in the space provided below. Indicate the **nuclear** and **cytoplasmic areas** of the cell.

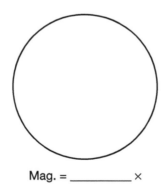

Mag. = _____ ×

Photograph Number 5

1. The cells shown here have come from human _____.

2. There are three different subtypes of cells shown here. What are they?

   a. _____

   b. _____

   c. _____

3. Which of the above cell types has a nucleus? _____

4. Sketch and label cell types A, B, C, and D.

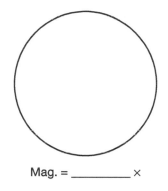

Mag. = _____ ×

Cell Models

Figure 5.1: Label the structures in the cross section of a typical animal cell.

Figure 5.2: Label the structures in the cross section of a typical plant cell.

1. Cite three major differences between plant and animal cells.

   a. _____

   _____

   b. _____

   _____

   c. _____

   _____

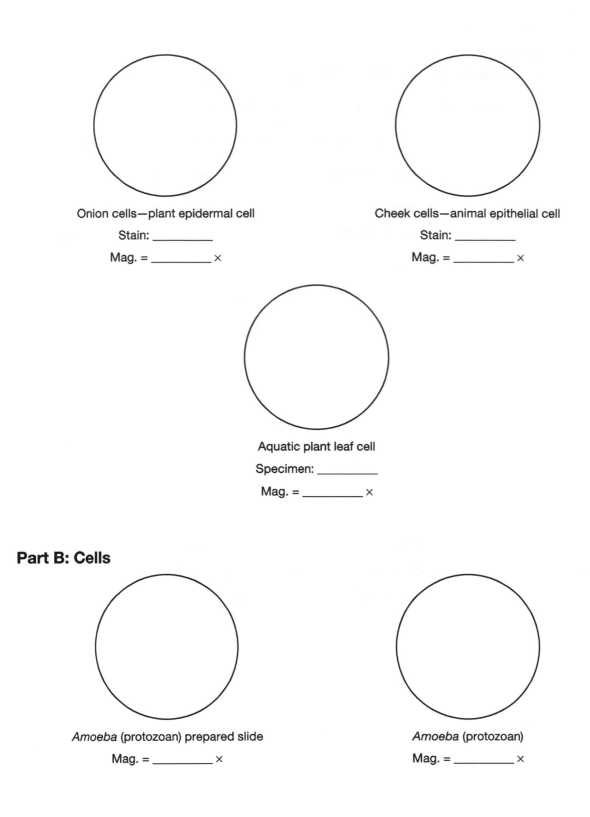

Onion cells—plant epidermal cell

Stain: _____

Mag. = _____ ×

Cheek cells—animal epithelial cell

Stain: _____

Mag. = _____ ×

Aquatic plant leaf cell

Specimen: _____

Mag. = _____ ×

Part B: Cells

Amoeba (protozoan) prepared slide

Mag. = _____ ×

Amoeba (protozoan)

Mag. = _____ ×

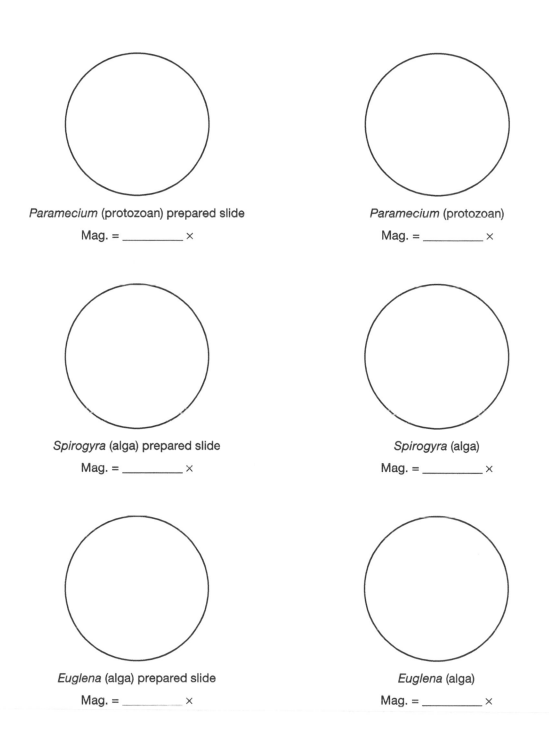

Paramecium (protozoan) prepared slide

Mag. = _____ ×

Paramecium (protozoan)

Mag. = _____ ×

Spirogyra (alga) prepared slide

Mag. = _____ ×

Spirogyra (alga)

Mag. = _____ ×

Euglena (alga) prepared slide

Mag. = _____ ×

Euglena (alga)

Mag. = _____ ×

The Molecules of Life

Exercise 6

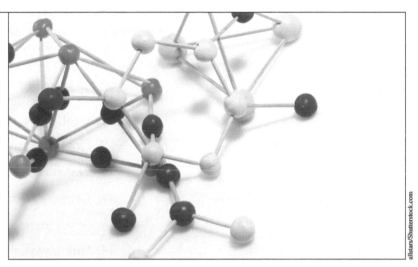

allstars/Shutterstock.com

Objectives

1. Learn the chemical tests, reagents, and outcomes for detection of the following macromolecules:

   a. Starch (polysaccharide)

   b. Sugars (monosaccharide, disaccharide)

   c. Proteins

   d. Lipids

Introduction

A living cell is an assemblage of both inorganic and organic molecules. Organic molecules are made primarily of carbon and hydrogen. Inorganic molecules lack carbon and hydrogen atoms as a major component of their molecular structure. The carbon atoms form the backbone of organic compounds and may exist as chains or rings. Of the complex and diverse array of organic molecules that exists in nature, there are four major groups of compounds that form the building blocks of cell, and serve as a source of energy and nutrients in all cells. These are: carbohydrates, proteins, lipids, and nucleic acids.

In this laboratory exercise, you will learn how to test solutions for the presence of three of these four types of molecules: carbohydrates (in the form of starch and glucose), proteins, and lipids. Each molecule will be detected with the use of a specific **reagent**. These reagents react differently depending on whether the molecule is present or absent in the solution. For each reagent, you will first observe how the appearance of a solution differs when the molecule is present (a **positive control**) and when it is absent (a **negative control**). Once you can correctly interpret positive and negative results, you will be able to apply this knowledge to analyze an unknown solution.

Materials

1. 2% starch solution
2. Iodine reagent
3. Egg albumin (protein) solution
4. Benedict's reagent
5. Biuret reagent
6. Sudan IV reagent
7. Vegetable oil
8. 5%, 0.5%, 0.05%, 0.005% glucose solutions
9. Test tube rack
10. Test tube holder
11. Plastic pipettes
12. Hot plate
13. Test tubes
14. Grease pencil
15. Small metric ruler
16. Unknown solution

Part A: Test for Carbohydrates

Method

1. Test for starch:

   a. Obtain two clean test tubes. Label one "–" and the other "+." These tubes will serve as the negative and positive controls, respectively.

   b. Place 1 cm of water (see illustration on the following page) in the "–" tube and add 4 drops of **iodine reagent**. Record the color of the solution on your data sheet.

   c. Place 1 cm of starch solution in the "+" tube and add 4 drops of iodine reagent. The appearance of a **blue-black** color is a **positive test** for starch. Record the color of the solution on your data sheet.

2. Test for sugar:

   a. Obtain and label five clean test tubes, #1–5.

   b. Place 1 cm of **Benedict's reagent** into each of the five test tubes. This reagent is used to test for simple sugars.

c. Add 1 cm of the following solutions to the tubes, as indicated below:

    i.   To tube #1: 1 cm of distilled water

    ii. To tube #2: 1 cm of 0.005% glucose

    iii. To tube #3: 1 cm of 0.05% glucose

    iv. To tube #4: 1 cm of 0.5% glucose

    v. To tube #5: 1 cm of 5% glucose

d. Carefully place all five tubes in a gently boiling water bath for three minutes. After heating, a **positive result** is indicated by **any change** from the original clear, bright aqua blue solution. Record the results on your data sheet.

Part B: Test for Proteins

Method

1. Test for proteins:

a. Obtain and label two clean test tubes "–" and "+."

b. Add 1 cm of water to the "–" tube. Add 3 drops of **Biuret reagent**. Record the color of the solution on the data sheet.

c. Add 1 cm of egg albumin (protein) to the "+" tube. Add 3 drops of Biuret reagent. A **lilac** or **purple** color is a **positive test** for protein. Record the color of the solution on your data sheet.

Part C: Test for Lipids

Method

1. Test for lipids:

a. Obtain and label two clean test tubes "–" and "+".

b. To each of the test tubes, add 1 cm of distilled water and 10 drops of **Sudan IV reagent.**

c. To the "–" tube, add another 1 cm of distilled water. (Because water is not a lipid, this water serves as a negative control.) Mix the tube vigorously. Wait 5 minutes before recording your results on your data sheet.

d. To the "+" tube, add 1 cm of vegetable oil. Mix the tube vigorously. Wait 5 minutes before recording your results on your data sheet. A **positive test** for lipids is the appearance of two layers, with a **deep orange/red** color in the top oil layer.

Example

2 cm

1 cm

Part D: Test for an Unknown Solution

Method

1. Obtain four clean test tubes and label them #1–4.

2. Add 1 cm of the unknown solution to each of the four test tubes. (Note: Mix the unknown solution thoroughly before removing a sample from it.)

3. Add the following to each of the tubes:

   a. To tube #1: 4 drops of iodine reagent.

   b. To tube #2: 1 cm of Benedict's reagent. Place this tube in a gently boiling water bath for three minutes.

   c. To tube #3: 3 drops of Biuret reagent.

   d. To tube #4: 1 cm of water and 10 drops of Sudan IV. Mix the tube thoroughly and wait five minutes before recording your results.

4. Based on the appearance of your tubes, determine which molecules are present in the unknown solution. Record the results in your data table.

Data Sheet

6

Name _____

Section _____   Date _____

Part A: Test for Carbohydrates

Starch Test

Reagent: _____

Tube	Color
–	
+	

Sugar Test

Reagent: _____

Tube	Solution	Color	Result ("–" or "+")
1	Water		
2	0.005% glucose		
3	0.05% glucose		
4	0.5% glucose		
5	5% glucose		

Part B: Test for Protein

Reagent: _____

Tube	Color
–	
+	

Part C: Test for Lipid

Reagent: _____

Tube	Appearance of Tube
–	
+	

Part D: Test for an Unknown Solution

Tube	Reagent Used	Molecule Being Tested for	Color/Appearance of Tube	Result ("–" or "+")
1				
2				
3				
4				

Membrane Transport

Exercise 7

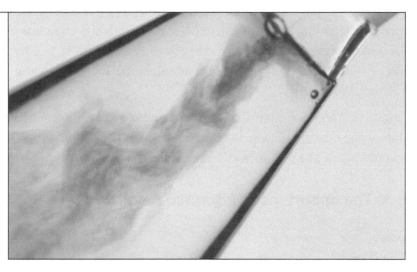

Objectives

1. Understand the importance of surface area to living organisms.

2. Describe the process of diffusion and osmosis.

3. Define hypotonic, isotonic, and hypertonic solutions, and predict the effect of each on living cells.

Introduction

The cells of living organisms require a constant supply of materials from their immediate surroundings. These substances may include food materials, such as glucose, and nonfood substances, such as oxygen. In addition, in multicellular plants and animals, the environment outside the cell may contain chemical messengers (for example, hormones) to direct essential activities within cells. Not only do materials have to pass into cells, but materials must leave the living cell. Whether materials are leaving or entering cells, they must pass through the **plasma** or **cell membrane,** which is selectively permeable.

During the course of this exercise, we will examine **diffusion** and **osmosis**, two common and vital methods used by cells to transport materials across cell membranes. Diffusion is the movement of molecules from an area of higher concentration to an area of lower concentration. Molecules will diffuse down their concentration gradient until **equilibrium** is reached. Many factors can affect diffusion, including molecular size and temperature. **Osmosis** is a special case of diffusion where water moves through a selectively permeable membrane from where the water concentration is high (thus, the **solute** concentration is low) to where the water concentration is low (thus, the solute concentration is high).

The tonicity of a solution describes its solute concentration compared to that of the solute concentration inside a cell. An **isotonic** solution is one in which solute and water concentrations are equal on both sides of the membrane. Therefore, there is no net movement of water across the membrane. In a **hypotonic** solution, the concentration of solute is lower than it is inside the cell. Therefore, water moves into the cell, causing **lysis** or **turgor pressure**. Finally, in a **hypertonic** solution, the concentration of solute is higher than it is inside the cell. Therefore, water moves out of the cell, causing **crenation** or **plasmolysis**.

It is important to remember that all living cells require water. The water and dissolved substances outside of the cell membrane is referred to as **extracellular fluid** (ECF). The water and dissolved substances inside the cell, including the cellular organelles, make up the cytoplasm.

Part A: The Importance of Surface Area to Volume Ratio

Materials

1. 50 ml beaker containing iodine reagent

2. One 5 mm and one 10 mm potato cube

Method

1. Obtain a small beaker that contains iodine reagent.

2. Select a 5 mm and a 10 mm cube from the labeled containers. Cube sizes are approximations and may not be exactly 5 mm and 10 mm, so trim your cubes. Add these cubes to the beaker of iodine reagent.

3. Wait at least 30 minutes and then remove the potato cubes. Save the iodine solution. Iodine reacts with the starch in the potato to give a blue-black color.

4. Following the direction of your laboratory instructor, determine the percentage of each of the cubes penetrated by the iodine solution. See the formula for percent penetration and the diagram of the cut potato cube on the data sheet.

5. Compare the percentage of iodine penetration to the surface area to volume ratio of each cube. **Note:** Your instructor will provide you with directions for determining the surface area to volume ratios of your cubes.

6. Record your observations and complete the computations on the data sheet.

Part B: Simple Diffusion

Materials
1. Iodine (I) powder
2. Methylene blue (MB) powder
3. Starch agar in a Petri dish
4. Small metric ruler
5. Toothpicks

Method
1. On the bottom of your Petri dish, place two labels approximately 4 cm apart: I and MB.
2. Dip the tip of a clean, dry toothpick into the provided beaker of water. Next, dip the wet tip of the toothpick into the iodine powder. Insert the powdered tip into the agar above your 'I' label.
3. Using a new, clean toothpick, repeat step 2 using methylene blue powder. Insert the powdered tip into the agar above your 'MB' label.
4. Examine the Petri dish at the end of 1 hour. Note any variation in the diffusion of the two molecules. Measure the colored zones in millimeters. Record your observations on the data sheet.

Part C: Tonicity

Materials
1. Set of beakers containing 0%, 10%, 20%, and 30% sucrose solutions and carrots
2. Electronic balances, weigh boats, and paper towels
3. Demonstration microscopes of plasmolysis

Method
1. Weight change:
   a. Obtain a set of beakers with carrots and varying concentrations of sucrose solution. **Note:** Set consists of 0%, 10%, 20%, and 30% sucrose solutions.
   b. Using the data sheet as a guide, obtain and record the necessary information about each carrot. Blot off any excess solution before weighing the carrots. The weights recorded on the beakers are the initial dry weights of the carrots. Plot your data on the graph provided on your data sheet. (**Note:** Any carrots that lost weight will result in a negative value for percent weight change and should therefore be graphed below the bolded x-axis.)

2. Plasmolysis:

   a. Note the difference between the plant samples shown in the two demonstration microscopes. One leaf is in water, and the other is in a 10% table salt solution.

   b. Compare the location of the cell wall, plasma membrane, and chloroplasts. Record your observations on the data sheet. Label the chloroplasts.

Part D: Diffusion and Osmosis Across a Selectively Permeable Membrane

Materials

1. String

2. Dialysis tubing (15-cm length)

3. 600 ml beaker

4. Salt–starch solution

5. Sodium chloride (NaCl) solution

6. Starch solution

7. Dropper bottle of 0.1 M **silver nitrate reagent**

8. Dropper bottle of **iodine reagent**

9. Test tube rack

10. 6 test tubes

Method

1. Obtain a dialysis tube and tie off one end of the tube with string.

2. Fill the sack with a salt–starch solution and tie off the open end.

3. Rinse the sack with distilled water and blot dry; weigh the sack and then record its (original) weight.

4. Place sack into a 600 ml beaker that has been previously filled with distilled water. Wait 20 minutes.

5. Meanwhile, obtain four clean test tubes, and number them 1–4. Prepare the following controls:

   a. To tube #1, add 1 cm of distilled water. Then add 2 drops of iodine reagent. This tube is your negative control for the starch test. Save this tube, and record your observation on the data sheet.

   b. To tube #2, add 1 cm of the starch solution. Then add 2 drops of iodine reagent. This tube is your positive control for the starch test. Save this tube, and record your observation on the data sheet.

c. To tube #3, add 1 cm of distilled water. Then add 2 drops of 0.1 M silver nitrate reagent. This tube is your negative control for the salt test. Save this tube, and record your observation on the data sheet.

d. To tube #4, add 1 cm of salt (NaCl) solution. Then add 2 drops of 0.1 M silver nitrate reagent. This tube is your positive control for the salt test. Save this tube, and record your observation on the data sheet.

6. Obtain two more test tubes, and number them 5 and 6. After the 20-minute incubation is complete, perform the following tests:

a. To tube #5, add 1 cm of water from the beaker. Test this beaker water for the presence of starch by adding 2 drops of iodine reagent. Compare this test tube to your starch controls (tubes #1 and #2) to determine whether starch is present in the beaker water. Record your results on the data sheet.

b. To tube #6, add 1 cm of water from the beaker. Test this beaker water for the presence of salt by adding 2 drops of silver nitrate reagent. Compare this test tube to your salt controls (tubes #3 and #4) to determine whether salt is present in the beaker water. Record your results on the data sheet.

7. Remove sack from beaker, blot dry, weigh, and record its present weight.

8. Over the sink, puncture sack, drain out liquid, and dispose of the used sack in the waste basket.

Membrane Transport

Data Sheet 7

Name _____

Section _____ Date _____

Part A: The Importance of Surface Area to Volume Ratio

Size of Cube	Surface Area 6(L × W)	Total Volume (L × W × H)	Surface Area to Volume Ratio	Size of Light Portion (in mm)	Volume of Light Portion (L × W × H)	% Iodine Penetration*
5 mm						
10 mm						

Total volume: see above data—Part A

Volume of light portion: (L × W × H) of light area

$$*\% \, penetration = \frac{Total \ Volume - Volume \ of \ light \ portion}{Total \ Volume} \times 100$$

Dark (iodine plus starch)

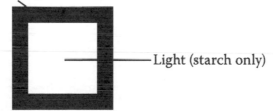

Light (starch only)

Figure 7.1. Cut surface of potato cube

1. Are your results as expected? _____

   Explain your answer: _____

Part B: Simple Diffusion

Molecule	Molecular Weight	Diameter of Diffusion Zone in mm
Iodine	127	
Methylene Blue	320	

1. Which molecule diffused faster? Why?

Part C1: Tonicity (Weight Change)

Sucrose Solution	Original Weight	Present Weight	Weight Change (present – original)	% Weight Change* (gain or loss)
0%				
10%				
20%				
30%				

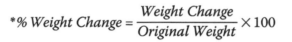

$$*\% \ Weight \ Change = \frac{Weight \ Change}{Original \ Weight} \times 100$$

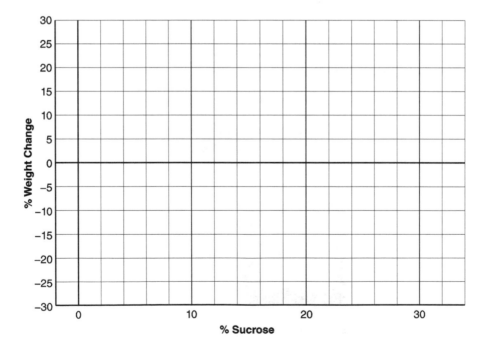

a. Draw a line to connect your data points. Where (at what % sucrose) does your line cross the bolded x-axis? What does this spot represent, *i.e.*, what is the percent weight change of the carrot at the point it crosses the x-axis?

b. Which concentration(s) of sugar is/are closest to isotonic?

c. Which concentration(s) of sugar is/are hypertonic?

d. Which concentration(s) of sugar is/are hypotonic?

Part C2: Tonicity (Plasmolysis)

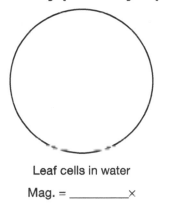

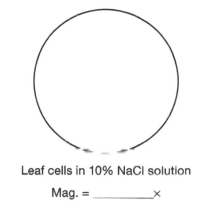

Leaf cells in water

Mag. = _____×

Leaf cells in 10% NaCl solution

Mag. = _____×

a. How does the distribution of the chloroplasts differ in the two demonstrations?

b. State the reason for the appearance of chloroplasts mentioned above.

c. Is 10% NaCl solution isotonic, hypotonic, or hypertonic compared to the plant cell?

Part D: Diffusion and Osmosis Across a Selectively Permeable Membrane

*Original weight of sack _____ g   *Present weight of sack _____ g

	Reagent Used (Test Solution)	Control Test Tube Appearance		Beaker Water	
		Distilled Water (–)	Starch Solution (+)	Beaker Water Test Appearance	Positive or Negative?
Starch Test					

	Reagent Used (Test Solution)	Control Test Tube Appearance		Beaker Water	
		Distilled Water (–)	Salt Solution (+)	Beaker Water Test Appearance	Positive or Negative?
Salt Test					

1. *What accounts for the weight change of the sack? Explain your answer, noting the type of transport involved.

2. What substance(s) went into the sack? Explain your answer, noting the type of transport involved.

3. What substance(s) went into the beaker? Explain your answer, noting the type of transport involved.

The Action of Enzymes

Exercise 8

Objectives

1. Define the terms **catalyst, variable, hydrolysis, substrate, product, active site,** and **metabolism.**
2. Explain the effect of time, temperature, and pH on enzyme activity.
3. Describe the effect of an inhibitor on enzyme activity.

Introduction

Almost all enzymes are complex protein molecules found in all living organisms. They function as catalysts in metabolic processes, such as photosynthesis, respiration, and digestion. Enzymes are able to speed up reactions at very low concentrations and at moderate temperatures that would otherwise require a long time, strong chemicals, and high temperatures, which would not be compatible with life.

Protein enzymes have a unique three-dimensional structure or **conformation**. Variations in the structure affect the enzyme's activity, since activity depends on how well a **substrate** binds to the **active site** of the enzyme. This also makes enzymes specific; a particular enzyme will only catalyze a particular reaction due to the compatibility of the fit between the substrate and the active site. Factors that alter the conformation affect enzyme activity. Many such factors are known. For example, extreme deviations from optimum temperature or pH (measure of acidity or alkalinity) change the enzyme's conformation, and the enzyme may lose some or all activity. The enzyme has been **denatured**. Metal ions may act as **inhibitors** of enzyme activity by interacting with the enzyme and altering its conformation or blocking its active site. The enzyme's activity is destroyed, and we say that the enzyme has been poisoned.

In this exercise, you will conduct a series of experiments designed to test the effect of time, temperature, pH, and the presence of heavy metal ions on enzyme activity. You will use the enzyme **amylase**, which **hydrolyzes** starch into simple sugar. Hydrolysis will be determined by the use of the iodine test for starch.

$$\text{starch} \xrightarrow{\text{amylase}} \text{maltose}$$

starch   maltose
(Substrate)   *(Enzyme)*   *(Product)*

Figure 8.1. Starch hydrolysis by the enzyme amylase yields the product maltose, a disaccharide

Part A: Effect of Time

Materials

1. Amylase
2. Wax pencil
3. Small metric ruler
4. Starch solution (room temperature)
5. Test tubes and rack
6. Iodine reagent
7. Plastic pipettes

Method

1. Place eight drops of prepared amylase into four numbered test tubes.

2. To each test tube, add 3 ml of starch solution.

3. Test tube #1 **immediately** for starch by adding two drops of iodine. Record your results on the data sheet.

4. Test tube #2 for starch by adding 2 drops of iodine after ___ minutes.

5. Test tube #3 after ___ minutes for starch, as before.

6. Test tube #4 after ___ minutes for starch, as before.

Part A: Effect of Time—Procedure

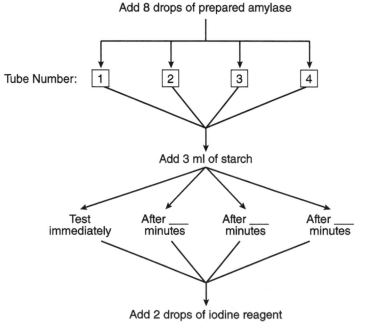

Part B: Effect of Temperature

Materials

1. Amylase
2. Wax pencil
3. Small metric ruler
4. Hot plate
5. Test tubes and rack
6. Starch solution (cold, room temperature, and warm)
7. Iodine reagent
8. Ice bath
9. Water bath (37 °C)
10. Plastic pipettes
11. Test tube clamps

Method

1. Place eight drops of prepared amylase into four numbered clean test tubes.

2. Place the test tubes in the following conditions for 15 minutes: tube #1 in a boiling water bath, tube #2 at room temperature, tube #3 in an ice bath, and tube #4 in the 37 °C water bath.

3. Using the test tube clamp, remove test tube #1 from the boiling water bath and allow it to cool for five minutes at room temperature. All other tubes can remain at their incubation temperatures during this five-minute waiting period.

4. Add starch to each test tube and incubate according to the following guidelines:

   a. To test tubes #1 and #2, add 3 ml of **room temperature** starch and incubate for 2 minutes at room temperature.

   b. To test tube #3, add 3 ml of **cold starch** and incubate for 2 minutes on ice.

   c. To test tube #4, add 3 ml of **warm** (37 °C) **starch** and incubate for 2 minutes in the 37 °C water bath.

5. After the 2-minute incubation is complete, test each tube for starch by adding two drops of iodine. Record your results on the data sheet.

6. What do you conclude about the heat stability of the enzyme?

Part B: Effect of Temperature—Procedure

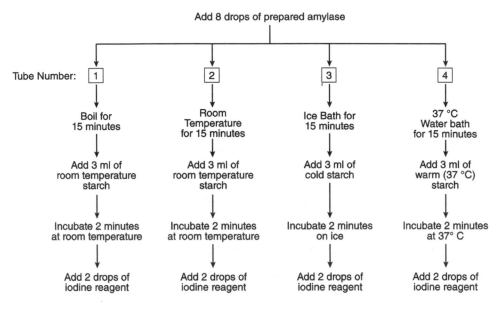

Part C: Effect of pH

Materials

1. Amylase
2. Starch solution (room temperature)
3. Test tubes and rack
4. Iodine reagent
5. Plastic pipettes
6. pH 4 buffer solution
7. pH 7 buffer solution
8. pH 9 buffer solution

Method

1. Label three test tubes: pH 4, pH 7, and pH 9.

2. Add eight drops of prepared amylase into each of the labeled test tubes.

3. Add 1 ml of the appropriate buffer solution into the marked test tubes.

4. Pipette 3 ml of starch solution into each of the three labeled test tubes. As you add the starch solution, start a six-minute timer.

5. After the six-minute incubation (i.e., when your timer goes off), add two drops of iodine reagent to the labeled test tubes.

6. Record your observations on the data sheet. At which pH was starch hydrolysis most efficient?

Part C: Effect of pH—Procedure

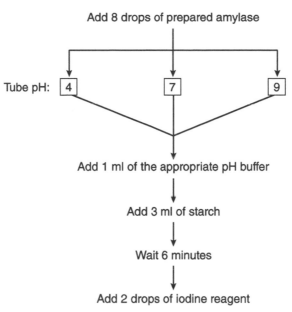

Add 8 drops of prepared amylase

Tube pH: 4   7   9

Add 1 ml of the appropriate pH buffer

Add 3 ml of starch

Wait 6 minutes

Add 2 drops of iodine reagent

Part D: Effect of Heavy Metal Ions (Copper)

Materials

1. Amylase
2. Starch solution (room temperature)
3. Test tubes in rack
4. 20% copper sulfate reagent
5. Iodine reagent
6. pH 7 buffer solution
7. Plastic pipettes
8. Small metric ruler
9. Distilled water

Method

1. Place eight drops of prepared amylase into each of two clean test tubes. Label the test tubes #1 and #2.

2. Add two drops of copper sulfate ($CuSO_4$) (heavy metal) reagent to test tube #1, and two drops of distilled water to test tube #2. Test tube #2 is your negative control.

3. Place the two test tubes in a test tube rack and wait five minutes.

4. Add 2 ml of starch solution to each of the test tubes.

5. Place the two test tubes back in the test tube rack and wait another five minutes.

6. Add two drops of iodine reagent to each tube. Record the results observed on your data sheet. Did the presence of heavy metal ions (copper) affect the result?

Note: Refer to the figure on the next page.

Part D: Effect of Heavy Metal Ions—Procedure

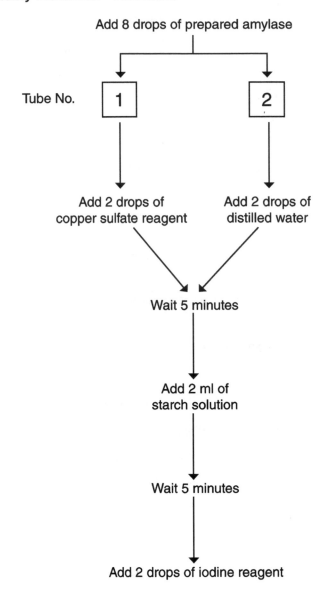

Data Sheet 8

Name _____

Section _____ Date _____

Part A: Effect of Time

Record the color and degree of amylase activity in each of the four tubes. Use ++ for complete starch hydrolysis, + for partial starch hydrolysis, and 0 for no starch hydrolysis. (**Hint**: A negative starch result indicates complete starch hydrolysis.)

Tube Number	1 (0 min)	2 (___ min)	3 (___ min)	4 (___ min)
Color of Solution				
Starch Hydrolysis				

Did the time difference between tube #1 and tube #2 alter the results? Explain the answer.

Did the time difference between tube #3 and tube #4 alter the results? Explain the answer.

Part B: Effect of Temperature

Record the color and degree of amylase activity in each of the four tubes. Use ++ for complete starch hydrolysis, + for partial starch hydrolysis, and 0 for no starch hydrolysis. (**Hint**: A negative starch result indicates complete starch hydrolysis.)

Tube Number	1 (100 °C)	2 (Room Temperature)	3 (0 °C)	4 (37 °C)
Color of Solution				
Starch Hydrolysis				

How did temperature affect the activity of the enzyme? Explain the results seen in each test tube.

Part C: Effect of pH

Record the color and degree of amylase activity in each of the three tubes. Use ++ for complete starch hydrolysis, + for partial starch hydrolysis, and 0 for no starch hydrolysis. (**Hint**: A negative starch result indicates complete starch hydrolysis.)

Tube Number	1 (pH 4)	2 (pH 7)	3 (pH 9)
Color of Solution			
Starch Hydrolysis			

At which pH was starch hydrolysis most efficient? At which pH is hydrolysis least efficient? Explain the results seen in each test tube.

Part D: Effect of Heavy Metal Ions

Record the color and degree of amylase activity in each of the two tubes. Use ++ for complete starch hydrolysis, + for partial starch hydrolysis, and 0 for no starch hydrolysis. (**Hint**: A negative starch result indicates complete starch hydrolysis.)

Tube Number	1 ($CuSO_4$)	2 (Negative Control)
Color of Solution		
Starch Hydrolysis		

How did the presence of heavy metal ions (copper) affect the results? Explain the results seen in each test tube.

Cellular Respiration

Exercise 9

Objectives

1. Distinguish between aerobic and anaerobic respiration.
2. Write the overall balanced equation for aerobic cellular respiration.
3. State and explain the effects of nutrient source on fermentation.
4. Define and perform a titration.

Introduction

Cellular respiration refers to a series of biochemical reactions employed by cells to extract and capture the chemical energy stored within molecules. In classifying respiratory reactions, two major categories are employed: **aerobic** and **anaerobic**. Aerobic respiration requires oxygen or a substitute. The following equation summarizes chemical events of aerobic cellular respiration.

$$C_6H_{12}O_6 \;+\; 6O_2 \;\rightarrow\; 6H_2O \;+\; 6CO_2 \;+\; \text{Energy}$$

$$\text{(glucose)} \qquad \text{(oxygen)} \qquad \text{(water)} \qquad \text{(carbon dioxide)} \qquad \text{(ATP–36/38 molecules)}$$

Here, glucose is completely broken down in the presence of oxygen to carbon dioxide and water and the energy released is used to make ATP. Carbon dioxide can dissolve in water, and some becomes carbonic acid.

$$CO_2 \;+\; H_2O \;\rightleftharpoons\; H_2CO_3 \;\rightleftharpoons\; H^+ \;+\; HCO_3^-$$

$$\text{(carbonic acid)} \qquad \text{(hydrogen ion)} \qquad \text{(bicarbonate ion)}$$

In part of this exercise, you will measure the amount of carbonic acid in a solution by using a method called **titration**. Titration is a technique used to determine an unknown amount of an acid or a base by using a neutralization reaction. We will use an indicator that changes color when the solution changes from acidic to basic (or vice versa).

Anaerobic respiration does not require oxygen. During one form of anaerobic respiration known as fermentation, glucose is incompletely broken down. Thus, less energy is released and fewer molecules of ATP are made during anaerobic respiration. This form of respiration is considerably less efficient.

Two common types of anaerobic respiration are alcohol fermentation and lactic acid fermentation. The following equations illustrate alcohol and lactic acid fermentation, respectively:

$$C_6H_{12}O_6 \quad \rightarrow \quad 2CH_3CH_2OH \quad + \quad 2CO_2 \quad + \quad Energy$$

(glucose)   (ethyl alcohol)   (carbon dioxide)   (ATP–2 molecules)

$$C_6H_{12}O_6 \quad \rightarrow \quad 2CH_3CH(OH)COOH \quad + \quad Energy$$

(lactic acid)   (ATP–2 molecules)

Note the production of carbon dioxide during alcohol fermentation but not during lactic acid fermentation.

ATP generated during cell respiration is used by cells to carry out innumerable cellular activities like active transport, biosynthesis, muscle contraction, etc. Indeed, ATP is the universal energy currency of cells.

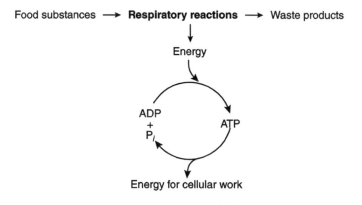

Part A: Effect of Nutrient Source on Fermentation

Materials

1. Wax pencil
2. 5 paper cups containing yeast
3. 5% glucose solution
4. 5% sucrose solution
5. 5% lactose solution
6. 1% starch solution
7. Distilled water
8. 50 ml graduated cylinder
9. 5 fermentation tubes
10. Wooden applicator sticks
11. Small metric ruler

Method

1. Select five paper cups containing yeast.
2. Label the paper cups glucose, sucrose, lactose, starch, and distilled water.
3. Add 40 ml of glucose solution to the paper cup labeled glucose. Mix the yeast and glucose solution thoroughly using a wooden applicator stick.
4. Repeat the procedure described in step 3 for the other paper cups, adding the appropriate solution to each paper cup.
5. Following the directions of your laboratory instructor, add the contents of each of the paper cups to separate, labeled fermentation tubes.
6. Observe and record gas production in the closed arm of the tube at 45 minutes. Use a ruler to measure gas accumulation in the arm of the fermentation tube to the nearest mm. (See diagram on the data sheet for measuring directions.)

Part B: Measurement of Respiration by Titration

Materials

1. Beaker with 250 ml of distilled water
2. 25 ml graduated cylinder
3. Dropper bottle of phenolphthalein
4. Six 50 ml beakers
5. Plastic pipettes
6. Dropper bottle of 0.0025 M sodium hydroxide (NaOH) solution
7. Wax pencil
8. Soda straw

Method

1. Using the wax pencil, label your six 50-ml beakers as follows:

   a. Two beakers are labeled "control"

   b. Two beakers are labeled "5-breath"

   c. Two beakers are labeled "10-breath"

2. Using the graduated cylinder, measure 25 ml water samples (from the large beaker) into both of the "control" beakers.

3. Using the soda straw, *gently* exhale 5 breaths into the large beaker of distilled water.

4. Using the graduated cylinder, measure 25 ml water samples (from the large beaker) into both of the "5-breath" beakers.

5. Using the soda straw, *gently* exhale 5 additional breaths into the large beaker of distilled water. (The water will now have a total of 10 breaths exhaled into it.)

6. Using the graduated cylinder, measure 25 ml water samples (from the large beaker) into both of the "10-breath" beakers.

7. For each of your six samples:

   a. Add three drops of the phenolphthalein indicator solution.

   b. Using a plastic pipette, carefully titrate each beaker with 0.0025 M sodium hydroxide (NaOH) solution following the directions given by your laboratory instructor. The end point is reached when the *first lasting tinge of a pink color appears*. This color change indicates that the neutralization of carbonic acid by sodium hydroxide has been completed; in other words, the end point of the titration has been reached. (**Note:** Please make sure to add drops of NaOH slowly and mix your sample carefully but thoroughly during the titration. However, do *not* use the tip of your pipette to stir the solution in your 50 ml beaker as you titrate it; doing so will cause you to contaminate the bottle of NaOH when you refill your pipette.)

   c. On your data sheet, record the number of drops of NaOH required to reach the end point.

8. Perform the calculations and answer the related questions on your data sheet (on the back of the page).

9. Dispose of titration waste in the designated waste container, as indicated by your instructor.

10. Remove wax pencil marks from the 50 ml beakers used for the titration by wiping them with a dry paper towel. Then, wash and rinse the beakers before returning them to the benchtop.

Part C: Resazurin Dye Reduction Test

Materials

1. 10 ml graduated cylinder
2. Milk samples (A and B)
3. Two screw-capped test tubes
4. Dropper bottle of Resazurin
5. Water bath at 37 °C

Method

1. Secure two clean, screw-capped test tubes and label them A and B.

2. Add 9.0 ml of the milk samples provided to the corresponding test tubes. (**Note:** One of these milk samples contains milk-spoiling bacteria. These bacteria can use Resazurin as their final electron acceptor during anaerobic respiration.)

3. Add 20 drops Resazurin dye solution to each of the tubes. Replace the caps, and gently mix the contents of the tubes just until a uniform color is achieved.

4. Place tubes in the water bath. Observe and record any color changes every 15 minutes for at least 1 hour. Do **not** shake the tubes when you check them. **Note:** Any color changes that occur are due to the reduction of Resazurin, which serves as a final electron (hydrogen) acceptor.

Part D: Lactic Acid Fermentation

Materials

1. 50 ml of warm whole milk
2. 100 ml beaker
3. 1 tsp. yogurt with active cultures
4. 1 wooden applicator stick
5. pH paper
6. One 600 ml beaker for the class

Method

Day 1

1. Using the graduations on your 100 ml beaker, measure approximately 50 ml of warm whole milk.
2. Test and record the pH.
3. Mix in 1 teaspoon of yogurt.

4. Pour the milk–yogurt mixture into the 600 ml beaker as indicated by your instructor.

5. This large beaker will be incubated at 37 °C until the next lab session.

Day 2

1. Observe the odor and consistency of the yogurt.

2. Test and record the pH of the yogurt.

Data Sheet

Name _____

Section _____ Date _____

Part A: Effect of Nutrient Source on Fermentation

	Distance (mm)
Yeast + Glucose	
Yeast + Sucrose	
Yeast + Lactose	
Yeast + Starch	
Yeast + Water	

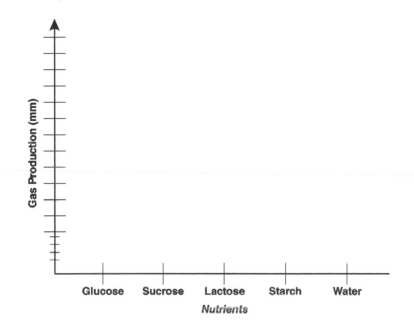

Gas bubbles

Measure this distance in mm

Yeast solution

Portion of closed arm of fermentation tube

Bar graph showing effect of nutrient source on fermentation.

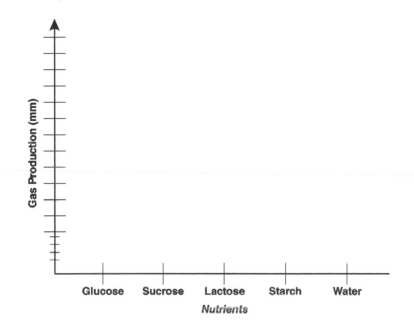

Gas Production (mm)

Glucose   Sucrose   Lactose   Starch   Water

Nutrients

1. Which nutrient source is best for yeast? How do you know?

2. What was the purpose of the yeast and water sample?

3. Why is starch not a good source of nutrition for yeast?

4. Why is lactose not a good source of nutrition for yeast?

5. Name the gas collected in the closed arm of the fermentation tube.

Part B: Measurement of Respiration by Titration

	Drops of NaOH Sample 1	Drops of NaOH Sample 2	Average Drops of NaOH*	Average Volume of NaOH (ml)**
Control				
5-breath				
10-breath				

 * Average number of drops = (Sample 1 + Sample 2) ÷ 2
** 1 drop = 0.05 milliliter (ml). Volume of NaOH = (Number of drops) × (0.05 ml)

1. What acid were you measuring in this titration experiment?

2. What is the role of phenolphthalein in this experiment?

3. Which sample required the least NaOH to reach the end point? Explain your answer.

4. Which sample required the most NaOH to reach the end point? Explain your answer.

Part C: Resazurin Dye Reduction Test

	0 minutes	15 minutes	30 minutes	45 minutes	60 minutes
Tube A					
Tube B					

1. Which tube changed color?

2. Which tube contained the spoiled milk?

3. What is the function of the Resazurin?

Part D: Lactic Acid Fermentation

pH of milk (Day 1): _____

pH of yogurt (Day 2): _____

1. What was the purpose of adding the yogurt to the warmed milk?

2. What accounts for the pH change?

3. Name another organism that can perform lactic acid fermentation.

Photosynthesis

Exercise 10

Gordon Swanson/Shutterstock.com

Objectives

1. Write the overall balanced equation for photosynthesis.

2. Identify photosynthetic organisms.

3. Explain and label the basic structures of a leaf and a chloroplast.

4. Evaluate and explain the effects of light intensity and color on photosynthesis.

5. Explain the role of carbon dioxide in photosynthesis.

6. Identify and evaluate the solubility of photosynthetic pigments using paper chromatography.

Introduction

Almost all life on earth depends upon green plants (**photoautotrophs** or **producers**) to trap the energy of sunlight through the process of **photosynthesis**. During photosynthesis, carbon dioxide combines with water in the presence of sunlight to produce glucose. Oxygen is produced as a by-product of this process and is the source of our atmospheric oxygen. The glucose from photosynthesis is a carbohydrate and serves as the source of energy and nutrients for **heterotrophs** or **consumers**. The carbon skeleton of glucose forms a framework on which other organic compounds can be built.

Where do you think the bulk of the world's photosynthesis occurs? If you said the forests of the world, you would be wrong. The oceans of the world contain the greatest concentration of photosynthetic organisms. They constitute the **phytoplankton** of the seas. The overall equation for the process of photosynthesis is shown below:

$$6CO_2 + 6H_2O \xrightarrow[\text{Light}]{\text{Chlorophyll}} C_6H_{12}O_6 + 6O_2$$

$$\text{(carbon dioxide)} \quad \text{(water)} \qquad\qquad\qquad \text{(sugar)} \quad \text{(oxygen)}$$

In this exercise, we will observe several important aquatic photosynthetic organisms. We will study the basic structure of a leaf, the photosynthetic organ of plants. We will also separate photosynthetic pigments using paper chromatography, a technique that is used to separate a mixture of molecules based on their solubility in a solvent.

Part A: Sites of Photosynthesis

Materials

1. Compound microscope

2. Microslide viewer

3. Microslide 79: "The Leaf of the Flowering Plant"

4. Prepared slide of diatoms

5. Live culture: diatom

6. Prepared slide of stomata

7. Prepared slides of leaf cross-section (monocot and dicot)

8. Leaf model

9. Chloroplast model

Method

1. Diatoms: These are microscopic algae that are among the most important groups of photosynthetic organisms in marine and freshwater environments. Prepare a wet mount from the diatom culture. You may need to use your high power (40×) objective. Locate the glass-like cell walls and the golden brown chloroplasts of the diatoms. Sketch and label a few diatom cells in the space provided on your data sheet. For additional representative diatoms, examine a prepared slide of diatoms.

2. A leaf is the major organ of photosynthesis in plants. It is a good example of how form fits function in biological systems. Label the leaf structures on Figure 10.1.

Chloroplast	Cell wall	Veins	Xylem
Palisade mesophyll	Spongy mesophyll	Phloem	Air space
Lower epidermis	Upper epidermis	Stoma	Nucleus
Guard cell	Cuticle		

3. View Microslide 79: "The Leaf of the Flowering Plant." The microslide gives an overview of the anatomy of a typical leaf. Identify the structures listed above, and complete the sketches and questions on your data sheet.

4. View the models of leaf and chloroplast. Between the two models, you should be able to identify all the structures listed above.

5. **Stomata** are microscopic openings located on the lower epidermis that allow the entrance of carbon dioxide into plant leaves with the simultaneous release of water and oxygen. The size of these openings is variable and is controlled by **guard cells**. Obtain a prepared slide of *Tradescantia* epidermis and locate the stomata–guard cell complexes on the leaves using the microscope.

6. View the prepared slides showing leaf cross-sections from a monocot and dicot, which are both available as demonstrations in the lab. As you sketch the cross-sections in the circles provided on your data sheet, identify and label the structures (listed in Method A2, on left) that you've already seen on the leaf cross-section model, diagram, and microslide images.

©Hayden-McNeil, LLC

Figure 10.1. Cross section of a dicot, *Privet (Ligustrum)* leaf

Part B: Effect of Light on Photosynthesis (white light/green light)

Materials
1. Volumeter
2. Test tube rack
3. Light source (lamp)
4. 1 sprig of aquatic plant
5. Beaker, 600 ml
6. Sodium bicarbonate ($NaHCO_3$) solution
7. Green food coloring in water
8. Grease pencil
9. Small metric ruler

Method
1. Set up the gas-collecting volumeter apparatus as shown in Figure 10.2 and as demonstrated by your instructor. Make sure the cut end of the plant sprig is up.

2. Fill the volumeter with enough sodium bicarbonate ($NaHCO_3$) such that the level of the fluid in the pipette is into the horizontal portion.

3. Arrange your volumeter apparatus such that the horizontal portion of the pipette is actually horizontal, or even angled up very slightly toward the open end. This will prevent the fluid from dripping out of the pipette and ruining your results.

4. Place the light source 10 cm from the tube containing the aquatic plant.

5. Place a beaker with water in between the volumeter and the light source.

6. Turn on the lamp and allow a 2-minute time period to elapse. Use a grease pencil to mark the level of liquid in the small glass tube. This is the initial reading.

7. After 5 minutes, draw a line to mark the level of liquid. Measure the distance between these lines in mm, and record it on your data sheet.

8. Move the light source back to a distance of 20 cm from the tube. Allow two minutes to pass, and mark the level of liquid. This line is your new initial reading.

9. After 5 minutes, draw another line to mark the level of liquid. Measure the distance between these lines in mm, and record it on your data sheet.

10. Turn off the lamp and place it 10 cm from your volumeter once again.

11. Remove the beaker of water, and replace it with the beaker of green water.

12. Turn on the lamp and allow 2 minutes to elapse. Draw a line to mark the level of liquid. This is the initial reading with the green light.

13. Allow 5 minutes to elapse, and draw a line to mark the level of liquid. Measure the distance between these lines in mm, and record it on your data sheet.

14. When you are finished recording your results, use a dry paper towel to wipe off all of the grease pencil marks you have made on the small glass tube.

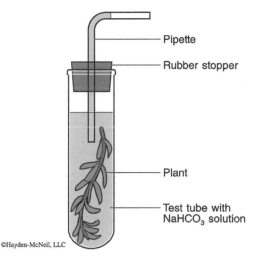

— Pipette

— Rubber stopper

— Plant

— Test tube with NaHCO₃ solution

©Hayden-McNeil, LLC

Figure 10.2. Volumeter. Observe the level of the solution in the pipette and the completely immersed plant

Part C: Carbon Dioxide—Uptake and Measurement

Materials

1. Two clean test tubes

2. Dropper bottle of phenol red solution

3. Soda straw

4. Test tube rack (wire)

5. Aquatic plants

6. Light source (lamp)

7. pH paper

Method

1. Secure two clean test tubes and fill them ½ full of tap water.

2. Add three drops of phenol red (acid–base indicator) and carefully shake tubes to turn the contents of the tubes light pink in color.

3. Determine the pH of the solution in each tube with pH paper. Record the color and pH of each solution on your data sheet.

4. Using a straw, exhale very gently into the tubes until a light-yellow color develops. **Carbon dioxide** (your breath) plus water will yield **carbonic acid**.

5. Determine the pH of the solution in each tube with pH paper. Record the color and pH of each solution on your data sheet.

6. Add a 6 cm sprig of the aquatic plant to one of the tubes.

7. Incubate the tubes in front of a light source for one hour or until a color change occurs.

8. Record the color and pH of each solution on your data sheet.

9. Dispose of the phenol red waste in the designated waste container, as indicated by your instructor.

Part D: Separation and Identification of Photosynthetic Pigments Using Paper Chromatography

Materials
1. Chromatography tube with cork
2. Strip of chromatography paper
3. Chromatography solvent
4. Leaves
5. Glass stirring rods

Method
1. See the demonstration beaker containing chlorophyll extract set up at the front of the laboratory. Read the accompanying material and carry out this simple and quick demonstration activity.

2. Secure a large test tube with cork stopper. Place 2–3 ml of chromatography solvent into the tube and replace the cork stopper.

3. Secure a chromatography strip, a small piece of leaf, and a small glass rod. Place the leaf section across the chromatography strip, directly above the pointed end. (See data sheet.) Using the glass rod, press the leaf section onto the surface of the chromatography strip as directed by your laboratory instructor. *Do this several times, using a fresh area of the leaf each time.*

4. Place the strip into the chromatography tube, taking care that only the tip touches the solvent. Seal the tube with the cork. Observe results over a one-hour period. **Pigments can move with the solvent up the chromatography paper; the more soluble the pigment, the farther it will travel.**

5. Record your observations on the data sheet. Draw and label each of the colored bands on the mock chromatography strip. The pigments commonly found in plant leaves and their colors are listed below:

   carotenes: yellow
   chlorophyll a: blue-green
   chlorophyll b: yellow-green

6. Dispose of the used chromatography solvent in the appropriate waste container at the front of laboratory. Return the chromatography tube to the front of the laboratory. **Note: Do not put water into the tube. Do not clean the tube.**

Data Sheet

Name _____

Section _____ Date _____

Part A: Sites of Photosynthesis

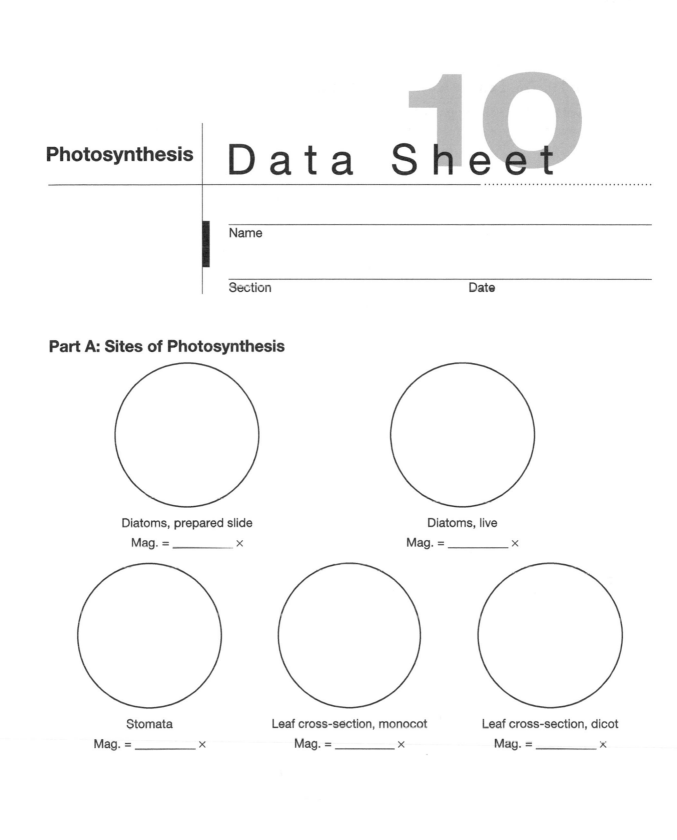

Diatoms, prepared slide
Mag. = _____ ×

Diatoms, live
Mag. = _____ ×

Stomata
Mag. = _____ ×

Leaf cross-section, monocot
Mag. = _____ ×

Leaf cross-section, dicot
Mag. = _____ ×

Microslide 79: The Leaf of a Flowering Plant

Working Layers of the Leaf: Images 2, 3, and 7

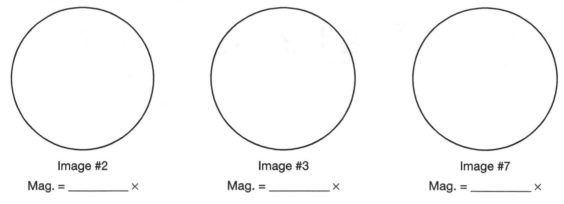

Image #2	Image #3	Image #7
Mag. = _____ ×	Mag. = _____ ×	Mag. = _____ ×

1. What do the following letters indicate in these images?

    a. E: _____

    b. P: _____

    c. Y: _____

    d. A: _____

    e. S: _____

2. Consider the arrow in Image #2.

    a. What does the arrow indicate?

    b. What is the function of this structure?

Chloroplast: Image 4

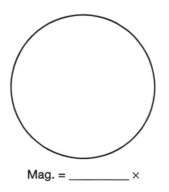

Mag. = _____ ×

1. What pigment molecule, which absorbs solar energy, is found within the chloroplast?

Epidermis with Stomata: Images 5 and 6

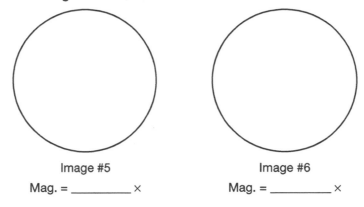

Image #5   Image #6

Mag. = _____ ×   Mag. = _____ ×

1. How many stomata do you see in Image #5? _____

2. What is the function of the guard cells that surround each stoma?

Part B: Effect of Light on Photosynthesis (white light/green light)

Rate of Photosynthesis (mm O_2 per 5 min.)—White Light	
10 cm from light source	20 cm from light source
mm	mm

Rate of Photosynthesis (mm O_2 per 5 min.)—Green Light
10 cm from light source
mm

a. Name the gas collected in this apparatus: _____ .

b. The gas molecules come from the splitting of _____ .

c. Did moving the light source away increase or decrease gas production? Is this as expected? Explain your answer.

d. Did changing the light source to green increase or decrease gas production? Is this as expected? Explain your answer.

e. Since the volumeter is stoppered, from where is the plant getting CO_2 to carry out photosynthesis?

Part C: Carbon Dioxide—Uptake and Measurement

	Initial		After Exhalation		After Incubation	
	Color	pH	Color	pH	Color	pH
Tube with plant						
Tube without plant						

a. What is the purpose of phenol red in the experiment?

b. What caused the color change, if any, after you exhaled into the tubes?

c. What caused the color change, if any, in the tube with the plant after incubation? Explain your answer.

d. What caused the color change, if any, in the tube without the plant after incubation? Explain your answer.

Part D: Separation and Identification of Photosynthetic Pigments Using Paper Chromatography

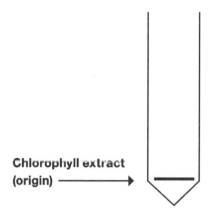

Chlorophyll extract
(origin)

a. Which pigment traveled the farthest? What can you tell about its solubility in the solvent?

b. Separation of photosynthetic pigments occur due to differences in _____.

c. Describe what you saw in the demonstration beaker containing chlorophyll extract (in Method 1).

Rat Anatomy

Exercise 11

Objectives

1. Describe the basic body plan of a mammal.

2. Locate the major body cavities.

3. Identify the major muscles and bones.

4. Identify and state the functions of major organs of the digestive, circulatory, respiratory, endocrine, and urogenital systems.

5. Identify the major vessels of the circulatory system.

Introduction

Rats, like humans, belong to the class **mammalia** in the phylum **chordata**, so their structural organization is similar to our own. Characteristics of mammals include mammary glands to nourish their offspring, hair at some time during their life cycle, and in most mammals, internal development of young. Compared to other animals, mammals also have a large, well-developed brain and greater intelligence.

In this exercise, you will study the anatomy of a rat using a technique called dissection. Dissection makes use of a set of instruments (such as a scalpel, scissors, forceps, blunt probe, etc.) to allow for observation of external and internal structures. We will study seven of the organ systems of the mammalian body. Major organs of each system, their location in the body cavities, and their functions will be identified.

Part A: External Anatomy and Skeleton

Materials

1. Preserved rat

2. Dissection pan

3. Rat skeleton

4. Human skeleton

5. Non-latex gloves

6. Dissection kit

7. Dissection chart

Method

1. Observe the general shape of the rat and the two main body cavities: **dorsal** and **ventral.** The dorsal cavity is further divided into the **cranial** and **vertebral** cavities. The divisions of the ventral cavity include the **thorax** and **abdominopelvic** cavities.

2. Rodents are characterized by long, gnawing, continually growing **incisor teeth** that must be worn down as they grow. Look inside the mouth. What types and how many teeth are located there? _____

3. Locate the **vibrissae** (whiskers) projecting from the snout. Observe the location of the other sense organs: **eyes, ears,** and **nose.** At the posterior end, find the **anus.**

4. In the **male,** the **scrotum,** which contains the **testes,** will be seen near the anus. Just anterior to the scrotum is the opening of the male urogenital system, the **penis.** In the **female,** there are three openings: **anus, vaginal opening** (anterior to anus), and **urinary opening** (anterior to the vagina). What is the sex of your rat? _____

5. Exchange your rat for one of the opposite sex with another group and observe the structures mentioned above.

6. Next, study and compare the skeleton of a rat to that of a human. Both are very similar in basic features and can be subdivided into an **axial skeleton,** consisting of a skull, vertebral column, ribs and sternum, and an **appendicular skeleton,** consisting of the bones attached to the axial skeleton. Differences observable in skull structure are correlated with difference in brain, sense organs, and feeding mechanisms. Differences in the appendicular skeleton result from posture: quadruped as opposed to biped.

7. Identify the bones listed below on a human skeleton:

Axial Skeleton

- Cranium
  - o Maxilla
  - o Mandible
- Vertebral column
  - o Cervical vertebrae
  - o Thoracic vertebrae
  - o Lumbar vertebrae
  - o Sacral vertebrae
  - o Coccyx
- Sternum
- Ribs

Appendicular Skeleton

- Pectoral girdle
  - o Clavicle
  - o Scapula
- Upper limb
  - o Humerus
  - o Radius
  - o Ulna
  - o Carpals
  - o Metacarpals
  - o Phalanges
- Pelvic girdle
  - o Os coxa
- Lower limb
  - o Femur
  - o Patella
  - o Tibia
  - o Fibula
  - o Tarsals
  - o Metatarsals
  - o Phalanges

Part B: Internal Anatomy

Materials

1. Preserved rat

2. Dissection pan

3. Dissection kit, pins, tag

4. Non-latex gloves

5. Dissection chart

Method

1. **Muscular system:**

   a. Dissection:

      i.   Place the rat on its back in the dissecting pan. Make a **midventral** incision with scissors through the **skin** from the **pelvis** to the **lower jaw**.

      ii. Lay back the skin in the thoracic area, exposing the underlying muscles and make a perpendicular incision extending just below the upper limb. Carefully skin a fore paw.

      iii. Lay back the skin in the abdominal area and make a perpendicular cut extending just above the lower limb. Skin a hind paw. Extend this cut around the back and gently pull away the skin along the dorsal surface up to the base of the head.

      iv. Next, carefully remove any superficial fat and connective tissue from a given region before attempting to identify the muscles. Observe the *direction* in which the muscle fibers run as an indication of dividing lines between muscles. Identify the muscles indicated in Figures 11.2 and 11.3.

   b. Anatomy of a muscle (optional):

      Skeletal muscles attach to bones by **tendons,** which pull on bones when the muscles contract (shorten). The tendon of the less movable end of the muscle during contraction is called the **origin**; the tendon at the more movable end of the muscle is the **insertion**. The part of the muscle between the origin and insertion is called the **belly**. Most movements involve the action of several muscles that are opposed to each other. Examples of muscle action are flexion and extension, abduction and adduction. A muscle that straightens or extends a limb is called an **extensor**; the opposing muscle that bends it is a **flexor**. **Abductors** are muscles that move a limb away from the midline of an animals's body, while an **adductor** moves a limb toward the midline.

2. **Digestive system:**

   Make a **midsagittal** cut through the thin abdominal muscles from the **pelvis** to the **sternum**. Without disturbing the **viscera**, observe the position of the organs in the abdominal cavity.

Locate the following:

a. **Mandibular (salivary) glands**: Prominently located around the oral cavity, these glands produce saliva, which contains the enzyme amylase.

b. **Diaphragm**: Thin muscular partition that forms a separation between the **abdominal** and **thoracic** cavities.

c. **Liver**: Most conspicuous and largest of all organs in the abdominal cavity; composed of several lobes. Determine if a **gallbladder** is present on the underside of the liver.

d. **Stomach**: Find it by lifting up the liver. Note the tubes connected to each end of it.

e. **Esophagus**: Anteriormost tube connected to the stomach. It passes down from the mouth, behind the trachea, through the diaphragm, and to the stomach.

f. **Small intestine**: Posterior tube connected to the stomach. Follow the small intestine along its length. The **duodenum, jejunum**, and **ileum** are successive parts of the small intestine, inseparable externally. Note the **mesentery** between the coils of the small intestine.

g. **Large intestine**: Joined to the small intestine. At the junction between them is a large sac called the **caecum**, the first part of the large intestine. Does the rat have an **appendix**? If present, it would be projecting from the caecum. The large intestine is subdivided into **ascending, transverse**, and **descending** parts. The descending part is connected to the anus by a short terminal segment, the **rectum**.

h. **Pancreas**: Lighter in color than the liver, irregular in shape, and located in the mesentery between the stomach and intestine. The head of the pancreas can be located inside the crook of the duodenum. Besides secreting digestive enzymes into the duodenum, it also produces the hormones insulin and glucagon.

3. **Respiratory system:**

a. Cut away the neck muscles of the rat to reveal the **trachea**. Trace the trachea down to where it bifurcates (branches) into two primary **bronchi**. Each primary bronchus connects with a **lung**. Observe the **cartilaginous rings** embedded in the walls of the trachea.

b. On the outer ventral surface of the trachea is the H-shaped **thyroid gland**, an essential endocrine organ. Near its attachment is the **larynx**. Locate the **thymus gland**, which lies against the trachea just above the heart.

4. **Circulatory system:**

The rat and all mammals have a **closed circulatory system** in which blood is contained within vessels. In your specimen, the blood vessels have been injected: **arteries**, which carry blood away from the heart, with red latex; **veins**, which carry blood toward the heart, with blue latex. Only one artery contains blue material. Name it and explain why. _____

Likewise, which vein(s) is red and why? _____

_____

a. Examine the **heart** in the thoracic cavity. It is enclosed by a membranous sac, the **pericardium**. Carefully remove it with your scissors and observe the heart more closely. It is composed of four chambers: two thin-walled anterior chambers, **atria**, and two thick-walled **ventricles**.

b. Identify the following major arteries:

   i. **Aorta**: Arises from the left ventricle and arches to the left as it leaves the heart.

   ii. **Innominate or brachiocephalic artery**: First short branch off the **aortic arch** from which arise the right **subclavian artery** going to the right forepaw and **right common carotid artery** that runs along the right side of the trachea.

   iii. **Left common carotid artery**: Second major branch off the aortic arch, lies on the left side of the trachea.

   iv. **Left subclavian artery**: Third major branch off the aortic arch, passes into the left foreleg.

c. Trace the aorta as it curves dorsally toward the vertebrae. Observe its penetration of the diaphragm. To follow it in the abdominal cavity, move the viscera to one side. Its main branches in this region are as follows:

   i. **Coeliac artery**: Whose three branches supply blood to the stomach, liver, and spleen.

   ii. **Superior (anterior) and inferior (posterior) mesenteric artery**: Superior (anterior) mesenteric artery is located slightly posterior to the coeliac. Trace its branches to see what structures it supplies. Posterior (inferior) mesenteric artery supplies the large intestine and rectum.

   iii. **Renal arteries**: Supply each kidney.

   iv. **Common iliac arteries**: Formed by bifurcation of the aorta in the pelvic area.

   v. **Spleen**: Dark-red, oblong organ located below and to the left of the stomach. This organ filters blood, removes old or damaged red blood cells, and plays a role in immunity.

d. Notice that most arteries are accompanied by veins that return blood to the heart. Locate the following veins, starting in the neck region:

   i. **Right or left jugular**: Large vein at the side of the neck.

   ii. **Right or left subclavian vein**: Comes from the foreleg and joins the jugular veins to form the **superior (anterior) vena cava**.

   iii. **Common iliac veins**: Located in the pelvic area, unite to form the posterior vena cava.

   iv. **Posterior (inferior) vena cava**: Main vein receiving all posterior circulation. Trace it along the dorsal body wall. Both the superior (anterior) and the posterior (inferior) vena cava enter the right atrium of the heart dorsally.

   v. **Renal veins**: Carry blood from the kidney into the posterior vena cava.

5. **Urogenital system:**

   a. In the rat, both the excretory and reproductive systems are combined for study, because their component parts are closely related embryologically and evolutionarily.

   b. Locate the **kidneys**. Each is connected to the **urinary bladder** via a **ureter**. At the anterior end of each kidney is an **adrenal gland**. This endocrine organ will appear as a small pink mass embedded in fatty tissue.

   c. In a male rat, observe the **scrotum**. Slit it ventrally and locate the **testes**. You may also find the testes in the lower abdominal cavity. In rodents, following breeding, the testes can be withdrawn into the body cavity. Observe the **spermatic cord**. It is composed of blood vessels and the **vas deferens**, which collects the sperm. Trace the spermatic cord into the abdominal cavity. Into what structure does it empty? _____

   d. In a female rat, find the **ovaries**. They are round, very small and located near the kidneys. Next, find the **oviducts**, which are highly convoluted tubes, adjacent to the ovaries. Each opens into one of the bifurcations of the **uterus**.

6. **Endocrine system:**

   Several endocrine glands have been located and identified with previously studied systems. Now, examine the following glands again as part of a separate system.

   a. The **H-shaped thyroid gland** (see respiratory system) is a small mass located atop the trachea. What does the thyroid gland control? _____

   b. The **thymus** (see respiratory system) lies across the front end of the heart, and extends into the base of the neck. Well developed in young mammals, this gland atrophies with age. What is its function? _____

   c. The **pancreas** (see digestive system) is an endocrine gland, as well as an exocrine gland of the digestive system. Its endocrine function is to produce the hormones insulin and glucagon. What is the role of these hormones? _____

   d. The **adrenal** or **suprarenal glands** area located atop the kidneys. The **ovaries** and **testes** (see urogenital system) not only produce sex cells, but also secrete hormones. These hormones are responsible for maintaining a functional reproductive system. Name these hormones:

      _____

   e. The **pituitary gland** is located at the base of the brain, and will be visible if you dissect out the rat brain. It secretes many hormones that control body functions and secretions of other glands. Can you name some of these hormones? _____

      _____

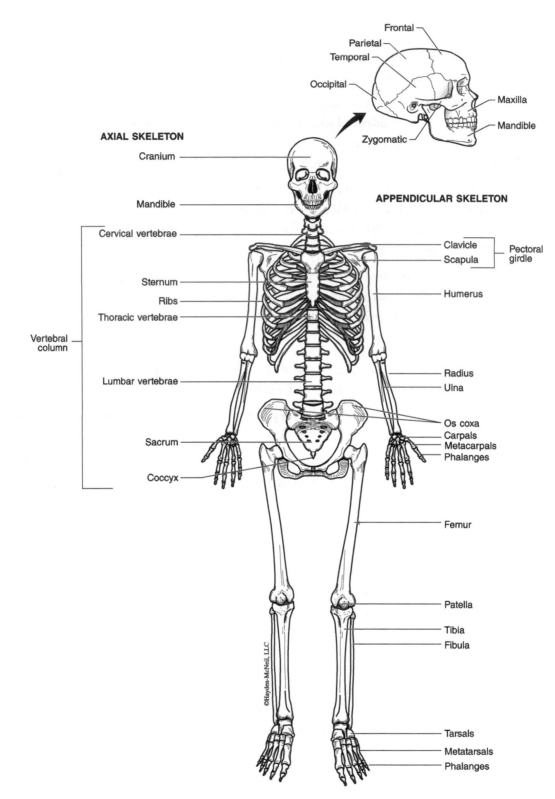

Figure 11.1. Human, skeletal system, ventral view

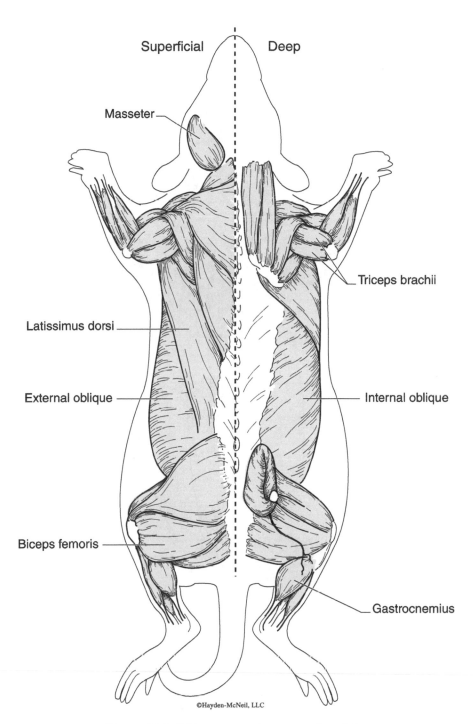

Superficial   Deep

Masseter

Triceps brachii

Latissimus dorsi

External oblique

Internal oblique

Biceps femoris

Gastrocnemius

©Hayden-McNeil, LLC

Figure 11.2. White rat, muscle system, dorsal view

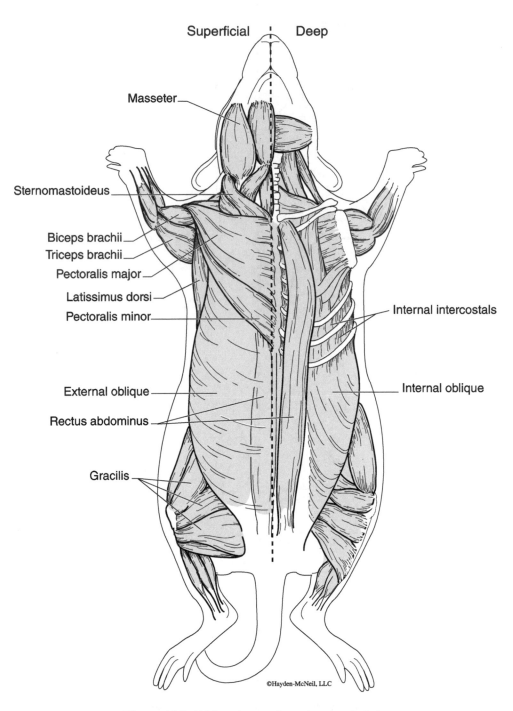

Superficial | Deep

Masseter

Sternomastoideus

Biceps brachii
Triceps brachii
Pectoralis major
Latissimus dorsi
Pectoralis minor

Internal intercostals

External oblique

Internal oblique

Rectus abdominus

Gracilis

©Hayden-McNeil, LLC

Figure 11.3. White rat, muscle system, ventral view

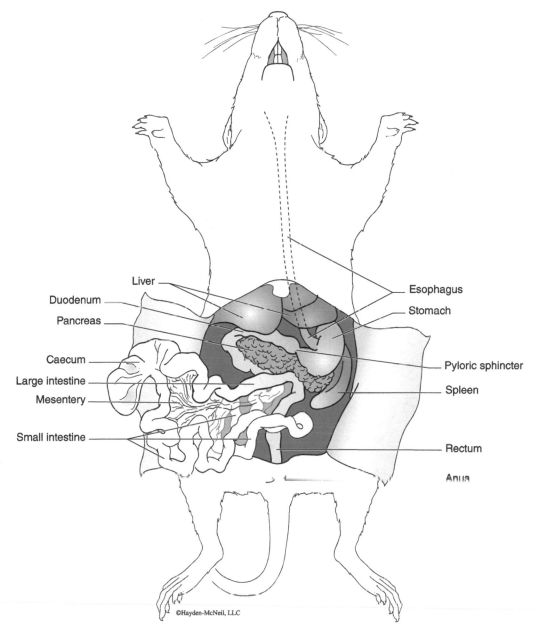

Liver
Duodenum
Pancreas
Caecum
Large intestine
Mesentery
Small intestine

Esophagus
Stomach
Pyloric sphincter
Spleen
Rectum
Anus

©Hayden-McNeil, LLC

Figure 11.4. White rat, digestive system, ventral view

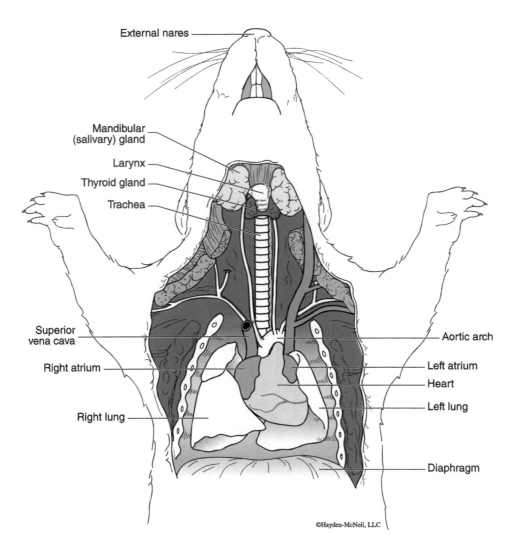

Figure 11.5. White rat, respiratory system, ventral view

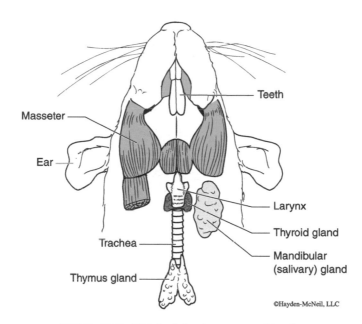

Teeth

Masseter

Ear

Larynx

Thyroid gland

Trachea

Mandibular
(salivary) gland

Thymus gland

©Hayden-McNeil, LLC

Figure 11.6. Detail of structures around trachea

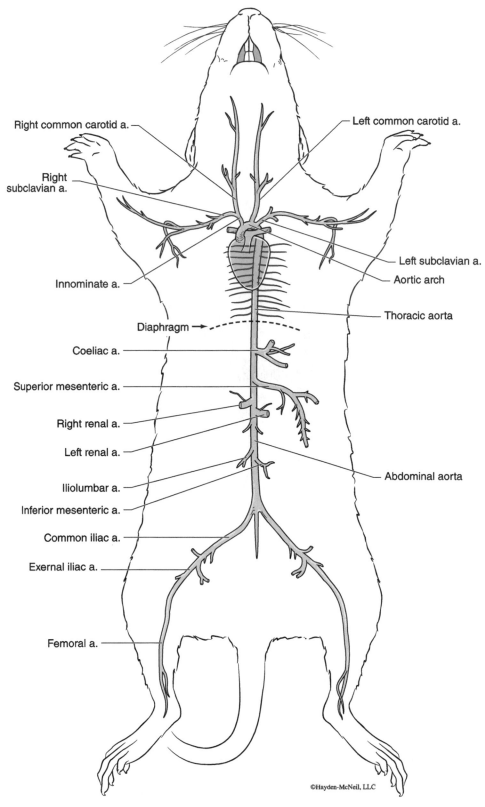

Right common carotid a.

Right subclavian a.

Innominate a.

Diaphragm →

Coeliac a.

Superior mesenteric a.

Right renal a.

Left renal a.

Iliolumbar a.

Inferior mesenteric a.

Common iliac a.

Exernal iliac a.

Femoral a.

Left common carotid a.

Left subclavian a.

Aortic arch

Thoracic aorta

Abdominal aorta

©Hayden-McNeil, LLC

Figure 11.7. White rat, arterial system, ventral view (injected with red latex)

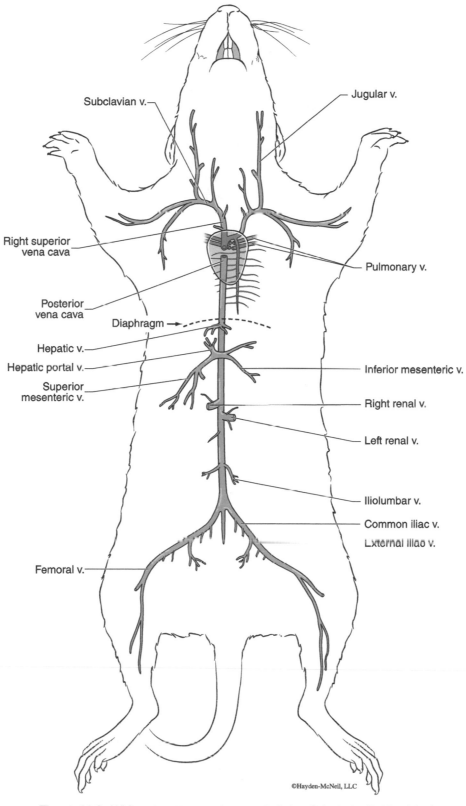

Subclavian v.

Jugular v.

Right superior
vena cava

Pulmonary v.

Posterior
vena cava

Diaphragm →

Hepatic v.

Hepatic portal v.

Inferior mesenteric v.

Superior
mesenteric v.

Right renal v.

Left renal v.

Iliolumbar v.

Common iliac v.

External iliac v.

Femoral v.

©Hayden-McNeil, LLC

Figure 11.8 White rat, venous system, ventral view (injected with blue latex)

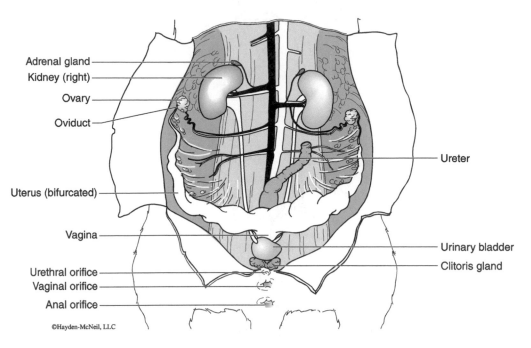

Adrenal gland
Kidney (right)
Ovary
Oviduct

Ureter

Uterus (bifurcated)

Vagina

Urinary bladder
Clitoris gland

Urethral orifice
Vaginal orifice
Anal orifice

©Hayden-McNeil, LLC

Figure 11.9. White rat, female urogenital system, ventral view

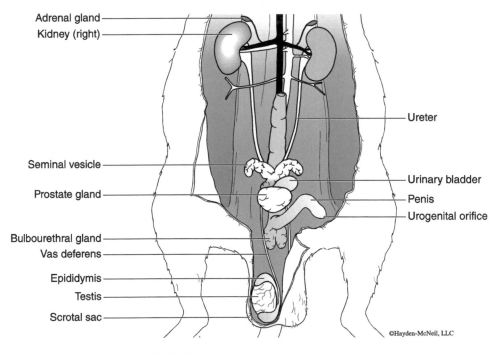

Adrenal gland
Kidney (right)

Ureter

Seminal vesicle

Urinary bladder

Prostate gland

Penis
Urogenital orifice

Bulbourethral gland
Vas deferens

Epididymis
Testis
Scrotal sac

©Hayden-McNeil, LLC

Figure 11.10. White rat, male urogenital system, ventral view

Asexual Reproduction

Exercise 12

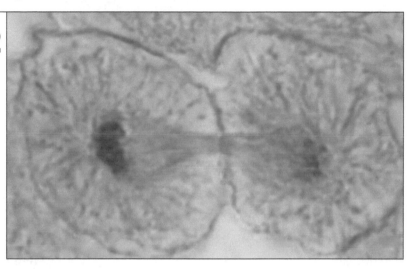

Objectives

1. Define asexual reproduction, mitosis, and cytokinesis.

2. Describe and identify the phases of the cell cycle in plant and animal cells.

3. State several forms of asexual reproduction and give examples of organisms that reproduce this way.

Introduction

One of the most important functions of any species is reproduction. Reproduction ensures continuation of the species for at least one more generation. Organisms may reproduce sexually or asexually. In **asexual reproduction**, offspring are produced without the fusion of **gametes** (sperm and egg). **Sexual reproduction** involves the fusion of gametes and will be discussed in Exercise 13. Forms of asexual reproduction include fission, budding, and sporulation, all of which will be examined in this laboratory exercise. During asexual reproduction, cells divide by mitosis followed by cytokinesis.

Mitotic division is fundamental not only to asexual reproduction, but to development and growth of organisms as well. **Mitosis** is division of the nucleus of a cell. This is followed by or overlaps with division of the cytoplasm, or **cytokinesis**. We will begin this laboratory exercise with a study of mitosis.

Part A: Mitosis—Animal Cell

Materials

1. Compound microscope

2. Microslide viewer

3. Models: Mitosis in Animal Cells

4. Prepared slide of whitefish blastula

5. Microslide 53: "Animal Mitosis"—*Ascaris* (a roundworm)

Method

1. Please view the set of models depicting the cell cycle in animal cells, which shows a typical animal cell as it proceeds from interphase through the phases of mitosis. Compare the models to Figure 12.1 below, and identify the following phases and structures:

Chromosomes	**Anaphase**	**Telophase**
Prophase	**Nucleus**	**Centrioles**
Metaphase	**Nuclear envelope**	**Spindle**
Cleavage furrow	**Cytokinesis**	

2. Proceed to study these phases and structures in Microslide 53: "Animal Mitosis."

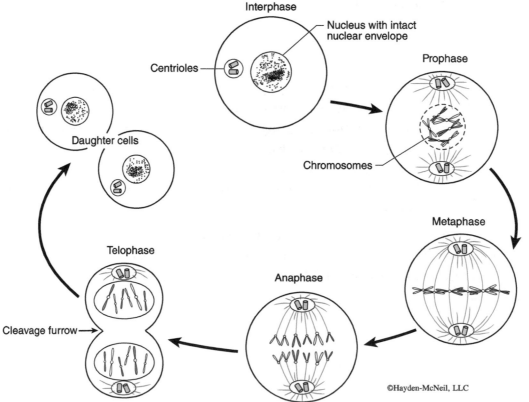

©Hayden-McNeil, LLC

Figure 12.1. Cell cycle in animal cells

3. Examine a prepared slide of whitefish blastula and, using the high-power objective (40×) of your microscope, locate cells in each stage of the cell cycle (interphase, prophase, metaphase, anaphase, and telophase). The blastula (a stage of embryonic development) of whitefish contains cells that are mitotically active. Record your observations on the data sheet.

Part B: Mitosis—Plant Cell

Mitotically active tissue is seen in the cells of the lateral and apical **meristems** of plants. The apical meristem includes the tips of shoots and roots. In this section, you will study mitosis in root tips.

Materials
1. Compound microscope
2. Microslide viewer
3. Models: Mitosis in Plant Cells
4. Prepared slide: Onion (*Allium*) root tip
5. Microslide 55: "Plant Mitosis"

Method

1. Please view the set of models depicting the cell cycle in plant cells, which shows a typical plant cell as it proceeds from interphase through the phases of mitosis. Compare the models to Figure 12.2, below, and identify the following phases and structures:

    Prophase   **Cytokinesis**   **Anaphase**

    Telophase   **Metaphase**   **Chromosomes**

    Nucleolus   **Interphase**   **Cell plate**

    Nucleus   **Nuclear envelope**

2. View Microslide 55: "Plant Mitosis." The eight photographs that make up this filmstrip show the phases of the cell cycle in onion root tip cells. As you look at the filmstrip, identify the phases and structures listed above.

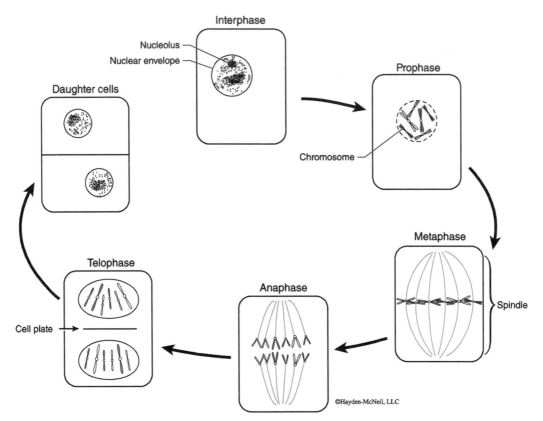

Figure 12.2. Cell cycle in plant cells

3. View the prepared slide of Onion (*Allium*) root tip. (This slide should be examined *after* you have looked at the microslide on plant mitosis.) The slide has three thin slices of onion root tip under the coverslip as shown in the following diagram.

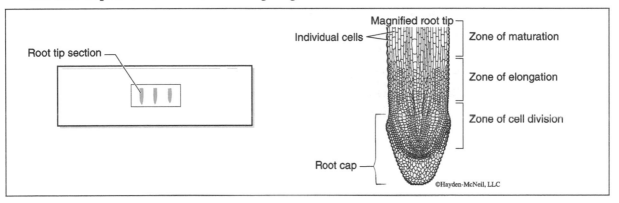

a. Examine the individual cells of the root tips using the high-power objective of your microscope (40×) and locate cells in **interphase**, **prophase**, **metaphase**, **anaphase**, and **telophase**. The presence of a well-formed nucleus containing a nucleolus or several nucleoli is indicative of interphase.

b. Draw a cell in *each of the phases* of the cell cycle in the space provided on your data sheet.

Part C: Fission

Fission or binary fission is common among many eukaryotic unicellular organisms as well as prokaryotic organisms. In eukaryotes, it involves mitosis followed by a separation of the parent cell into two equal portions (organisms).

Materials

1. Microslide 64: "Binary Fission"

2. Prepared slides of *Paramecium* undergoing fission

Method

1. View Microslide 64: "Binary Fission," which will explain this type of asexual reproduction.

2. After viewing Microslide 64, examine the prepared slide of *Paramecium* undergoing fission. Record your observations on your data sheet.

Part D: Sporulation

Rhizopus is a fungus commonly called the "bread mold." This organism will form a cottony mass of thread-like strands as it grows on the surface of bread or other suitable substrates. This mass is collectively called the **mycelium**, and individual threads are called **stolons** or **hyphae** (Figure 12.3). *Rhizopus* commonly reproduces via an asexual form known as sporulation. During sporulation, rising above the mycelium at intervals will be aerial shoots called **sporangiophores**. These are capped by black globe-like structures called **sporangia**. Each sporangium contains hundreds of small, asexually produced, single-celled structures called **spores**. Once mature, the spores are released from the sporangium. If they land on a suitable environment, they will germinate and grow into another *Rhizopus* mold.

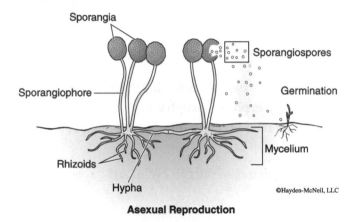

Asexual Reproduction

Figure 12.3. *Rhizopus:* sporulation

Materials

1. Compound microscope

2. Prepared slide: *Rhizopus* spores

Method

1. Examine the prepared slide of *Rhizopus* sporangia (Figure 12.3). Many of these sporangia will not contain spores. Examine the slide, first with the low-power objective. When you have located a sporangium bearing spores (indicated by a brown to golden coating), shift to high power and carefully examine it to see if you can identify the individual spores. Place your drawing of the sporangium and spores on the data sheet. You should be able to identify this organism in the future as being *Rhizopus* as well as the **sporangia**, **spores**, and **hyphae**.

Part E: Budding

Budding is similar to fission in that it occurs among both unicellular and multicellular organisms. However, it is different in that the parent and resulting offspring or bud are of unequal size. The larger portion may be considered the parent, the smaller portion the offspring. When detached from the parent, the bud can develop into a full-sized adult capable of forming buds. In this section you will observe budding in plants and animals.

Materials

1. Compound microscope

2. *Bryophyllum* plant

3. Prepared slides showing **budding in *Hydra*** (see Figure 12.4)

Method

1. Examine a prepared slide of *Hydra* showing budding. *Hydra* are simple animals of the phylum Cnidaria found in both fresh and marine environment. The bud will appear as an outgrowth from the body of the parent. (See Figure 12.4.) Sketch a budding *Hydra* in your data sheet.

Adult *Hydra*

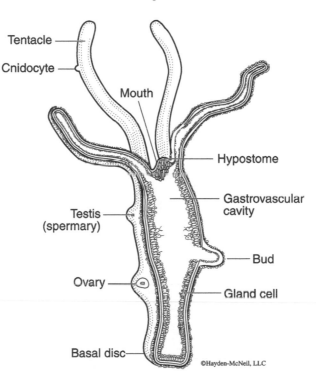

Figure 12.4. Adult with asexual bud

2. Observe the large *Bryophyllum* plant. This plant is commonly called the "pregnant plant." Its common mode of reproduction is to produce buds or small plantlets, complete with roots, on the margins of its leaves. When the plantlets are mature, they drop off the leaves, land on soil and take root growing a new *Bryophyllum* plant. The plantlets are produced as a result of mitosis followed by cell specialization in the leaf margin. View the *Bryophyllum* plant and make a drawing on your data sheet of a single leaf and a few of the attached plantlets.

Data Sheet 12

Name _____

Section _____ Date _____

Part A: Mitosis—Animal Cell

Make a sketch of a whitefish cell in each stage of the cell cycle, noting the position and structure of the chromosomes. Mag. = _____ ×

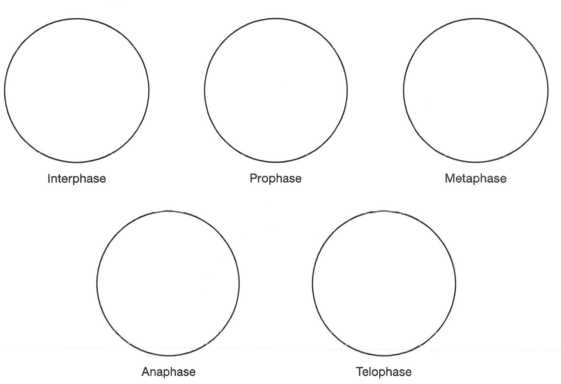

Interphase   Prophase   Metaphase

Anaphase   Telophase

Part B: Mitosis—Plant Cell

Make a sketch of an onion cell in each stage of the cell cycle, noting the position and structure of the chromosomes. Mag. = _____×

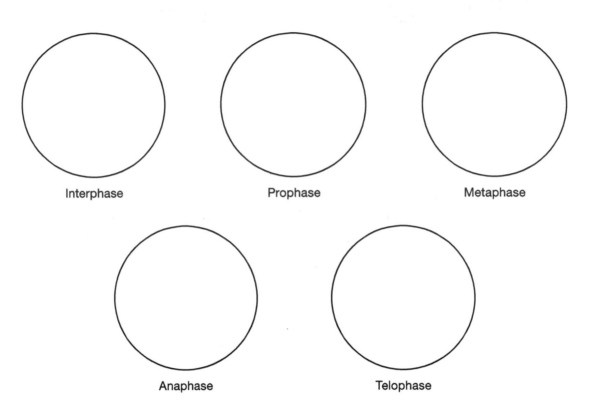

Interphase   Prophase   Metaphase

Anaphase   Telophase

Part C: Fission

Make a sketch of a *Paramecium* undergoing fission.

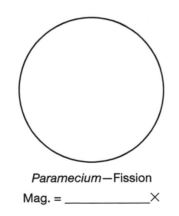

Paramecium—Fission

Mag. = _____×

Part D: Sporulation

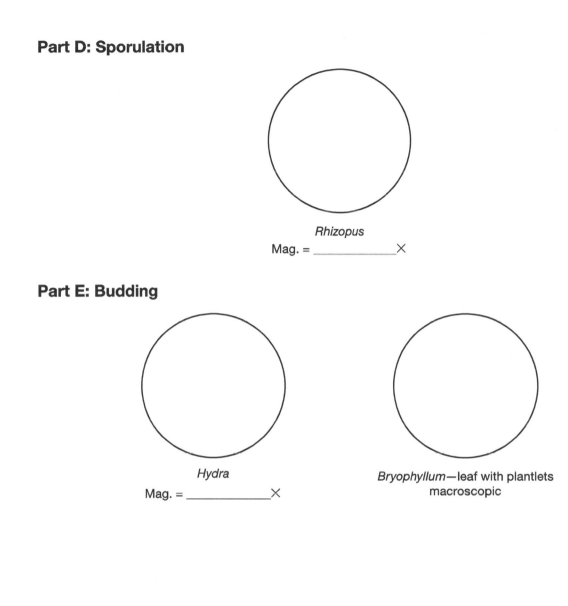

Rhizopus

Mag. = _____ ×

Part E: Budding

Hydra

Mag. = _____ ×

Bryophyllum—leaf with plantlets
macroscopic

Sexual Reproduction and Development

Exercise 13

Tono Balaguer/Shutterstock.com

Objectives

1. Describe and identify the different stages of conjugation, and list the organism that performs it.

2. Identify parts of a flower, including the female and male reproductive organs.

3. Describe and identify different phases of meiosis.

4. Recognize the location of, and role of meiosis in, gamete production in plants and animals.

5. Identify and describe the stages of embryonic development.

Introduction

As was mentioned in the previous lab exercise, one of the most important functions of any species is reproduction, which ensures the continuation of the species. Sexual reproduction in particular offers a species an opportunity to reshuffle its genetic material. This recombination is necessary if the species is to adjust to a changing environment.

There are a variety of reproductive methods, classified as either **asexual** or **sexual**. In asexual reproduction, offspring are produced without fusion of **gametes** (**sperm** and **egg**). In sexual reproduction, the fusion of egg and sperm results in the formation of a **zygote**, the first cell of the new organism. The developing zygote must undergo a series of **physiological** and **morphological** changes before it can assume its role in the environment. These changes, referred to as developmental stages, mark the organism's progress from fertilization to birth. After birth, the organism may continue further development as a **larval** or **juvenile** form, depending upon the species.

Reproduction and development depend upon **cell division**. Basically, a cell divides to produce two cells. The production of **daughter** cells involves the division of the **nucleus** and **cytoplasm**. If the resulting nuclei have the same number of chromosomes as the parent cell, we refer to the nuclear division as being mitotic. If the division results in cells with one-half the number of chromosomes as the parent cell, we refer to the nuclear division as being **meiotic**. Division of the cytoplasm is specifically called **cytokinesis**.

Mitotic division is fundamental to asexual reproduction, development, and growth. Meiotic division is confined to the production of gametes, and occurs only in the **gonads**—ovaries or testes. In this exercise, we will look at sexual reproduction in plants and animals.

Part A: Conjugation

Spirogyra is a common **filamentous green alga** found in ponds, drainage ditches, and lakes in Michigan. This alga normally reproduces asexually by mitosis coupled with a fragmentation process involving the filaments. During periods of environmental stress, it will undergo a sexual reproductive phase called **conjugation** that results in the formation of a diploid zygote (see Figure 13.1).

Materials

1. Compound microscope

2. Prepared slide: conjugating *Spirogyra*

Method

1. Examine a prepared slide of conjugating *Spirogyra*. As you view the filaments from right to left, you will see **a mature gametophyte, paired filaments** with **conjugation tubes, gametes undergoing syngamy**, and **zygospore**. Sketch each of the four stages on your data sheet.

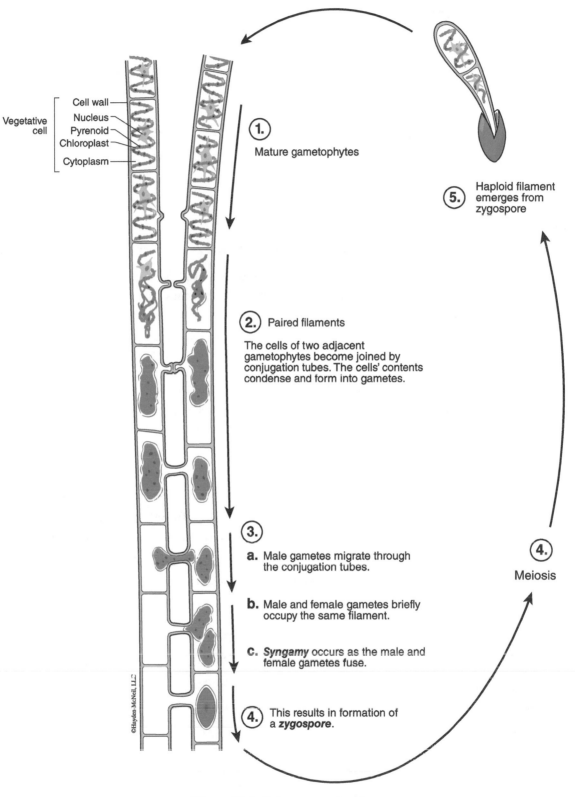

Vegetative cell
- Cell wall
- Nucleus
- Pyrenoid
- Chloroplast
- Cytoplasm

1. Mature gametophytes

5. Haploid filament emerges from zygospore

2. Paired filaments

The cells of two adjacent gametophytes become joined by conjugation tubes. The cells' contents condense and form into gametes.

3.
a. Male gametes migrate through the conjugation tubes.

b. Male and female gametes briefly occupy the same filament.

c. *Syngamy* occurs as the male and female gametes fuse.

4. This results in formation of a **zygospore**.

4. Meiosis

©Hayden-McNeil, LLC

Figure 13.1. *Spirogyra:* conjugation

Part B: Sexual Reproduction in Plants

The flower is the primary reproductive structure in **angiosperms** or flowering plants. Flowers contain both the male and female reproductive organs—**stamen** and **pistil**, respectively. The result of fertilization in plants is the **fruit** and **seed**, formed from the **ovary** and **ovule**, respectively.

Materials

1. Flower structure Riker mount

2. Flower model

3. Soaked bean seeds

Method

1. View the model of a typical dicot flower and identify the structures mentioned below.

   a. **Sepals.** These modified leaves are the outermost parts of the flower and are collectively called the **calyx**. They are usually green, but in certain flowers may be colored. They are thought to be protective in nature.

   b. **Petals.** These are usually the brightly colored parts of the flower. They serve both a protective and insect-attracting role. The petals are collectively called the **corolla**.

   c. **Stamens.** These are the male reproductive organs of the flower. They are located inside the corolla and consist of a stalk called a **filament**, which bears a terminal capsule or sac called the **anther**. It is within the anther that the pollen grains are produced.

   d. **Pistil.** This is the female reproductive organ of the flower. These structures consist of: a flattened top, specialized to receive pollen grains, called the **stigma**; a slender stalk or **style**; and an expanded base, the **ovary**. Within the ovary, meiosis occurs with the subsequent production of the egg cell. Also found within the ovary are the **ovules** that, after fertilization occurs, develop into **seeds**. The ovary will also undergo development and the expanded ovary with its seeds will form a fruit.

2. View the flower structure Riker mount, and identify the structures listed above.

3. Label the following structures in Figure 13.2 on the next page:

Stamen	**Anther**	**Filament**	**Pollen grains**
Pollen tube	**Stigma**	**Style**	**Ovary**
Pistil	**Ovule**	**Petal**	**Sepal**
Receptacle			

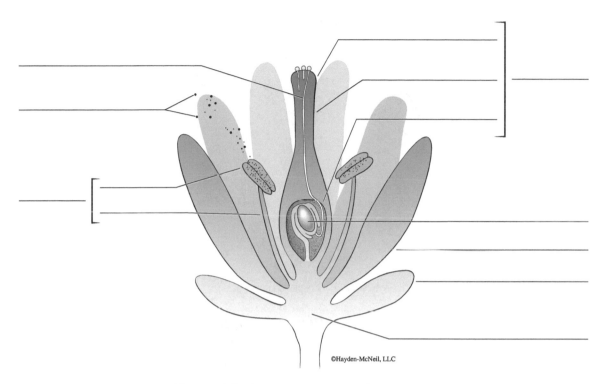

©Hayden-McNeil, LLC

Figure 13.2. Generalized structure of a dicot flower

4. Examine a soaked bean seed (Figure 13.3).

   a. **External anatomy.** Identify the following structures:

      i. **Hilum:** This is the large, very prominent scar of the seed and represents the attachment point of the developing seed to the wall of the ovary.

      ii. **Caruncle:** This is a dark lump at one end of the hilum. It facilitates the entrance of water into the seed during germination

      iii. **Micropyle:** A small, pit-like depression at the outer end of the hilum. It is the scar resulting from the penetration of the pollen tube into the ovule prior to the fertilization of the egg.

   b. **Internal anatomy.** Using a dissecting needle and forceps, carefully strip away the reddish-brown covering—the seed coat. Locate the two large, leaf-like structures that constitute the bulk of the embryo. These are called the **cotyledons**. Locate the following parts of the embryo.

      i. **Plumule:** the first pair of true leaves in the plant.

      ii. **Hypocotyl:** That part of the embryo that will give rise to the lower portion of the stem and root system

      iii. **Epicotyl:** That part of the embryo above the point of attachment of the cotyledons. This part of the embryo will give rise to the upper reaches of the plant.

c. Record your observations concerning the external and internal anatomy of the seed on the data sheet.

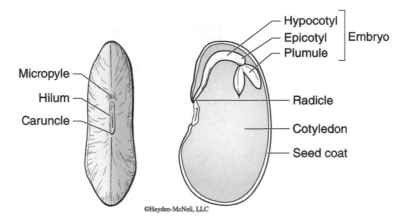

Figure 13.3. Structure of the seed

Part C: Meiosis and Sexual Reproduction in Animals

Meiosis consists of two consecutive cell divisions that reduce the chromosome number in half producing **haploid (N)** gametes. In females, meiosis occurs in ovaries and produces eggs. This process is specifically called **oogenesis.** Male gametes or sperm are produced in the testes and the process is specifically called **spermatogenesis.**

Materials

1. Compound microscope

2. Models: Meiosis in Animal Cells

3. Prepared slide of mammalian ovary cross-section

4. Prepared slide of mammalian or grasshopper testis cross-section

Method

1. View the models of meiosis in animal cells. Be able to identify the following phases and structures:

Interphase	**Spindle apparatus**	**Centrioles**
Prophase I	**Prophase II**	**Nucleus**
Metaphase I	**Metaphase II**	**Crossing-over**
Anaphase I	**Anaphase II**	**Synapsis**
Telophase I	**Telophase II**	

2. View a slide showing **spermatogenesis** in animal testis. A mammalian testis is made up of a many coils called **seminiferous tubules**, the site of development of sperm. Within each tubule are sperm cells (spermatocytes) in various stages of meiosis. In between seminiferous tubules are **interstitial cells**, which produce the hormone **testosterone.** Identify all of the parts labeled in Figure 13.4a.

3. View a slide showing **oogenesis** in mammalian ovary. Eggs cells or oocytes are present surrounded by follicular cells. Together, this is called a follicle. The follicular cells produce **estrogen** and **progesterone.** In the cross section of the ovary are follicles in various stages of development. Identify all of the parts labeled in Figure 13.4b.

4. Record your observations on the data sheet.

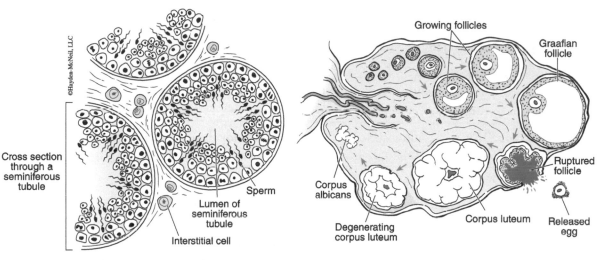

a. Cross section of mammalian testis   b. Cross section of mammalian ovary

Figure 13.4.

Part D: Animal Embryonic Development

Although the developmental sequence varies for any given species, most animals follow a general pattern once fertilization is completed. This generalized developmental pattern is typified by starfish.

Materials

1. Models of starfish development

2. Microslide 60: "Starfish Cleavage"

3. Prepared slide showing starfish embryology

Method

1. View the models showing starfish development and look for the stages: zygote, 2-, 4-, 8- and 16-cell cleavage stages, morula, blastula, gastrula, larva, and adult starfish.

2. View the microslide showing starfish development and look for the following stages.

   a. **Zygote**: This is a single cell with a "lifted membrane"—the fertilization membrane.

   b. **Cleavage stages**: Find 2-, 4-, 8-, and possibly 16-cell stages. Beyond this last stage, it is difficult to count the cells. Careful focusing will be necessary. The embryo at the 16–32-cell stage is a solid ball of cells called the **morula**.

   c. **Blastula**: This is a hollow sphere of cells. The interior cavity is called the blastocoel. Note that while the cell number has greatly increased, the actual mass of the embryo is no greater than the zygote.

   d. **Gastrula**: One side of the blastula is indented as if it were pushed in, similar to forcing a finger into a balloon. There are many stages of gastrulation on the slide: some show the process just beginning while others show the process completed. During gastrulation the germ layers are established—**ectoderm, endoderm**, and **mesoderm.** Name the first organ system that is formed at this time: _____.

   e. **Larva**: Most animal species form a larval stage. The larva of the starfish, called a bipinnaria, swims about in the sea for some time before settling to the bottom and metamorphosing into the adult starfish. With careful searching you may see a small **mouth, gut**, and **anus.**

3. Next, secure a slide showing starfish "cleavage" and look for the same developmental stages. Record observations on the data sheet.

Part E: Extra-Embryonic Membranes—Demonstration

The evolution of the extra-embryonic membranes made possible the development of vertebrate embryos on land. These membranes, which surround and cover the embryos of reptiles, birds, and mammals, are known as the **amnion, chorion, allantois,** and **yolk sac.** The **amnion** is a protective membrane filled with amniotic fluid that surrounds the embryo and cushions it from mechanical shock. In the chick, the chorion lies just under the porous shell and functions in gas exchange. In mammals, the **chorion** becomes part of the placenta where nutrients, gases, and wastes are exchanged with maternal blood. The **allantois** functions as a metabolic waste container in birds and reptiles, while in placental mammals, its blood vessels (umbilical blood vessels) connect the embryo with the placenta. In bird and reptilian eggs, the **yolk sac** surrounds the yolk and has a nutritive function, but in mammals, it functions in blood production for the first month, and then usually detaches and shrinks in size.

Materials

1. Slide of human umbilical cord c.s.

2. Models of development and extra-embryonic membranes.

Method

1. View the demonstration slide of a human umbilical cord in cross section. Record your observation on the data sheet. Note the umbilical blood vessels.

2. Observe the models and photographs of showing development and extra-embryonic membranes in the hall cabinet.

Data Sheet

13

Name _____

Section _____ Date _____

Part A: Conjugation

Mature gametophyte generation

Mag. = _____×

Paired filament

Mag. = _____×

Gametes undergoing syngamy

Mag. = _____×

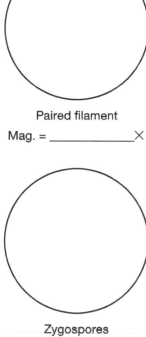

Zygospores

Mag. = _____×

Part B: Sexual Reproduction in Plants

The Flower

1. What are the male reproductive organs of flowers? _____

2. What is the female reproductive organ of the flower? _____

The Bean Seed

External Anatomy   Internal Anatomy

Part C: Meiosis and Sexual Reproduction in Animals

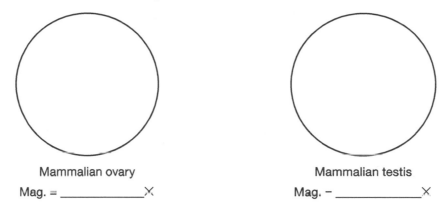

Mammalian ovary

Mag. = _____ ×

Mammalian testis

Mag. – _____ ×

Make a sketch of the meiosis phases showing the position and structure of chromosomes and high-lighting important events.

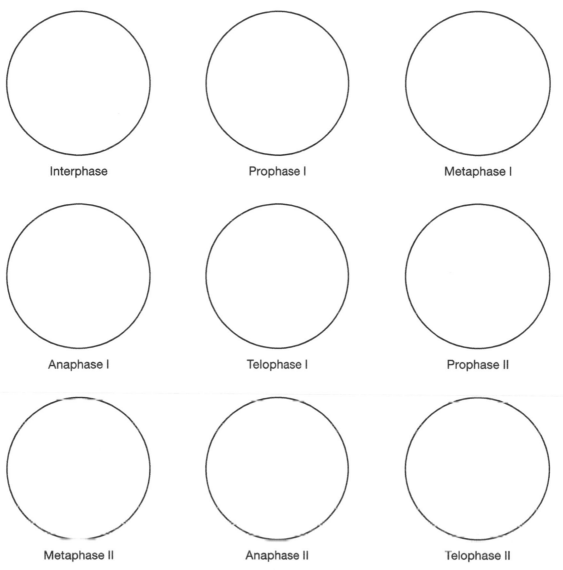

Interphase	Prophase I	Metaphase I
Anaphase I	Telophase I	Prophase II
Metaphase II	Anaphase II	Telophase II

Part D: Animal Embryonic Development

Make a sketch of the starfish *developmental stages*. Mag. = _____ ×

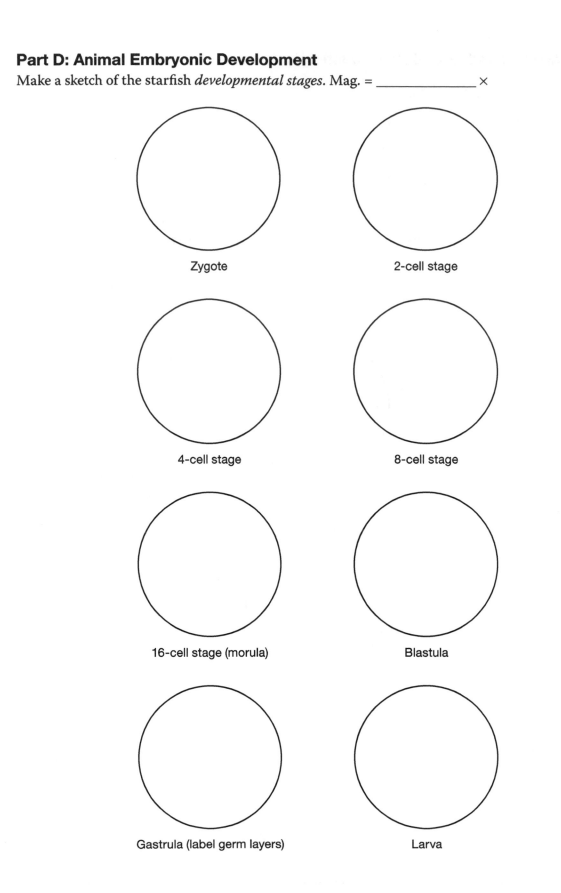

Zygote

2-cell stage

4-cell stage

8-cell stage

16-cell stage (morula)

Blastula

Gastrula (label germ layers)

Larva

Part E: Extra-Embryonic Membranes

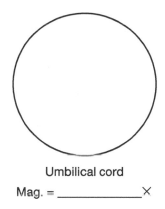

Umbilical cord

Mag. = _____ ×

Mendelian Genetics

Exercise 14

Objectives

1. Identify chromosomes.

2. Define gene, monohybrid, dihybrid, genotype, phenotype, allele, locus, dominant, recessive, and chromosomes.

3. Solve monohybrid, monohybrid test, and dihybrid cross problems.

4. Explain the inheritance of human ABO blood types, and list which genotype(s) are associated with each phenotype.

5. Analyze and interpret blood typing plates.

Introduction

Gregor Mendel, an Augustinian monk, is regarded as the father of modern genetics. In 1865, he formulated and published his laws of inheritance. The first law, **the law of segregation**, states:

- An individual has two **alleles** for each trait.

- The alleles segregate during the formation of gametes.

- Each gamete has only one allele for each trait.

- Fertilization restores two alleles for each trait in the offspring.

An allele is an alternate form of a gene. Alleles occur at a specific location on a chromosome called a **locus.** An allele may be **dominant** (A), in which case they are always expressed, or they may be recessive (a), in which case they are only expressed in an individual with the **homozygous recessive** (aa) **genotype.** Such an individual would exhibit the recessive **phenotype** or appearance.

An individual with two dominant alleles (AA; **homozygous dominant**) or one dominant and one recessive allele (Aa; **heterozygous**) would exhibit the dominant phenotype.

The second law, **the law of independent assortment**, states:

* Each pair of alleles for a trait separate into gametes independently of the pairs of alleles for other traits.

In this lab, you will use genetic corn ears to illustrate Mendel's laws of inheritance. The law of segregation can be demonstrated with a simple monohybrid cross, while the law of independent assortment requires a dihybrid cross.

Part A: Fruit Fly and Human Chromosomes

Materials
1. Prepared slide of fruit fly (*Drosophila melanogaster*) chromosomes
2. Prepared slide of human chromosomes
3. Compound microscope

Method
1. View the prepared slide showing polytene chromosomes from the salivary glands of *Drosophila* on demonstration at the front desk.
2. Sketch the chromosomes on your data sheet.
3. Observe the demonstration slide showing human chromosomes.
4. Sketch the chromosomes on the data sheet.

Part B: Monohybrid and Dihybrid Crosses

Materials
1. Genetic corn ears
2. Riker mounts of genetic corn crosses
3. Class data

Method
Select one corn ear from each group (green, red, and blue).
1. A color code is painted on the end of the corn ear to identify the type of cross from which it resulted.
2. Count the number and type of individual kernels on the ear. Record this information on your data sheet in the appropriate table, and submit it to your instructor for inclusion in class data.

3. Using class data, determine which traits are dominant and recessive. In addition, give the Mendelian ratio of the kernels. This is the F_2 generation. Now figure out and record the genetic makeup of the F_1 generation, which are the parents that produced the corn ear that you counted.

4. Repeat steps 1 through 3 with a corn ear from each of the remaining two groups.

Part C: Multiple Allelic Trait—Human Blood Groups

Blood type is based on the presence or absence of specific genetically determined glycoproteins, called **antigens,** on the surface of red blood cells (RBC). Human ABO blood typing is one **trait** that is influenced by **multiple alleles**: I^A, I^B, and i. These alleles control the presence of a glycoprotein on the surface of red blood cells. The I^A allele encodes the "A" version of the glycoprotein, the I^B allele encodes the "B" version of the glycoprotein, and the i allele corresponds with the absence of glycoprotein.

Antibodies are a class of glycoproteins made by the immune system that attach to non-self antigens. When antibodies attach to non-self antigens, they can cause **agglutination** (clumping).

For example, if you have type A blood, your red blood cells do not have the B glycoprotein on their surface; your immune system produces anti-B antibodies. Due to the presence of these anti-B antibodies, agglutination would occur if you were to receive type B blood because the surfaces of the donated red blood cells have the B antigen. For this reason, a person's blood is typed prior to receiving a transfusion.

BLOOD TYPE	ANTIGEN ON RBC	ANTIBODY PRODUCED
A	A	Anti-B
B	B	Anti-A
O	None	Anti-A and Anti-B
AB	A and B	Neither Anti-A nor Anti-B

Since each individual inherits two genes, one from each parent, that control the synthesis of the ABO glycoproteins, an individual may have one of six blood genotypes:

$$I^A I^A \qquad I^A i \qquad I^B I^B \qquad I^B i \qquad I^A I^B \qquad ii$$

Materials

1. Blood typing demonstration

Methods

1. View blood typing demonstration, and record agglutination results.

2. Based on these results, determine the blood type of each sample.

3. Fill in all possible genotypes associated with each phenotype.

Part D: Human Inheritance—Making Babies

Human inheritance is also subject to the same laws of inheritance. Below is a list of human traits that follow simple dominant/recessive patterns of inheritance.

Materials

1. Coin

2. Colored pencils

Method

1. You will be working in pairs (2) for this exercise.

2. Toss a coin two times to determine the sex of the child:

   a. 2 heads or 2 tails = female

   b. 1 head, 1 tail = male

3. Toss a coin two times for each of the listed traits:

   a. Heads = dominant allele

   b. Tails = recessive allele

4. Draw the face of the child on your data sheet.

Face shape

Round	(RR, Rr)
Square	(rr)

Chin prominence

Very prominent	(LL, Ll)
Less prominent	(ll)

Chin shape: Only flip coins for this trait if chin genotype is LL or Ll. A genotype of ll prevents the expression of the next two pairs of genes.

Round	(RR, Rr)
Square	(rr)
Dimple present	(AA, Aa)
Absent	(aa)

Hair type

Curly	(CC)
Wavy	(Cc)
Straight	(cc)

Hairline

Widow's peak	(WW, Ww)
Straight	(ww)

Skin pigmentation

Freckles	(FF, Ff)
No freckles	(ff)

Eyebrow color

Very Dark	(HH)
Medium Dark	(Hh)
Light	(hh)

Eyebrow thickness

Bushy	(BB, Bb)
Fine	(bb)

Eyebrow placement

Not connected	(NN, Nn)
Connected	(nn)

Eye traits: Determine the phenotype of the next four traits before drawing the eyes.

Eye—Interpupillary distance

Close together	(EE)
Average	(Ee)
Far apart	(ee)

Eyes—Size

Large	(EE)
Medium	(Ee)
Small	(ee)

Eyes—Shape

Almond	(AA, Aa)
Round	(aa)

Eyes—Slantedness

Horizontal	(HH, Hh)
Upward slant	(hh)

Eyelashes

Long	(LL, Ll)
Short	(ll)

Eye color: The determination of eye color is very complicated. For purposes of this lab, we will assume there are two gene pairs involved. Determine the genotype of the first pair (AA, Aa, aa) and then the second pair (BB, Bb, bb).

Genotype	Phenotype
AABB	Dark brown
AABb	Brown
AaBB	Brown
AAbb	Dark blue
AaBb	Dark blue
aaBB	Dark blue
aaBb	Light blue
Aabb	Light blue
aabb	Pale blue

Mouth—Size

Long	(MM)
Average	(Mm)
Short	(mm)

Lips

Thick	(TT, Tt)
Thin	(tt)

Protruding lower lip

Protruding	(HH)
Slight	(Hh)
Absent	(hh)

Dimples

    Dimpled   (DD, Dd)

    No dimples (dd)

Nose size

    Big   (NN)

    Medium   (Nn)

    Small   (nn)

Nose shape

    Rounded   (RR, Rr)

    Pointed   (rr)

Nostril shape

    Rounded   (RR, Rr)

    Pointed   (rr)

Earlobe attachment

    Free   (FF, Ff)

    Attached   (ff)

Darwin's earpoints

    Present   (DD, Dd)

    Absent   (dd)

Hairy ears: The trait is sex-limited to males.

    Absent   (HH, Hh)

    Present   (hh)

Skin color: This is a polygenic trait. We will assume there are three gene pairs involved. Flip your coins to determine the genotype of the first pair of genes (AA, Aa, aa). Then flip again to determine the genotype of the second pair of genes (BB, Bb, bb). Flip for the third and last time to determine the third pair of genes (CC, Cc, cc). You *flip three times* for a total of *six letters.* If your gene pairs are —1— (see below) then the skin color is —2—.

—1—	—2—
6 capitals	Very dark brown
5 capitals	Very dark brown
4 capitals	Dark brown
3 capitals	Medium brown
2 capitals	Light brown
1 capital	Light tan
no capitals	White

Data Sheet

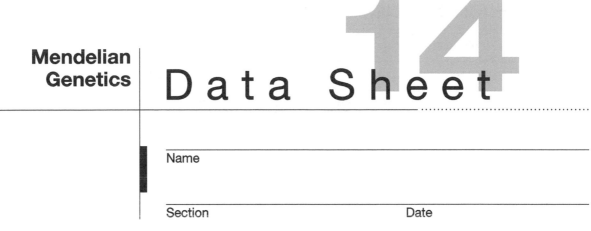

Name _____

Section _____ Date _____

Part A: Fruit Fly and Human Chromosomes

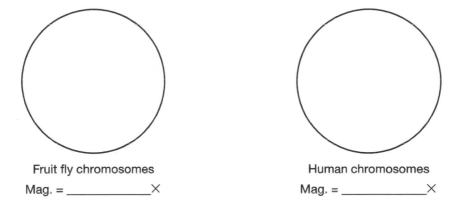

Fruit fly chromosomes

Mag. = _____×

Human chromosomes

Mag. = _____×

1. The bands seen in the fly chromosomes represent _____.

2. What is a gene?

3. From which stage of the cell cycle were the human chromosomes harvested? Explain your answer.

Part B: Monohybrid and Dihybrid Crosses

Green: _____ cross

Your Group Data		Entire Class Data	
Type of Kernels	**Number of Kernels**	**Type of Kernels**	**Number of Kernels**
Your calculated ratio:		Your calculated ratio:	
Expected Mendelian ratio of this cross:		Expected Mendelian ratio of this cross:	
Genotypes of the F_1 parents of this cross:		Genotypes of the F_1 parents of this cross:	

Red: _____ cross

Your Group Data		Entire Class Data	
Type of Kernels	**Number of Kernels**	**Type of Kernels**	**Number of Kernels**
Your calculated ratio:		Your calculated ratio:	
Expected Mendelian ratio of this cross:		Expected Mendelian ratio of this cross:	
Genotypes of the F_1 parents of this cross:		Genotypes of the F_1 parents of this cross:	

Blue: _____ cross

Your Group Data		Entire Class Data	
Type of Kernels	**Number of Kernels**	**Type of Kernels**	**Number of Kernels**
Your calculated ratio:		Your calculated ratio:	
Expected Mendelian ratio of this cross:		Expected Mendelian ratio of this cross:	
Genotypes of the F_1 parents of this cross:		Genotypes of the F_1 parents of this cross:	

Part C: Multiple Allelic Trait—Human Blood Groups

Blood Sample	Agglutination/Clumping with Anti-A Antibody Solution (Yes or No)	Agglutination/Clumping with Anti-B Antibody Solution (Yes or No)	Blood Type (Phenotype)	Genotype(s)
I				
II				
III				
IV				

Part D: Human Inheritance—Making Babies

Draw a picture of the child's face, below.

Molecular Biology and Biotechnology

Exercise 15

Objectives

1. Define semi-conservative, reading frame, point mutation, pleiotropy, restriction enzyme, and recognition site.

2. Explain the structures of DNA and RNA, noting the differences between them.

3. Explain the process of DNA replication, and perform DNA replication by generating a complementary strand of DNA.

4. Explain the process of transcription, and perform transcription to generate an mRNA transcript.

5. Explain the process of translation, and perform translation to generate a protein.

6. Explain DNA fingerprinting. Perform and interpret results of gel electrophoresis.

Introduction

A series of landmark experiments implicated **deoxyribonucleic acid** (DNA) as the genetic material, and in 1953, the correct structure of DNA was first presented by James Watson and Francis Crick. Much was discovered in the last half of the 20th century. Molecular biology has progressed tremendously in the past 25 years. Genetic engineering and recombinant DNA technology has resulted in great advances in the fields of agriculture and medicine.

During this exercise, you will examine the structure of DNA, practice DNA replication, and translate a protein. You will examine the impact of one particular DNA mutation in red blood cells and observe how one gene can impact multiple phenotypes. You will use one of the most important tools of molecular biology—**gel electrophoresis**—to determine the DNA fragment patterns of several individuals in a DNA fingerprint.

Part A: DNA Structure and Replication

DNA is a nucleic acid polymer made up of nucleotide monomers. Nucleotides of DNA are composed of the sugar deoxyribose, a phosphate group and one of four different nitrogenous bases:

- **The Purines:** Adenine (A) and Guanine (G)

- **The Pyrimidines:** Thymine (T) and Cytosine (C)

As suggested by Watson and Crick in 1953, complementary base-pairing makes DNA replication easy. **DNA replication** is the process by which two new double helices are formed. DNA replication is **semi-conservative** because each new molecule consists of one old strand and one new strand.

Materials

1. Model of DNA

Method

1. Observe the double helix structure shown in the model of DNA.

2. Answer the questions on your data sheet.

Part B: RNA Structure, Transcription, and Translation

RNA, also a polymer of nucleotide monomers, differs from DNA by having ribose sugar nucleotides attached to the phosphate group. The nitrogenous bases of RNA are adenine (A), guanine (G), and cytosine (C) as in DNA, but thymine (T) is replaced with the pyrimidine uracil (U). RNA is generally single-stranded.

Information encoded in DNA is first transcribed to messenger RNA (mRNA) before being translated to the amino acid sequence of proteins. The central dogma of molecular biology is:

$$\text{DNA} \xrightarrow{\text{Transcription}} \text{RNA} \xrightarrow{\text{Translation}} \text{Proteins}$$

A mutation in DNA can impact the sequence of RNA and in turn the amino acids making up a protein. An example of this is seen in sickle-cell anemia, an autosomal recessive disorder causing abnormal hemoglobin. In sickle-cell anemia, there is a **point mutation** in DNA that leads to a change in the amino acids incorporated in the hemoglobin. This change in hemoglobin structure causes red blood cells to sickle, leading to multiple symptoms.

Materials

1. Genetic code table

2. Prepared microscope slide of normal human blood smear

3. Prepared microscope slide of blood smear with sickled red blood cells

Method

1. Using the genetic code table, complete the transcription and translation on your data sheet. Complete the corresponding questions.

2. Observe and compare the prepared slides of normal blood and sickle-cell anemia blood at 400✕. Record your observations on the data sheet.

Part C: Multiple Effects of a Gene on an Organism (Pleiotropy)

Pleiotropy is an inheritance pattern in which one gene affects multiple phenotypic traits. Two varieties of peas will be compared to demonstrate this phenomenon. The **one gene** that is different between these two pea varieties encodes an enzyme that catalyzes the formation of starch from glucose-1-phosphate. This difference in enzyme activity—which you will investigate during this lab—ultimately leads to changes in appearance (wrinkled versus round), water uptake, and the structure of starch granules.

Materials

1. Presoaked wrinkled and round peas

2. Mortar and pestle

3. Centrifuge and centrifuge tubes

4. Grease pencil

5. Iodine solution

6. Glucose-1-phosphate agar in Petri dish

7. Sand

8. Samples of pre-weighed and soaked round and wrinkled peas

Hypotheses to Be Tested

1. Wrinkled peas absorb more water per gram than round peas.

2. Round peas will exhibit more enzyme activity than wrinkled peas.

Method

1. Determine the water uptake per gram by the sample of round and wrinkled pre-weighed peas, based on the data provided. These peas are in specially marked beakers.

2. Obtain ten of the soaked round peas and place them into a mortar with a pinch of sand, and grind to a paste. Continue grinding while gradually adding 10 ml of water. Grind until fairly smooth.

3. Once a smooth consistency is reached, transfer 8 ml of the mixture into a centrifuge tube. Using a paper towel, wipe any remaining sample into a garbage can.

4. Repeat steps 2 and 3 with a sample of wrinkled peas.

5. Following the directions of your laboratory instructor, centrifuge the samples that you have prepared.

6. Following centrifugation, place a drop of each of the enzyme extracts (clear solution in the centrifuge tubes) onto a Petri dish containing glucose-1-phosphate agar. (Do not allow drops to mix.)

7. Allow each of the drops to remain undisturbed for 30 minutes.

8. At the end of 30 minutes, add a small drop of iodine solution to each of the drops to determine enzyme activity.

   What color is the area with the extract from the wrinkled pea? _____

   What color is the area with the extract from the round pea? _____

9. Record results for Step 8 on the data sheet provided.

Part D: DNA Paternity Test Simulation

An offspring's DNA is a composite of its parents' DNA. So, comparison of DNA fragmentation patterns between a child and mother will reveal a partial match; bands in a child's DNA fingerprint that are not present in the mother's fingerprint must be contributed by the father.

DNA samples from mother, child, male 1, and male 2 in this case have been cut with **restriction enzymes**. Restriction enzymes cut DNA at specific nucleotide sequences called **recognition sites**. No two individuals (except for identical twins) have exactly the same pattern of restriction enzyme recognition sites due to variations in their DNA. Thus, treating DNA samples with the same restriction enzymes reveals a unique collection of different fragments. The fragments have been amplified using polymerase chain reaction (PCR).

In this experiment you will be analyzing DNA fragment patterns using gel electrophoresis to determine if male 1 or male 2 is the biological parent of the child.

Materials

1. Agarose gel (prepared by lab staff)

2. Power supply

3. DNA samples

4. TAE (1×) buffer

5. DNA stain (1×)

6. Staining trays

7. Micropipettes and tips

8. White light box

9. DNA cooler

10. Petri dishes with practice wells

11. Nitrile gloves

12. Bags for gel storage

Method

Day 1

1. Obtain aliquots of DNA samples from your instructor—keep on ice.

2. Pour enough TAE buffer solution to completely immerse the gel (approx. 175 ml).

3. Load the DNA samples as directed by your instructor.

NOTE:

• **Do not puncture wells when loading!**

• **Remember to use a different pipette tip for each sample.**

• **Do not release plunger of micropipette until tip is out of the well and chamber!**

4. When all samples have been loaded, cover the chamber and attach the electrodes first to the chamber and next to the power supply.

5. Your instructor will turn on the power supply to run your gels at 125V.

6. After 30–40 minutes turn off and unplug the power supply.

7. Detach electrodes from your chamber.

8. Lift the tray with gel out of chamber and slide onto a staining tray. Do not rip gel!
    Caution: Buffer solution may be hot!

9. Cover gel with 25 ml of 1× DNA stain solution for five minutes.

10. Carefully pour stain into the *used* stain beaker/bottle.

11. Rinse your gel several times with tap water, being careful not to rip it.

12. Carefully place your gel into a bag (labeled with your name) and add enough tap water to surround/cover the gel. Remove as much air from the bag as possible before you seal it, and place your bag into the storage container, as indicated by your instructor, to continue destaining until the next lab session.

13. Dispose of used TAE buffer in the designated waste container. Rinse and dry the gel chamber before reassembling it on your bench.

Day 2

1. Obtain your bag from the class container. If needed, you may continue to destain your gel by placing it in a staining tray and rinsing it in several changes of tap water. **Note:** Gently agitating the tray and frequently changing the water will expedite the destaining process.

2. Discard the water, and carefully place your gel on the white light box. (Position your gel with the wells across the top and the ladder on the left.)

3. Analyze your gel to determine which male is the father of this child, following the directions provided by your instructor. **Note:** Remember, to determine paternity, you must find bands that the child has that the mother does not, and assess which potential father could have contributed this piece of DNA to the child.

4. On your data sheet, draw a picture of the bands you observed in each sample, and answer the accompanying questions.

Data Sheet

Name _____

Section _____   Date _____

Part A: DNA Structure and Replication

1. How many strands do you see? _____

2. Which molecules form the backbone of each strand? _____

3. What pairs with the base adenine? _____

4. What pairs with the base guanine? _____

5. Name the type of bonding that attaches purines to pyrimidines: _____

Replicate the complementary strand, given the following nucleotide sequence:

– T A C C A T G A G T A G A C T –

_____

Part B: RNA Structure, Transcription, and Translation

DNA Template Strand	mRNA Codon (Complement to DNA Template Strand)	Amino Acid
GGG		
		Start (methionine)
	GUG	
GTG		
	CUG	
		Threonine
	CCU	
CTC		
		Glutamate
TTC		
	UGA	

1. What is the **start codon** and its importance to the **reading frame**?

2. What is the consequence of changing CTC to CTT in the DNA template strand?

3. What is the consequence of changing CTC to CAC in the DNA template strand? (**Note:** This is the point mutation that causes sickle-cell anemia.)

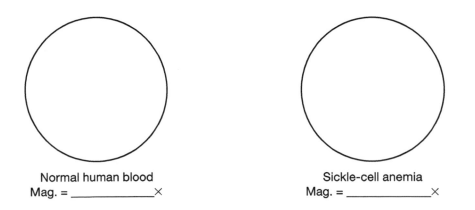

Normal human blood
Mag. = _____×

Sickle-cell anemia
Mag. = _____×

Part C: Multiple Effects of a Gene on an Organism (Pleiotropy)

Peas	Original Weight (g)	Present Weight (g)	Water Uptake/g*	Starch Test Result	Enzyme Activity (++/+/0)
Round					
Wrinkled					

$$*Water\ uptake/g = \frac{Weight\ Difference = Present\ Weight - Original\ Weight}{Original\ Weight}$$

1. Which pea absorbed the most water?

2. Which pea exhibited the most enzyme activity?

   How can you tell this?

3. Do the data support the hypotheses?

Part D: DNA Paternity Test Simulation

1. What does each stained band represent?

2. Who is the father of this child? Explain your answer.

Community Ecology: Symbiosis

Exercise 16

Alan Kraft/Shutterstock.com

Objectives

1. Define ecology, producer, consumer, decomposer, and symbiosis.

2. Define commensalism, and give an example.

3. Define mutualism, and give examples of mutualistic associations.

4. Define parasitism, and give examples of parasitic associations.

Introduction

Ecology is the study of interactions between organisms and between organisms and their environment. One important interaction is the trophic (feeding) relationship between producers and consumers. A **producer** is an autotroph, an organism capable of making its own food. Plants are producers. A **consumer** is a heterotroph, an organism that obtains its food from other living things. Animals are consumers. **Decomposers** are consumers that feed on dead organic matter. Bacteria and fungi are decomposers.

A close interaction between species is called **symbiosis**. Symbiotic relationships may be categorized as:

Commensalism: An association where one member benefits and the other is unaffected.

Mutualism: An association where both members benefit from each other's presence.

Parasitism: An association where one member benefits (parasite) and the other member (host) is harmed.

In this lab exercise, we will study each of these symbiotic relationships.

Part A: Commensalism

Materials
1. Prepared slide of *Obelia* with *Ephelota*
2. Compound microscope

Method
1. Examine the prepared slide of the Cnidarian *Obelia* with the commensalistic Protozoan *Ephelota*. *Ephelota* benefits from this relationship by obtaining food scraps, while *Obelia* is unaffected.
2. Draw and label *Obelia* with *Ephelota* on your data sheet.

Part B: Mutualism

Materials
1. Living cultures of *Paramecium bursaria*
2. Specimens of lichens
3. Prepared *Physcia* (lichen) slide
4. Compound microscope, glass slide, coverslip

Method
1. Make a wet mount slide of *Paramecium bursaria* and examine it under high power.
2. Note the green cytoplasmic inclusions; these are algal cells. How do they benefit the *Paramecium*?

   _____

   How does the *Paramecium* benefit the algal cells?

   _____

3. View the series of **lichens**. These are plants that have an **algal** and **fungal** "component." How does one benefit the other?

   _____

4. Obtain and examine a *Physcia* (lichen) slide. Note the algal (red) and the fungal (green) components of the lichen.
5. Make a sketch in your data sheet.

Part C: Parasitism

Materials

1. Plant galls

2. Prepared slide of *Trichinella* in muscle cysts

3. Prepared slide of tapeworm (*Taenia*)

4. Prepared slide of liver fluke (*Clonorchis*)

5. Demonstration parasites

Method

1. Examine the plant gall with the aid of a dissection microscope. The organism you observe is an insect larva.

2. Make a study of the following human parasites.

   a. Examine a prepared slide of the roundworm parasite *Trichinella*—causative agent of the disease trichinosis (see life cycle diagram). The stage that you are viewing on the slide shows the larvae (immature worms) encysted in skeletal muscle. Your instructor may review the life cycle of the worm with you and explain the method that this parasite uses in gaining entry to its **host**. Record your observations on the data sheet. See Figure 16.1.

   b. Study a tapeworm (*Taenia*) slide next. Adult tapeworms are restricted to the digestive tracts. Draw the head and several proglottids (body segments). See Figure 16.2.

   c. Next, view the prepared slide of the liver fluke (*Clonorchis*). Trace the life cycle of this human pathogen. The "intermediate" hosts of this parasite are snails and fish, and the adult worms are found in the human liver. Complete the life cycle outline on the data sheet. See Figure 16.3.

3. View additional parasites that may be on display, as directed by your instructor.

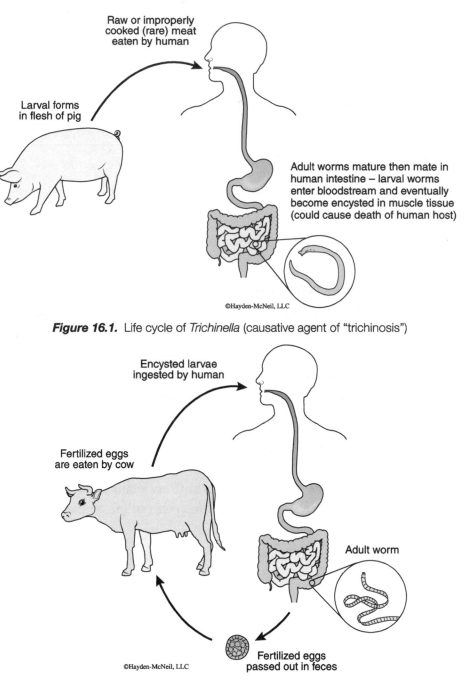

Figure 16.1. Life cycle of *Trichinella* (causative agent of "trichinosis")

Figure 16.2. Life cycle of *Taenia saginata* (beef tapeworm)

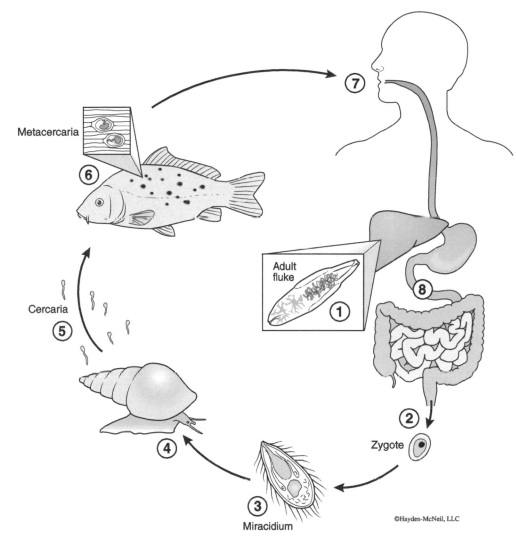

Figure 16.3. Life cycle of *Clonorchis sinensis* (human liver fluke)

1. **Adult liver fluke** develops and lives in liver of human host.

2. **Zygote** leaves adult fluke and is passed from human host in feces.

3. Zygote develops into **miracidium** and then penetrates the snail.

4. Inside snail, the miracidium develops into a **sporocyst**, which gives rise to several **redia**. Each redia develops into several **cercaria**.

5. **Cercaria** leave snail.

6. Cercaria attach to fish and discard tails. They then penetrate under fish's scales and encyst in tissues, becoming **metacercaria**.

7. Metacercaria enter human host when poorly cooked fish tissue is ingested.

8. **Immature fluke** emerges from metacercaria in duodenum, migrates through bile ducts to liver, and matures to adult.

Data Sheet

16

Name _____

Section _____ Date _____

Part A: Commensalism

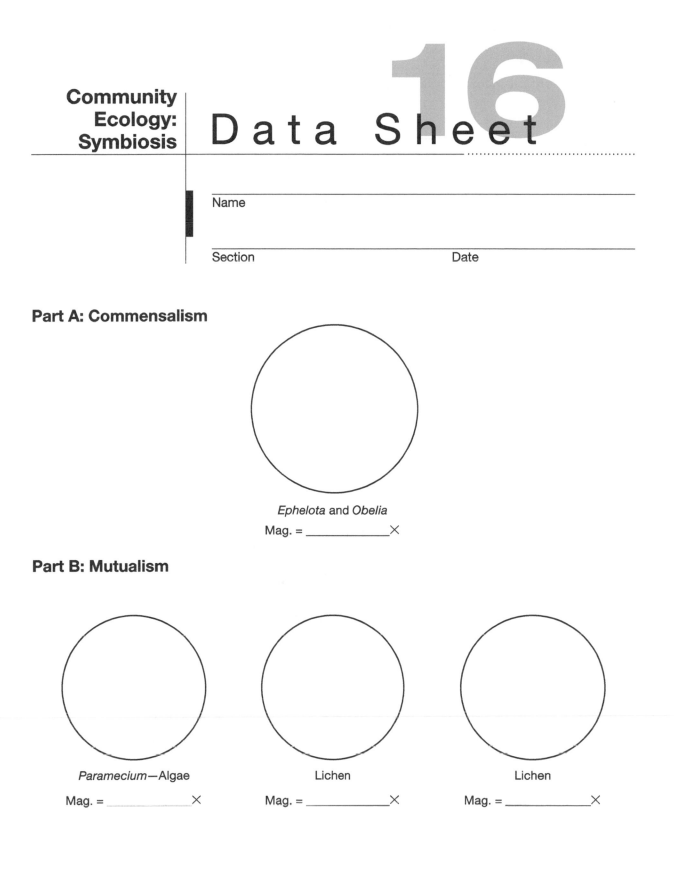

Ephelota and *Obelia*

Mag. = _____ ✕

Part B: Mutualism

Paramecium—Algae

Mag. = _____ ✕

Lichen

Mag. = _____ ✕

Lichen

Mag. = _____ ✕

Part C: Parasitism

Make a sketch of the following relationships.

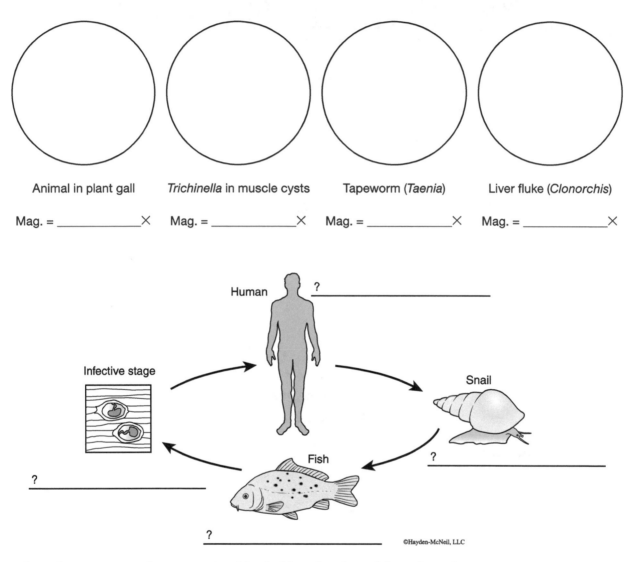

Animal in plant gall Mag. = _____×

Trichinella in muscle cysts Mag. = _____×

Tapeworm (*Taenia*) Mag. = _____×

Liver fluke (*Clonorchis*) Mag. = _____×

Human ? _____

Infective stage

Snail

Fish

? _____

? _____

? _____

©Hayden-McNeil, LLC

Place these terms in the appropriate blanks(?) in the above life cycle outline.

Second intermediate host

Infected fish muscle

First intermediate host

Adult worm

Community Ecology: Predation

Objectives

1. Define population, community, ecology, and predation.
2. Define the differences between predator and prey.
3. Describe the population dynamics of predator-prey cycling and what causes it.

Introduction

Recall from Exercise 16 that **ecology** is the study of **ecosystems**, which includes the interactions of organisms with both other organisms and with their physical and chemical environment; therefore, both **biotic** (living) and **abiotic** (non-living) components must be considered. These interactions amongst organisms include all of the interactions within the biotic **community**, which includes all of the different populations present in the local environment. A **population** is made of all the interacting organisms within one species.

During Exercise 16, you explored symbiotic relationships between two species. Another example of how two species within a community can interact is **predation**. Predation occurs when one species is a resource (i.e., food) for another species. The **predator** consumes the **prey**. For example, a lion is a predator on its zebra prey. The predator population benefits, while the prey population is harmed.

During this lab, you will explore the concept of predation and the impact it has on both predator and prey populations. An interesting aspect of the predator-prey interaction is how each species' population size is affected by the other: the presence of predators can decrease prey population size through predation, which in turn will decrease predator population size because of lack of food. With fewer predators, the prey population can increase once again. This alternating increase and decrease in predator and prey population sizes is called **predator-prey cycling** (Figure 17.1).

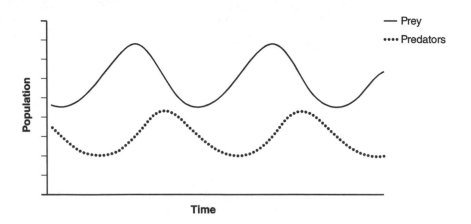

Figure 17.1. Predator-prey cycling. An increase in the prey population soon causes an increase in the predator population because more food is available. As the predator population increases, the prey population declines from increased predation. Fewer prey means less food for the predator, whose population then declines. Lower predation causes the prey population to increase and begins the cycle once again.

Part A: Simulation of Predator-Prey Cycling

This exercise will simulate predation using you (and a spoon) as the predator and beads as the prey. Predation will occur, and surviving prey will reproduce, as will predators that have captured enough food/prey to be able to reproduce. You will track the population size of both the predator and prey populations over time.

Materials

1. Small plastic beads

2. Plastic spoons

3. Plastic weigh boats, bowls, trays, or petri dishes

4. 250 ml beakers

Background

A new meadow develops in a forest as the result of a forest fire. Mice move into the meadow and begin to eat the plants and insects there and reproduce. Weasels, attracted by the mice as a food resource, also migrate into the meadow. The weasels eat the mice and, if they capture enough mice, also reproduce.

- A small tray, bowl, or dish will simulate the meadow habitat.

- Beads will simulate the mice.

- Each scoop of a spoon through the meadow simulates predation by one weasel on the mouse/bead population.

The following rules apply to every generation:

1. **Rules for the Mouse Population:**

    - **There are always at least 10 mice initially present.**

        ○ If there are not 10 mice after reproduction, assume mice migrate in from a nearby meadow.

    - **The surviving mice after predation reproduce by doubling their numbers.**

        ○ Example: If 22 beads remain in the tray after predation, add 22 more beads for a total of 44.

    - **There are never more than 100 mice present.**

        ○ Assume 100 is the meadow's **carrying capacity** — the maximum size population of mice that the meadow can support.

            ▪ Example: If you have 55 surviving mice, then doubling the mice equals 110, which exceeds 100 ($2 \times 55 = 110$), so only place 100 beads in the meadow.

2. **Rules for the Weasel Population:**

    - **There is always at least one weasel initially present.**

        ○ If no weasels survive from the previous generation, assume a weasel migrates in from a nearby meadow.

    - **For a weasel to survive it must capture at least 5 mice.**

        ○ If a weasel captures fewer than five mice, assume it starves to death or emigrates to another meadow in search of food.

    - **For *every 5 mice* a weasel catches, the weasel produces 1 weasel offspring.**

        ○ Example: There are three weasels in a generation. One weasel captures 11 mice, one captures 7 mice, and one captures 2 mice.

            ▪ Weasel 1 captures 11 mice. It survives and reproduces 2 offspring. ($1 + 2 = 3$)

            ▪ Weasel 2 captures 7 mice. It survives and reproduces 1 offspring. ($1 + 1 = 2$)

            ▪ Weasel 3 captures 2 mice. It dies or leaves the meadow. (0)

                - In the next generation there will be a total of 5 weasels.

                    ○ Weasel 1 plus 2 offspring (3)

                    ○ Weasel 2 plus 1 offspring (2)

How to add and capture mice:

- One partner plays the role of predator and one the role of data keeper.

- The data keeper:

    ○ Adds mice each generation

    ○ Gently shakes the tray once, distributing the mice

    ○ Records the data on the data sheets

- The predator:

    ○ Scoops once quickly through the length of the tray capturing mice with the spoon

        ▪ The predator should not tilt the tray or deliberately try to capture all the mice. Just capture what is easy to scoop up with one quick scoop through the length of the tray.

General Method

1. Obtain a "meadow" container, a spoon, and a beaker with beads.

Start

2. Hold 1 spoon, and place 10 bead "mice" in the "meadow."

    a. Record 1 weasel and 10 mice in the *Population Data Table* as the initial population size for Generation 1.

Generation 1

3. The "weasel" will scoop once through the meadow capturing mice with the spoon. Place the mice in the beaker "stomach."

    a. Record the number of mice captured by the weasel in the *Weasel Predation Data Table* for Generation 1.

    b. Calculate the total number of surviving weasels plus new offspring weasels.

        i. If a weasel captures 5 or more mice it survives.

        ii. For every 5 mice a weasel captures, it produces 1 weasel offspring.

4. Double the number of surviving mice remaining in the meadow.

    a. The mice population is never below 10 or above 100.

5. Record the total number of mice and total surviving weasels plus offspring in the *Population Data Table* for Generation 2.

Generation 2 and higher

6. Repeat the steps of Generation 1 for each weasel calculated above:

    a. Scoop once through the meadow with the spoon for each weasel, capturing mice.

b.   Record the number of mice captured by that weasel in the *Weasel Predation Data Table*.

c.   After all weasels have fed:

i.   Calculate the total number of weasels for the next generation in the *Weasel Predation Data Table*.

ii.   Double the surviving bead/mice.

d.   Record the mice and weasel numbers in the *Population Data Table*.

e.   Continue until you reach Generation 19.

f.   Calculate the initial populations in Generation 20.

Graph your Data and Answer the Questions

7.   Plot the mice and weasel populations over Generations 1 through 20 on the graph provided.

a.   Use an 'm' to plot each mouse data point.

b.   Use a 'w' to plot each weasel data point (or use two different colors).

c.   Connect each mouse data point with a straight line.

d.   Connect each weasel data point with a separate straight line.

8.   Analyze the graph and data to answer the questions.

Example for the First Four Generations—Start here then continue on your own

Use these "practice" generations to help you figure out how to fill out the Data Tables. You will generate your own data starting with Generation 5 and higher.

Generation 1

1.   Begin with 10 mice and one weasel in the meadow (place 10 beads in the tray).

2.   Fill in Generation 1 of the *Population Data Table*.

3.   The capture of mice by the weasel is simulated by scooping the spoon once through the tray for each weasel present.

a.   Scoop through the tray but pretend your weasel (scoop) caught no mice (beads).

4.   In the *Weasel Predation Data Table* enter a 0 for prey captured by predator 1 of the first generation. Also enter a 0 for offspring produced by the predator.

a.   Add up the total mice caught and record it in the "Captured Mice" column.

b.   Calculate the number of weasels (scoops) for the second generation. This will be zero—no surviving weasels and no offspring. Record a zero in the last column marked "Surviving Predators + Offspring."

Generation 2

1. Fill in Generation 2 of the **Population Data Table**.

   a. The 10 surviving mice reproduce and double their numbers; add 10 more beads to the tray for a total of 20 beads.

   b. No weasels survived, so one new weasel migrates into the meadow.

   c. Record 20 mice, 1 weasel.

2. Scoop once through the tray for one weasel, picking up 4 beads. Place the beads into the beaker, representing the stomach of the predator.

3. In the **Weasel Predation Data Table** enter 4 for prey captured by predator 1 of the second generation and 0 for predator offspring.

   a. Add up the total mice caught and record it in the "Captured Mice" column.

   b. Calculate the number of weasels (scoops) for the third generation. This will be zero—no surviving weasels and no offspring. Record zero in the "Surviving Predators + Offspring" column.

Generation 3

1. Fill in Generation 3 of the **Population Data Table**.

   a. Sixteen mice survive; add 16 more beads to the tray since the surviving mice of a generation always double their numbers.

   b. No weasels survived, so one new weasel migrates into the meadow.

   c. Record 32 mice and 1 weasel.

2. Scoop once through the tray, picking up 7 beads.

3. In the **Weasel Predation Data Table** enter 7 for prey captured by predator 1 of the third generation. Also enter 1 for the offspring produced by this predator since the weasel reproduces for every 5 captured mice.

   a. Add up the total mice caught and record it in the "Captured Mice" column.

   b. Calculate the number of weasels (scoops) for the fourth generation. The weasel caught 7 mice, so it survives, and also reproduces 1 offspring. Record a 2 in the "Surviving Predators + Offspring" column.

Generation 4

1. Fill in Generation 4 of the **Population Data Table**.

   a. Twenty-five mice survive (32 − 7 = 25); add 25 more beads to the tray.

   b. There were two weasels at the end of Generation 3, one survivor and one offspring.

   c. Record 50 mice and 2 weasels.

2. There are 2 predators in Generation 4. Scoop **once** through the tray for **each** predator.

   a. Scoop once through the tray for the first predator, picking up 13 beads.

      i. In the *Weasel Predation Data Table* enter 13 for prey captured by predator 1 of the fourth generation and 2 for the offspring produced by this predator.

   b. Scoop again through the tray for the second predator, picking up 7 beads.

      i. In the *Weasel Predation Data Table* enter 7 for prey captured by predator 2 of the fourth generation, and 1 for the offspring produced by this predator.

3. Calculate the number of captured mice and number of weasels (scoops) for the fifth generation.

   a. Add up the total mice caught and record it in the "Captured Mice" column.

   b. Weasel 1 plus two offspring, weasel 2 plus one offspring = 5 weasels. Record this in the "Surviving Predators + Offspring" column.

Generation 5

1. Fill in Generation 5 of the *Population Data Table*.

   a. Thirty mice survive (50 − 13 − 7 = 30); add 30 more beads to the tray.

   b. There were 5 weasels at the end of Generation 4.

   c. Record 60 mice and 5 weasels.

Completing the Exercise

1. Continue as outlined above to complete the *Population Data Table*.

2. Important: In simulating the capture of mice by the predator, scoop the spoon through the length of the tray, and do not deliberately attempt to scoop up all the beads.

3. In the *Population Data Table* remember that

   a. **Initial Prey** never falls below 10 or over 100; and

   b. **Initial Predators** never fall below 1.

4. When you have completed 20 generations and the *Population Data Table* is complete, graph the results as directed.

5. Then answer the questions on the data sheet.

Weasel Predation Data Table

A weasel must capture at least 5 mice to survive, and for each 5 mice it captures it produces one offspring.

Weasel (scoop) Number →		1	2	3	4	5	6	7	8	9	10	11	12	13	14	15	16	17	18	19	20	Total Mice Captured	Surviving Predators + Offspring
→ Generation																							1
Start																							
1	Mice Captured	0																					
	Offspring Produced	0																				0	0
	Predators for next Generation	0																					
2	Mice Captured	4																					
	Offspring Produced	0																				4	0
	Predators for next Generation	0																					
3	Mice Captured	7																					
	Offspring Produced	1																				7	2
	Predators for next Generation	2																					
4	Mice Captured	13	7																				
	Offspring Produced	2	1																			20	5
	Predators for next Generation	3	2																				
5	Mice Captured																						
	Offspring Produced																						
	Predators for next Generation																						
6	Mice Captured																						
	Offspring Produced																						
	Predators for next Generation																						

Continued on next page

Weasel (scoop) Number →		1	2	3	4	5	6	7	8	9	10	11	12	13	14	15	16	17	18	19	20	Total Mice Captured	Surviving Predators + Offspring
→ Generation																							
7	Mice Captured																						
	Offspring Produced																						
	Predators for next Generation																						
8	Mice Captured																						
	Offspring Produced																						
	Predators for next Generation																						
9	Mice Captured																						
	Offspring Produced																						
	Predators for next Generation																						
10	Mice Captured																						
	Offspring Produced																						
	Predators for next Generation																						
11	Mice Captured																						
	Offspring Produced																						
	Predators for next Generation																						
12	Mice Captured																						
	Offspring Produced																						
	Predators for next Generation																						

Continued on next page

Weasel (scoop) Number →	1	2	3	4	5	6	7	8	9	10	11	12	13	14	15	16	17	18	19	20	Total Mice Captured	Surviving Predators + Offspring
↓ Generation																						
13 — Mice Captured																						
13 — Offspring Produced																						
13 — Predators for next Generation																						
14 — Mice Captured																						
14 — Offspring Produced																						
14 — Predators for next Generation																						
15 — Mice Captured																						
15 — Offspring Produced																						
15 — Predators for next Generation																						
16 — Mice Captured																						
16 — Offspring Produced																						
16 — Predators for next Generation																						
17 — Mice Captured																						
17 — Offspring Produced																						
17 — Predators for next Generation																						
18 — Mice Captured																						
18 — Offspring Produced																						
18 — Predators for next Generation																						
19 — Mice Captured																						
19 — Offspring Produced																						
19 — Predators for next Generation																						

Population Data Table

Generation ↓	Initial Mice	−	Total Mice Captured	=	Surviving Mice	Initial Weasels
Generation ↓	Never < 10 Never > 100		Copied from Weasel Predation Data Table		× 2 = Initial mice for next generation (to mimic mouse reproduction)	Copied from Weasel Predation Data Table (If surviving weasels = "0," then 1 migrates in)
1	Start with 10	−	0 mice captured	=	10 × 2 = 20	Start with 1
2	20	−	4	=	16 × 2 = 32	1
3	32	−	7	=	25 × 2 = 50	1
4	50	−	20	=	30 × 2 = 60	2
5	60	−		=		5
6		−		=		
7		−		=		
8		−		=		
9		−		=		
10		−		=		
11		−		=		
12		−		=		
13		−		=		
14		−		=		
15		−		=		
16		−		=		
17		−		=		
18		−		=		
19						
20						

Data Sheet

17

Name _____

Section _____ Date _____

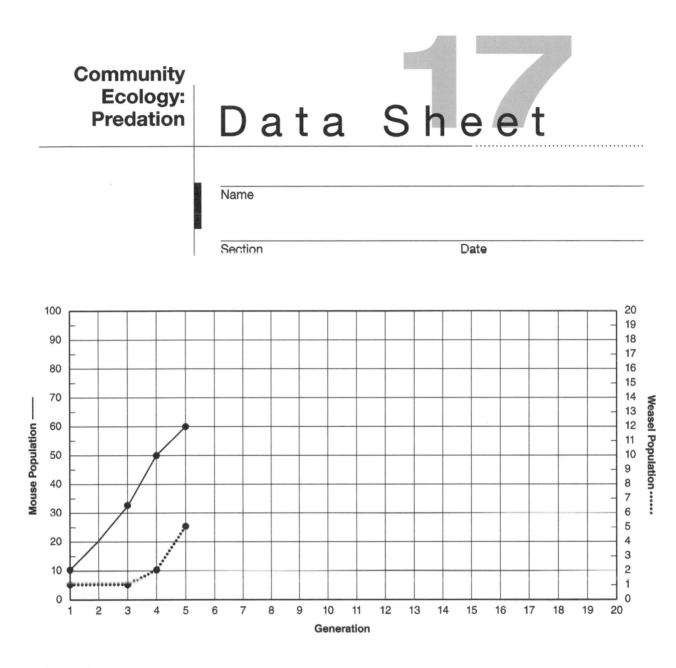

Questions

1. Which population (predator or prey) shows the **first** increase in numbers?

2. A **peak** in the weasel population comes _____ a peak in the mouse population.

    a. before

    b. after

    c. at the same time as

3. What is your explanation for this?

4. A **drop** in the mouse population comes _____ a peak in the weasel population.
   a. before
   b. after
   c. at the same time as

5. What causes this decline in mouse population?

6. What factor most determines the size of the weasel population in the meadow in any given generation?

7. What would happen to the mouse population if there were no weasels and no predation on the mouse population?

8. What would happen to the weasel population if the mouse population decreased because of a viral disease in addition to loss through predation?

Evolution

Exercise 18

Eric Isselee/Shutterstock.com

Objectives

1. Define evolution, natural selection, fitness, genetic drift, bottleneck effect, allele frequency, adaptation, gene flow, and random mating.

2. List the five forces that cause evolution.

3. Calculate and monitor allele frequencies in a population to determine whether evolution is occurring.

4. Explain how camouflage affects natural selection in a population of prey.

5. Explain the link between genetic drift and population size.

Introduction

Evolution can be defined as descent with modifications over time. Evolution results in a change in the genetic makeup (**allele frequency**) of a population over time. The most important mechanism driving evolution is **natural selection**, proposed simultaneously by **Charles Darwin** and **Alfred Russell Wallace**. Natural selection can result in the increase of **alleles** that produce advantageous traits (**adaptations**) and the decrease of those alleles that produce less favorable traits. As a result, individuals in the population become better adapted to their environment over time. Their **Darwinian fitness** (their survival and reproduction) increases.

Genetic drift is another cause of evolution. Genetic drift is the change in allele frequencies due to **random events**. Genetic drift has a larger effect on smaller populations. The **bottleneck effect** is genetic drift caused by a drastic reduction in population size. Both natural selection and genetic drift can cause an allele to be lost or fixed, but only natural selection can lead to adaptation.

Natural selection and genetic drift are two forces that can cause evolution, and they will be investigated during this lab. Different colored beads will represent different alleles. Other forces that lead to evolution are **mutations, gene flow,** and **non-random mating**.

Part A: Natural Selection by Simulated Predator

Individuals are more likely to survive if they possess a coloration that helps them elude predators (better camouflage). These individuals will then survive and pass on more of their genes to the next generation. Thus, we can say they exhibit greater **fitness**.

Materials

1. Two different colors of beads (40 of each color)

2. Two 250 ml beakers

3. Trays lined with paper

Method

1. Place 20 beads of each color (40 beads total) into the tray. Mix the beads thoroughly.

2. Acting as a predator, quickly select the prey that *stand out* against the paper background. As a predator, you must act quickly to capture your food before it escapes—aim for 10 draws in 10 seconds.

   Note: Pick out *two beads* at a time. These two beads represent the two alleles in the genotype that determine the color of your prey.

   • Place beads in a "waste" beaker as they are being pulled out.

3. The survivors (the beads left in the tray) will establish the next generation's gene pool as follows:

   • Count the number of each color bead (allele) remaining in the tray.

   • Multiply by two.

   • This will be the number of beads of each color to be placed in the tray to start the next generation. There should always be 40 beads in the tray at the start of each generation.

4. Repeat for up to 10 generations or until only one color (allele) remains in the population.

5. Calculate the allele frequencies of the dominant and recessive allele in each generation. Plot the progression of the dominant allele over time in your data sheet. Your instructor will indicate which color of bead is considered dominant.

Part B: Genetic Drift by the Bottleneck Effect

Because you are randomly picking only half of the population, this activity demonstrates the bottleneck effect, which is a type of genetic drift.

Materials

1. Two different colors of beads (40 of each color)

2. Two 250 ml beakers

3. Trays lined with paper

Method

1. Place 20 beads of each color (40 beads total) into the tray.

2. Mix the beads thoroughly.

3. **Without looking,** remove one pair of beads (a pair of alleles) at a time. Record the color combination (genotype) on the data sheet. Your instructor will indicate which color of bead is to be considered the dominant allele and which color should be identified as the recessive allele.

   Bead color of dominant allele_____

   Bead color of recessive allele _____

4. Select *10 pairs* of beads. They are the parents of the next generation.

5. Remove all unpicked beads from the tray and place in "waste" beaker.

6. Construct the next generation's gene pool as follows:

   • Count the actual number of each color bead (allele) that you selected from the tray.

   • Multiply that number by two.

   • This will be the number of beads of each color to be placed in the tray for the next generation.

   • There should always be 40 beads in the tray at the start of each generation.

7. Repeat steps 3 through 6 until you have reached the 20th generation or until one color (allele) has disappeared.

Data Sheet

18

Name _____

Section _____ Date _____

Part A: Natural Selection by Simulated Predator

Population	Dominant Beads (____)	Recessive Beads (____)	Total
Initial—0	20	20	40
1st Generation			
2nd Generation			
3rd Generation			
4th Generation			
5th Generation			
6th Generation			
7th Generation			
8th Generation			
9th Generation			
10th Generation			

Generation	Frequency of the Dominant Allele (p)*	Frequency of the Recessive Allele (q)*
Initial—0	0.5	0.5
1st Generation		
2nd Generation		
3rd Generation		
4th Generation		
5th Generation		
6th Generation		
7th Generation		
8th Generation		
9th Generation		
10th Generation		

$$*Frequency\ of\ Dominant\ Allele = p = \frac{\#\ of\ dominant\ alleles}{\#\ of\ total\ alleles} = \frac{\#\ of\ dominant\ alleles}{40}$$

$$*Frequency\ of\ Recessive\ Allele = q = \frac{\#\ of\ recessive\ alleles}{\#\ of\ total\ alleles} = \frac{\#\ of\ recessive\ alleles}{40}$$

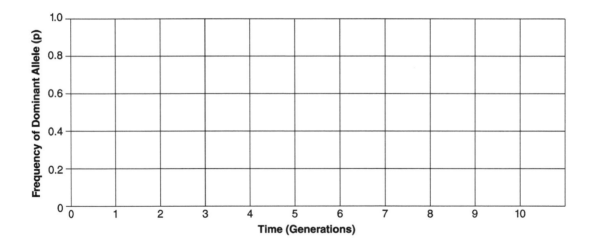

1. What force is causing the change in the frequencies of the colored beads (alleles)?

2. What is happening to the frequency of the dominant allele?

3. At the end of this experiment, is the population better adapted or less adapted to its environment (tray)? Explain your answer. (Hint: Think about camouflage.)

4. What would be the result if the paper were:

   a. the opposite color?

   b. white?

5. What do you think would happen in this experiment if you were to repeat it blindfolded?

Part B: Genetic Drift by the Bottleneck Effect

Generation	AA	Aa	aa	Frequency of Dominant Allele (p)*	Frequency of Recessive Allele (q)*
0 – Start					
1					
2					
3					
4					
5					
6					
7					
8					
9					
10					
11					
12					
13					
14					
15					
16					
17					
18					
19					
20					

*Refer to the equations on page 182.

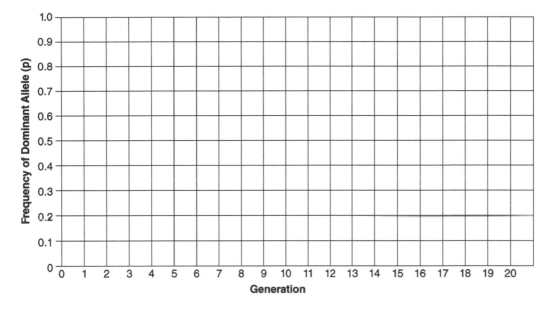

1. What force is causing the change in the frequencies of the colored beads (alleles)?

2. What happened to the frequency of the dominant allele?

3. Do you think you would get the same result if you repeated the experiment? Explain.

4. At the end of this experiment, is the population better adapted to its environment (tray)?

5. What would be the difference in your results if there were 1000 beads in the tray instead of 40?

6. Describe and explain the differences between your graph in Part A and your graph in Part B. Discuss how these differences relate to adaptation.

Plant Anatomy

Exercise 19

Objectives

1. Distinguish between monocots and dicots.
2. Identify features of a monocot stem.
3. Identify features of a dicot stem and root.
4. Identify the features of a woody stem.

Introduction

Although this laboratory exercise is entitled plant anatomy, we will still study only one group of plants, the **Angiospermae**. These are more commonly called **flowering plants**. Although these are the most recent members of the plant kingdom, they are the dominant group of plants on the earth's land surfaces at the present time. The majority of plants that are familiar to you, with the exception of the evergreen trees, are members of the Angiospermae group. This group includes the **typical flowering plants** (example: geranium plants), the **grasses** (example: front lawns, corn, wheat, and rice), and the **broad-leafed trees** (example: maples, oaks, and elms). Taxonomically, the Angiospermae group has been divided into two large subgroups, the **Monocotyledoneae (monocots)** and the **Dicotyledoneae (dicots)**.

Monocots derive their name from the fact that their embryos exhibit a **single cotyledon**. The mature plants of this group are characterized by **parallel leaf veination**, **scattered vascular bundles** in their stems, and **floral parts** in multiples of three. The grasses constitute the most common members of this group.

The dicots derive their name from the fact that the embryos of these plants exhibit **two cotyledons**. The mature plants of this group are characterized by **nonparallel leaf veination**, a **circular arrangement of vascular bundles** in their stems, and **floral parts** arranged in multiples of four or five. The broad-leafed trees, such as maples and oaks, as well as many of the typical flowers, such as geraniums and petunias, are examples of dicots.

Materials

1. Models: Root Tip, Monocot Stem, Dicot Stem, Woody Stem

2. Compound microscope

3. Prepared slides: *Ranunculus* root c.s., *Zea mays* stem c.s., *Helianthus* stem c.s., *Tilia* 3-year-old stem c.s.

Method

1. ***Ranunculus* root:**

    Since the roots of both monocot and dicot exhibit great similarity, only a cross section of *Ranunculus* (a dicot) will be examined. You are advised to begin your study of this material with the scanning power of the microscope, switching to higher power as the need arises. As this and the other prepared slides are examined, you should be aware that the specimens have been stained to highlight certain tissues, hence the variety of colors that you will see. As you view the *Ranunculus* slide, use your textbook as a guide to the structures that you are to locate.

    Examination of the interior of the root should reveal a definite circular structure, the **stele** or **vascular region** of the root. It is within this region that you should be able to identify **vascular tissue** (**xylem** and **phloem**) of the root. The **xylem** cells will be thick-walled and stained red, while those of the **phloem** will be thin-walled and blue-green in color. The phloem cells will be located between the arms of the **xylem** tissue. To the outside of the stele is a great mass of thin-walled cells containing small purplish granules. This is the **cortex** area of the root and serves mainly as a storage area. The numerous purple granules are **starch granules**. The outermost cells of the root, those on its surface, constitute the **epidermis** of the root. Once your observations have been completed, it is recommended that you draw a representative section through the root in the indicated area on the data sheet for this exercise.

2. ***Zea mays* stem:**

    The corn stem provides you with an example of the typical **monocot stem**. The rather large nature of this specimen makes it advisable to start your examination with the scanning power of the microscope. You can then switch to higher levels of magnification as the need arises. As you view the *Zea mays* slide, use your textbook as a guide to the structures that you are to locate.

Upon examination of this section, you should first note the **scattered vascular bundles**, which are the prime characteristic of the **monocot stem**. The large mass of tissue that these bundles are embedded in is the cortex of the stem. Within the vascular bundles, you should be able to find the thick-walled, large diameter, red staining cells of the functional **xylem tissue** and those of the thin-walled, blue-green staining cells of the **phloem tissue**. The very outer surface of the stem constitutes the **epidermis** of this stem. Once your observations have been completed, it is recommended that you draw a representative section through the stem in the indicated area on the data sheet that is at the end of this exercise.

3. *Helianthus* **stem:**

The sunflower provides you with the opportunity to examine the anatomy of the typical **herbaceous (nonwoody) dicot stem**. The large nature of this specimen makes it advisable that you begin your observations with the scanning power of the microscope. You can then switch to the higher levels of magnification as the need arises. As you view the *Helianthus* slide, you should use your textbook as a guide to locate the structures described below.

Upon examination of this section, you should first note the **circular arrangement of the vascular bundles**. This is a distinctive characteristic of the herbaceous **dicot stem**. The mass of thin-walled cells within the circle of vascular bundles is the **pith** of the stem, while that to the outside of the circle is the **cortex** of the stem. Within a single vascular bundle, you should be able to locate the relatively large diameter, thick-walled, red staining cells of the functional **xylem tissue**. The thin-walled, blue-green staining cells are those of the functional **phloem**. You should be able to find a distinct "cap" of thick-walled, narrow diameter, red staining cells. These are **sclerenchyma (fiber cells)**, which serve to protect the functional parts of the vascular bundle, as well as to help support the stem. The very outer surface of the stem constitutes the **epidermal** layer of the stem. Once your observations have been completed, it is recommended that you draw a representative section through this stem in the indicated area on the data sheet for this exercise.

4. *Tilia* **stem:**

The *Tilia* provides you with the opportunity to examine the stem anatomy of the typical **woody dicot**. The extremely large nature of this specimen makes it advisable to start your examination with the scanning power of the microscope. You can then employ the higher levels of magnification as the need arises. As you examine the *Tilia* slide, use your textbook as a guide to the structures you are to locate.

Upon examination of this section, you should notice the **absence of distinct vascular bundles**. The bulk of the tissue in this stem is a solid mass of **xylem** (wood) tissue. As examination of this "woody" area will reveal the existence of "annual rings" whose appearance is created by xylem cells of different diameters. Within a single annual ring, you should be able to locate the narrow diameter xylem of the **summer wood** and the much larger diameter xylem of the **spring wood**. At the very center of the stem you should see a relatively small amount of a tissue consisting of thin-walled cells called **pith**. Using your textbook as a guide, locate the **vascular cambium** of this stem. Although it is a very narrow band of tissue, it is of great importance to the stem. The repeated divisions of this layer create both new xylem and phloem tissue as it is required by the plant. This constant addition of new tissue leads to a continual increase in stem diameter for the life of this plant. Locate the somewhat pyramid-shaped masses of **phloem** that lie just to the outside of the xylem (wood) tissue of this stem. The actual functional phloem tissue will be blue-green in color. The reddish to orange material mixed in with the functional phloem cells are **protective fiber cells**. The very outside of this stem is made up of cork. Once your observations have been completed, it is recommended that you draw a representative section through this stem in the indicated area on the data sheet for this exercise.

Data Sheet

19

Name _____

Section _____   Date _____

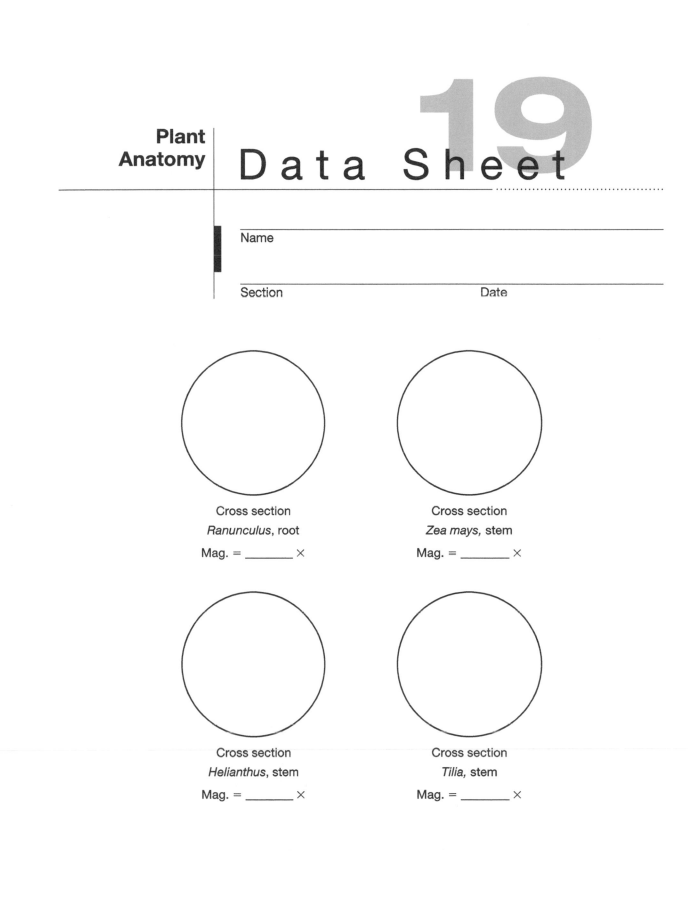

Cross section
Ranunculus, root

Mag. = _____ ×

Cross section
Zea mays, stem

Mag. = _____ ×

Cross section
Helianthus, stem

Mag. = _____ ×

Cross section
Tilia, stem

Mag. = _____ ×

What is the Microsoft ® Office Specialist Program?

The Microsoft Office Specialist Program enables candidates to show that they have something exceptional to offer – proven expertise in certain Microsoft programs. Recognized by businesses and schools around the world, over 4 million certifications have been obtained in over 100 different countries. The Microsoft Office Specialist Program is the only Microsoft-approved certification program of its kind.

What is the Microsoft Office Specialist Certification?

The Microsoft Office Specialist certification validates through the use of exams that you have obtained specific skill sets within the applicable Microsoft Office programs and other Microsoft programs included in the Microsoft Office Specialist Program. The candidate can choose which exam(s) they want to take according to which skills they want to validate.

The available Microsoft Office Specialist Program exams include*:
- Using Windows Vista®
- Using Microsoft® Office Word 2007
- Using Microsoft® Office Word 2007 - Expert
- Using Microsoft® Office Excel® 2007
- Using Microsoft® Office Excel® 2007 - Expert
- Using Microsoft® Office PowerPoint® 2007
- Using Microsoft® Office Access® 2007
- Using Microsoft® Office Outlook® 2007
- Using Microsoft SharePoint® 2007

The Microsoft Office Specialist Program 2010 exams will include*:
- Microsoft Word 2010
- Microsoft Word 2010 Expert
- Microsoft Excel® 2010
- Microsoft Excel® 2010 Expert
- Microsoft PowerPoint® 2010
- Microsoft Access® 2010
- Microsoft Outlook® 2010
- Microsoft SharePoint® 2010

What does the Microsoft Office Specialist Approved Courseware logo represent?

The logo indicates that this courseware has been approved by Microsoft to cover the course objectives that will be included in the relevant exam. It also means that after utilizing this courseware, you may be better prepared to pass the exams required to become a certified Microsoft Office Specialist.

For more information:

To learn more about Microsoft Office Specialist exams, visit www.microsoft.com/learning/msbc

To learn about other Microsoft approved courseware from Axzo Press, visit http://www.axzopress.com.

* The availability of Microsoft Office Specialist certification exams varies by Microsoft program, program version and language. Visit www.microsoft.com/lcarning for exam availability.

Contents

Proofing and delivering presentations   8-1

Course summary   S-1

Glossary   G-1

Index   I-1

Introduction

After reading this introduction, you will know how to:

A Use ILT Series manuals in general.

B Use prerequisites, a target student description, course objectives, and a skills inventory to properly set students' expectations for the course.

C Set up a classroom to teach this course.

D Get support for setting up and teaching this course.

Topic A: About the manual

ILT Series philosophy

Our goal is to make you, the instructor, as successful as possible. To that end, our manuals facilitate students' learning by providing structured interaction with the software itself. While we provide text to help you explain difficult concepts, the hands-on activities are the focus of our courses. Leading the students through these activities will teach the skills and concepts effectively.

We believe strongly in the instructor-led class. For many students, having a thinking, feeling instructor in front of them will always be the most comfortable way to learn. Because the students' focus should be on you, our manuals are designed and written to facilitate your interaction with the students, and not to call attention to manuals themselves.

We believe in the basic approach of setting expectations, then teaching, and providing summary and review afterwards. For this reason, lessons begin with objectives and end with summaries. We also provide overall course objectives and a course summary to provide both an introduction to and closure on the entire course.

Our goal is your success. We encourage your feedback in helping us to continually improve our manuals to meet your needs.

Manual components

The manuals contain these major components:

- Table of contents
- Introduction
- Units
- Course summary
- Glossary
- Index

Each element is described below.

Table of contents

The table of contents acts as a learning roadmap for you and the students.

Introduction

The introduction contains information about our training philosophy and our manual components, features, and conventions. It contains target student, prerequisite, objective, and setup information for the specific course. Finally, the introduction contains support information.

Units

Units are the largest structural component of the actual course content. A unit begins with a title page that lists objectives for each major subdivision, or topic, within the unit. Within each topic, conceptual and explanatory information alternates with hands-on activities. Units conclude with a summary comprising one paragraph for each topic, and an independent practice activity that gives students an opportunity to practice the skills they've learned.

The conceptual information takes the form of text paragraphs, exhibits, lists, and tables. The activities are structured in two columns, one telling students what to do, the other providing explanations, descriptions, and graphics. Throughout a unit, instructor notes are found in the left margin.

Course summary

This section provides a text summary of the entire course. It is useful for providing closure at the end of the course. The course summary also indicates the next course in this series, if there is one, and lists additional resources students might find useful as they continue to learn about the software.

Glossary

The glossary provides definitions for all of the key terms used in this course.

Index

The index at the end of this manual makes it easy for you and your students to find information about a particular software component, feature, or concept.

Manual conventions

We've tried to keep the number of elements and the types of formatting to a minimum in the manuals. We think this aids in clarity and makes the manuals more classically elegant looking. But there are some conventions and icons you should know about.

Item	Description
Italic text	In conceptual text, indicates a new term or feature.
Bold text	In unit summaries, indicates a key term or concept. In an independent practice activity, indicates an explicit item that you select, choose, or type.
`Code font`	Indicates code or syntax.
`Longer strings of ▶ code will look ▶ like this.`	In the hands-on activities, any code that's too long to fit on a single line is divided into segments by one or more continuation characters (▶). This code should be entered as a continuous string of text.
	In the left margin, provide tips, hints, and warnings for the instructor.
Select **bold item**	In the left column of hands-on activities, bold sans-serif text indicates an explicit item that you select, choose, or type.
Keycaps like (↵ ENTER)	Indicate a key on the keyboard you must press.
	Warnings prepare instructors for potential classroom management problems.
	Tips give extra information the instructor can share with students.
	Setup notes provide a realistic business context for instructors to share with students, or indicate additional setup steps required for the current activity.
	Projector notes indicate that there is a PowerPoint slide for the adjacent content.

Instructor note/icon

Instructor notes.

⚠ *Warning icon.*

✔ *Tip icon.*

Setup icon.

Projector icon.

Hands-on activities

The hands-on activities are the most important parts of our manuals. They are divided into two primary columns. The "Here's how" column gives short directions to the students. The "Here's why" column provides explanations, graphics, and clarifications. To the left, instructor notes provide tips, warnings, setups, and other information for the instructor only. Here's a sample:

Do it!

Take the time to make sure your students understand this worksheet. We'll be here a while.

A-1:   Creating a commission formula

Here's how	Here's why
1 Open Sales	This is an oversimplified sales compensation worksheet. It shows sales totals, commissions, and incentives for five sales reps.
2 Observe the contents of cell F4	F4 ▼ = =E4*C_Rate
	The commission rate formulas use the name "C_Rate" instead of a value for the commission rate.

For these activities, we have provided a collection of data files designed to help students learn each skill in a real-world business context. As students work through the activities, they will modify and update these files. Of course, students might make a mistake and therefore want to re-key the activity starting from scratch. To make it easy to start over, students will rename each data file at the end of the first activity in which the file is modified. Our convention for renaming files is to add the word "My" to the beginning of the file name. In the above activity, for example, students are using a file called "Sales" for the first time. At the end of this activity, they would save the file as "My sales," thus leaving the "Sales" file unchanged. If students make mistakes, they can start over using the original "Sales" file.

In some activities, however, it might not be practical to rename the data file. Such exceptions are indicated with an instructor note. If students want to retry one of these activities, you will need to provide a fresh copy of the original data file.

PowerPoint presentations

Each unit in this course has an accompanying PowerPoint presentation. These slide shows are designed to support your classroom instruction while providing students with a visual focus. Each presentation begins with a list of unit objectives and ends with a unit summary slide. We strongly recommend that you run these presentations from the instructor's station as you teach this course. A copy of PowerPoint Viewer is included, so it is not necessary to have PowerPoint installed on your computer.

The ILT Series PowerPoint add-in

The CD also contains a PowerPoint add-in that enables you to do two things:

- Create slide notes for the class
- Display a control panel for the Flash movies embedded in the presentations

To load the PowerPoint add-in:

1   Copy the Course_ILT.ppa file to a convenient location on your hard drive.

2   Start PowerPoint.

3   Choose Tools, Macro, Security to open the Security dialog box. On the Security Level tab, select Medium (if necessary), and then click OK.

4   Choose Tools, Add-Ins to open the Add-Ins dialog box. Then, click Add New.

5   Browse to and double-click the Course_ILT.ppa file, and then click OK. A message box will appear, warning you that macros can contain viruses.

6   Click Enable Macros. The Course_ILT add-in should now appear in the Available Add-Ins list (in the Add-Ins dialog box). The "x" in front of Course_ILT indicates that the add-in is loaded.

7   Click Close to close the Add-Ins dialog box.

After you complete this procedure, a new toolbar will be available at the top of the PowerPoint window. This toolbar contains a single button labeled "Create SlideNotes." Click this button to generate slide-notes files in both text (.txt) and Excel (.xls) format. By default, these files will be saved to the folder that contains the presentation. If the PowerPoint file is on a CD-ROM or in some other location to which the slide-notes files cannot be saved, you will be prompted to save the presentation to your hard drive and try again.

When you run a presentation and come to a slide that contains a Flash movie, you will see a small control panel in the lower-left corner of the screen. You can use this panel to start, stop, and rewind the movie, or to play it again.

Topic B: Setting student expectations

Properly setting students' expectations is essential to your success. This topic will help you do that by providing:

- Prerequisites for this course
- A description of the target student
- A list of the objectives for the course
- A skills assessment for the course

Course prerequisites

Students taking this course should be familiar with personal computers and the use of a keyboard and a mouse. Furthermore, this course assumes that students have completed the following course or have equivalent experience:

- *Windows XP: Basic, Windows Vista: Basic,* or *Windows 7: Basic*

Target student

The target student for the course is an individual who wants to learn the basic features of PowerPoint to create effective presentations by using the drawing tools, clip art, WordArt, charts, and tables. Students need little or no experience using PowerPoint, but should be comfortable using a personal computer and Microsoft Windows XP or Vista, or preferably Windows 7.

Course objectives

You should share these overall course objectives with your students at the beginning of the day. This will give students an idea about what to expect, and it will help you identify students who might be misplaced. Students are considered misplaced when they lack the prerequisite knowledge or when they already know most of the subject matter to be covered.

Note: In addition to the general objectives listed below, specific Microsoft Office Specialist exam objectives are listed at the beginning of each topic (where applicable) and are highlighted by instructor notes.

After completing this course, students will know how to:

- Identify components of the PowerPoint environment; open and run a presentation; use Help; and close a presentation and PowerPoint.

- Create a presentation and add slides to it; save a presentation; rearrange and delete slides; and insert slides from another presentation.

- Format text and bulleted lists; use the Find, Replace, Cut, Copy, and Paste commands; and align text.

- Draw objects by using tools in the Drawing group; format, modify, move, rotate, align, and delete drawn objects; and add text to drawn objects.

- Use WordArt to create visually appealing text objects; add and modify pictures; and add and modify clip art images.

- Add a table to a presentation, enter text in the table, and format the table; create and format a chart; and insert a SmartArt hierarchy chart and modify it.

- Create a presentation from a template; use slide masters to make global design changes; specify slide transitions and timings; add speaker notes and footers to slides; and set up a slide show for a speaker and for a kiosk.

- Proof a presentation for mistakes; preview and run a presentation; and print a presentation, a range of slides, an individual slide, handouts, and notes pages.

Skills inventory

Use the following form to gauge students' skill levels entering the class (students have copies in the introductions of their student manuals). For each skill listed, have students rate their familiarity from 1 to 5, with five being the most familiar. Emphasize that this is not a test. Rather, it is intended to provide students with an idea of where they're starting from at the beginning of class. If a student is wholly unfamiliar with all the skills, he or she might not be ready for the class. A student who seems to understand all of the skills, on the other hand, might need to move on to the next course in the series.

Skill	1	2	3	4	5
Opening and closing presentations					
Navigating in a presentation					
Creating presentations					
Adding, rearranging, and deleting slides					
Adding, editing, and formatting slide text					
Saving a presentation					
Inserting slides from other presentations					
Changing bullet styles					
Applying character formatting					
Applying paragraph formatting					
Copying text formatting					
Finding and replacing text					
Copying and pasting text					
Drawing and formatting shapes					
Duplicating, deleting, and moving objects					
Resizing, rotating, and aligning objects					
Adding text to objects and using text boxes					
Adding and modifying WordArt					
Inserting and modifying pictures					
Arranging and grouping overlapping items					
Inserting and modifying clip art					
Adding, modifying, and formatting tables					

Skill	1	2	3	4	5
Creating and formatting charts and diagrams					
Creating presentations based on templates					
Applying design themes					
Creating and modifying slide masters					
Specifying slide transitions and timings					
Adding and formatting speaker notes					
Setting up slide shows					
Proofing presentations					
Previewing and running presentations					
Printing presentations					

Topic C: Classroom setup

All our courses assume that each student has a personal computer to use during the class. Our hands-on approach to learning requires that they do. This topic gives information on how to set up the classroom to teach this course.

Hardware requirements

Each student's personal computer should have:

- A keyboard and a mouse
- A 1GHz or faster processor
- 256 MB RAM (or higher)
- At least 2GB of available hard drive space after operating system install
- DVD-ROM drive
- SVGA monitor at 1024 × 768 or higher resolution
- A printer is required to complete Activity C-3 in the "Proofing and delivering presentations" unit, although students can opt not to print.

Software requirements

You will need the following software:

- Microsoft Windows 7
- Microsoft Office 2010 (minimally, you can install only PowerPoint and Excel)
- A printer driver (An actual printer is not required, but students will not be able to complete "Printing presentations" in the "Proofing and delivering presentations" unit unless a driver is installed.)

Network requirements

The following network components and connectivity are also required for this course:

- Internet access, for the following purposes:
    - Downloading the latest critical updates and service packs
    - Opening Help files, downloading templates, and accessing clip art from Office.com. If online Help is not available, students will not be able to complete Activity B-1 in the unit titled "Getting started." Students will also need Internet access to complete activities in the units titled "Working with graphics" and "Modifying presentations."
    - Downloading the Student Data files from www.axzopress.com (if necessary)

Classroom setup instructions

Before you teach this course, you will need to perform the following steps to set up each student computer.

1   Install Windows 7 on an NTFS partition according to the software publisher's instructions. After installation is complete, if the student machines have Internet access, use Windows Update to install any critical updates and Service Packs.

Note: You can also use Windows Vista or Windows XP, but the screen shots in this course were taken in Windows 7, so students' screens might look different.

2   With flat-panel displays, we recommend using the panel's native resolution for best results. Color depth/quality should be set to High (24 bit) or higher.

3   Install Microsoft Office 2010 according to the software manufacturer's instructions. Perform a default installation. You'll need both PowerPoint and Excel installed.

4   Start Microsoft Office PowerPoint 2010. Then do the following.

   a   Activate the software. After activation, the Welcome to the 2010 Microsoft Office System dialog box appears.

   b   Select "Don't make changes" and click Finish.

5   Disable Protected View settings for PowerPoint as follows:

   a   On the File tab, click Options.

   b   Select Trust Center and click Trust Center Settings.

   c   Select Protected View and "clear Enable Protected View for files originating from the Internet."

   d   Click OK twice to save settings. Close PowerPoint.

6   If you have the data disc that came with this manual, locate the Student Data folder on it and copy it to the desktop of each student computer.

   If you don't have the data disc, you can download the Student Data files for the course:

   a   Connect to www.axzopress.com.

   b   Under Downloads, click Instructor-Led Training.

   c   Browse the subject categories to locate your course. Then click the course title to display a list of available downloads. (You can also access these downloads through our Catalog listings.)

   d   Click the link(s) for downloading the Student Data files. You can download the files directly to student machines or to a central location on your own network.

   e   Create a folder named Student Data on the desktop of each student computer.

   f   Double-click the downloaded zip file(s) and drag the contents into the Student Data folder.

7   Move the Student Data folder from C:\ to the My Documents folder of each student's user account.

8   Start Microsoft Office PowerPoint 2010. Then do the following:

    a   Activate the software. After activation, the Welcome to the 2010 Microsoft Office System dialog box appears.

    b   On the Privacy Options screen, verify that "Search Microsoft Office Online for Help content when I'm connected to the Internet" is checked.

    c   Verify that "Download a file periodically that helps determine system problems" is cleared.

    d   Verify that "Sign up for the Customer Experience Improvement Program" is cleared.

    e   Click Next.

    f   Select "I don't want to use Microsoft Update." Click Finish.

CertBlaster software

CertBlaster pre- and post-assessment software is available for this course. To download and install this free software, students should complete the following steps:

1   Go to www.axzopress.com.

2   Under Downloads, click CertBlaster.

3   Click the link for PowerPoint 2010.

4   Save the .EXE file to a folder on your hard drive. (**Note:** If you skip this step, the CertBlaster software will not install correctly.)

5   Click Start and choose Run.

6   Click Browse and navigate to the folder that contains the .EXE file.

7   Select the .EXE file and click Open.

8   Click OK and follow the on-screen instructions. When prompted for the password, enter **c_pp2010**.

Topic D: Support

Your success is our primary concern. If you need help setting up this class or teaching a particular unit, topic, or activity, please don't hesitate to get in touch with us.

Contacting us

Please contact us through our Web site, www.axzopress.com. You will need to provide the name of the course, and be as specific as possible about the kind of help you need.

Instructor's tools

Our Web site provides several instructor's tools for each course, including course outlines and answers to frequently asked questions. To download these files, go to www.axzopress.com. Then, under Downloads, click Instructor-Led Training and browse our subject categories.

Unit 1

Getting started

Unit time: 30 minutes

Complete this unit, and you'll know how to:

A Explore the PowerPoint environment.

B Get help by using PowerPoint's Help options.

Topic A: The PowerPoint window

This topic covers the following Microsoft Office Specialist exam objective for PowerPoint 2010.

#	Objective
1.1	**Adjust views**
	1.1.1 Adjust views by using the Ribbon
	1.1.2 Adjust views by using status bar commands
	1.2.1 Manipulate the PowerPoint window

The PowerPoint 2010 interface

Explanation

PowerPoint 2010 is part of the Microsoft Office suite. You can use PowerPoint to create presentations that can combine text, graphics, charts, clip art, and WordArt. These presentations can then be shown to a single person or to a large audience.

If you're accustomed to older versions of PowerPoint, you might initially be disoriented by the current interface. However, PowerPoint 2010 is designed to give you easy access to every command and feature of PowerPoint, and the new features will make creating visually appealing slide shows much easier.

Starting PowerPoint

To start PowerPoint, click the Start button and choose All Programs, Microsoft Office, Microsoft PowerPoint 2010. Every time you start PowerPoint, a new blank presentation appears in the application window and the Home tab is active by default.

The File tab

The Office button in PowerPoint 2007 and the File menu in previous versions of PowerPoint have been replaced by the File tab, located in the window's top-left corner, as shown in Exhibit 1-1. Click the File tab to display *Backstage view,* which in some ways resembles a traditional File menu. The File tab contains:

- Commands for opening, saving, and closing presentations.
- Commands for displaying file information, opening recently used presentations, using templates to create new presentations, printing and sharing presentations, and getting Help.
- Commands for displaying application options and closing PowerPoint.

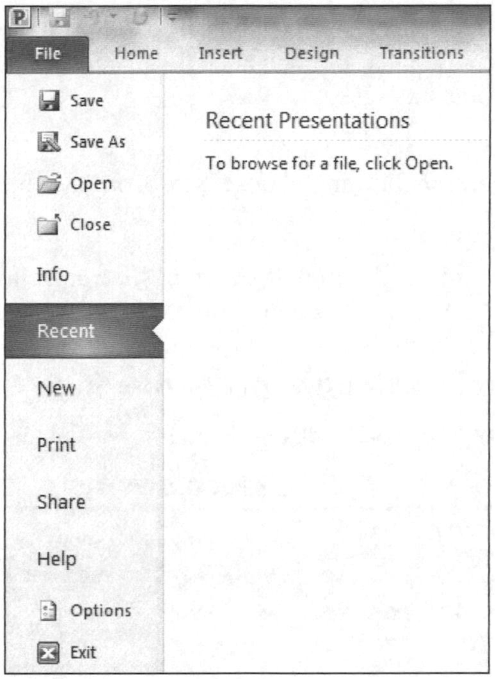

Exhibit 1-1: The File tab

Opening presentations

To open a presentation:

1 Click the File tab and click Open. The Open dialog box appears.

2 Navigate to the desired folder and select the file name for the presentation you want to open.

3 Click Open.

Running presentations

Objective 1.1.1

After you open a presentation, you can start adding text to the slide that appears in the PowerPoint window. When you're ready to display a presentation to your intended audience, you'll need to run a slide show.

There are multiple ways to run a slide show. Here's one way:

1 Click the Slide Show tab on the Ribbon. The *Ribbon* is the panel located at the top of the application window. It contains various tabs divided by function. The Slide Show tab contains groups of buttons and icons that you can use to start a slide show.

2 Click From Beginning to begin playing the slide show from the first slide.

Moving between slides

When you run a slide show, PowerPoint displays one slide at a time. You can advance the slides manually, or have PowerPoint advance them automatically. To move to the next slide in the show, you can:

- Click the mouse.
- Right-click the current slide and choose Next from the shortcut menu.
- Press the Page Down key.

To move to the previous slide, right-click the current slide and choose Previous, or press the Page Up key. To end the slide show at any time, press the Escape key.

Do it!

A-1: Opening and running a presentation

The files for this activity are in Student Data folder **Unit 1\Topic A**.

Here's how	Here's why
1 Click **Start** and choose **All Programs**, **Microsoft Office**, **Microsoft PowerPoint 2010**	To start Microsoft PowerPoint. By default, a new, blank presentation opens.
Observe the screen	You'll see the PowerPoint window, which contains a blank presentation.
2 Click the **File** tab	To display commonly used file commands.
Click **Open**	To display the Open dialog box.
3 Navigate to the current topic folder	The files for this activity are in Student Data folder Unit 1\Topic A.
4 Select **Outlander Spices**	You'll open this presentation.
5 Click **Open**	To open the presentation. The first slide appears in the PowerPoint window.

This tab serves the same purpose as the File menu in older versions of PowerPoint.

TIPS *Tell students they can also press Ctrl+O.*

Help students navigate to the Student Data folder.

Objective 1.1.1

6   Click the **Slide Show** tab at the top of the window

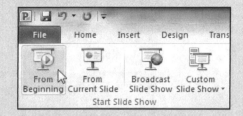

To display the Slide Show controls on the Ribbon.

TIPS
Tell students they can also press F5.

In the Start Slide Show group, click **From Beginning**

To start the slide show from the first slide.

Remind students that during this course, they will learn the techniques needed to create the slides in this presentation.

7   Observe the first slide

This is the title slide.

8   Click the mouse

To move to the next slide. You'll see a slide titled "Redesign Website."

9   Click the mouse again

To see a slide with text and clip art.

10 Move to the next slide

(Click the mouse.) This is the fourth slide; it contains a table.

11 Move to the next slide

To see the fifth slide, which contains a chart.

12 Press PAGE UP

To move to the previous slide. You can use the Page Up and Page Down keys to view all the slides in the presentation.

13 Right-click the slide

To display a shortcut menu.

    Choose **Previous**

To move to the previous slide.

14 Click the left mouse button three times

To move three slides forward to see a slide containing an organization chart.

Tell students that by default, slide shows end with a black screen.

    Click once more

To end the slide show. You'll see a black screen.

15 Click the mouse

To exit the show and return to the first slide.

The PowerPoint environment

Explanation

The PowerPoint window has several components that help you interact with the program. Exhibit 1-2 shows some of these components. If you're accustomed to older versions of PowerPoint, you'll notice that this new version uses the interface introduced in PowerPoint 2007, with some additional changes.

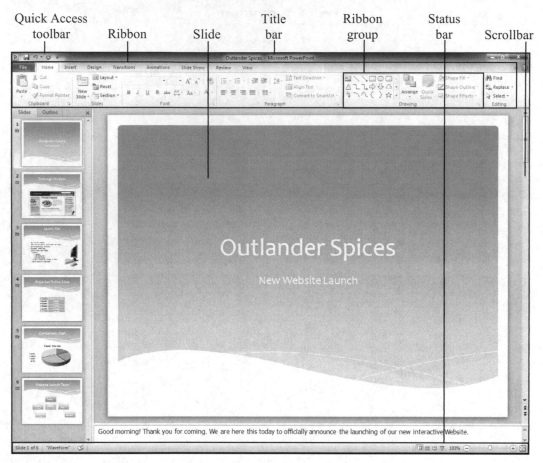

Exhibit 1-2: The components of the PowerPoint 2010 window

The following table describes the components of the PowerPoint window.

Item	Description
Title bar	Displays the name of the current document.
Quick Access toolbar	Contains frequently used commands (by default, Save, Undo, and Repeat/Redo). Can be customized to include the commands you specify.
Ribbon	Contains PowerPoint's primary tools, commands, and other features, divided among tabs named File, Home, Insert, Design, Transitions, Animations, Slide Show, Review, and View, as well as several contextual tabs. The items on each tab are organized into several groups.
Ribbon groups	Contain sets of related controls. Each tab contains several groups.
Slide	Displays the text and graphics that you type and edit. When you click a text placeholder, a flashing vertical line, called the *insertion point*, is displayed in the document area. It indicates the location where text will appear as you type.
Status bar	Contains presentation status information, buttons for switching views, and the document zoom slider.
Scrollbars	Used to view parts of the presentation that don't currently fit in the window.

Gallery and list previews

In PowerPoint 2010, one way you can apply settings is to select an option from a gallery or list. The items in a gallery and in some lists are displayed as sample previews of how they will affect the current slide, rather than simply as a list of named options. For example, the Themes gallery on the Design tab displays thumbnails of how each theme will look when applied to a slide.

In addition, some galleries and lists use the *Live Preview* feature. When you move the pointer over options in a gallery or list that uses Live Preview, each option is previewed on the current slide. For example, moving the pointer over each font in the Font list causes any selected text on the current slide to appear in that font temporarily.

Do it!

A-2: Examining the PowerPoint environment

Here's how	Here's why
1 Observe the title bar	Outlander Spices - Microsoft PowerPoint
	The title bar displays the current presentation's name (Outlander Spices) and the program name (Microsoft PowerPoint).
2 Observe the Ribbon	(Located under the title bar, at the top of the PowerPoint window.) Most of PowerPoint's tools and commands are divided among the tabs on the Ribbon.
3 Click the **Home** tab	To display the Home tab's options and tools.
4 Observe the groups on the Home tab	The Home tab contains the Clipboard, Slides, Font, Paragraph, Drawing, and Editing groups.
5 Click the **Insert** tab	To display the Insert tab's options and tools.
In the Images group, point to **Picture**, as shown	
	A ScreenTip appears, describing the functionality of the button.
6 Click the **Design** tab	
In the Themes group, point to one of the theme icons	
	To see a Live Preview of the theme applied to the current slide.
Point away from the icons in the Themes group	The current slide returns to its original appearance.

⚠ *Be sure that your students don't click the icon.*

Help students find the Dialog Box Launcher. Explain that not every group on the Ribbon has a Dialog Box Launcher.

7 In the Background group, click the Dialog Box Launcher, as shown

> Background Styles ▾
> ☐ Hide Background Graphics
> Background

To open the Format Background dialog box. In the bottom-right corner of some groups, you'll see a Dialog Box Launcher, which opens a dialog box containing additional settings related to that group.

Click **Close**

To close the dialog box.

8 Observe the slide

It has a title layout with text on it.

9 Point to the text on the slide

The pointer changes to an I-beam.

Click the text

> Outlander

To place the insertion point in the text.

10 Observe the scrollbar

Use the vertical scrollbar to navigate among the slides while you're creating them.

Objective 1.1.2

11 Observe the status bar

Tell students that the window was resized for this screen shot. The status bar might look slightly different on their screens.

> Slide 1 of 6 | "Waveform" | ▤ ▦ ▤ ♀ 38% ⊖ ▽ ⊕ ⊠

(At the bottom of the PowerPoint window.) The left part of the status bar indicates which slide is selected and the total number of slides. The status bar also includes the name of the current theme, the view buttons, and magnification controls.

Presentation views

Explanation

You can display a presentation in any one of four views: Normal, Slide Sorter, Slide Show, and the new Reading view. You switch between these views by clicking the corresponding button.

Objective 1.1.2

View	Button	Description
Normal		The default view, which you'll usually work in as you create slides. It contains two tabs on the left (Slides and Outline) and a Slide pane on the right.
Slide Sorter		Provides a miniature view of all slides in a presentation so you can view multiple slides at once. You can change the order of the slides in this view.
Slide Show		Provides a full-screen view of your presentation. Any special effects you add to your presentation, such as transitions and timings, are visible during the slide show.
Reading View		Provides a full-screen view of your presentation, just like Slide Show view, but with the PowerPoint status bar and the Windows taskbar still visible. This view is a better option when you want to view a presentation on a computer instead of using a projector. When using Reading view, you can quickly and easily switch to other views. Consider using this view when you're creating a presentation and want to quickly view a draft as a slide show.

The Outline and Slides tabs

In Normal view, there are two tabs to the left of the Slide pane: the Slides tab and the Outline tab. The Slides tab displays thumbnails of the slides. The Outline tab displays the slide text as an outline that you can use to organize and develop the content of the presentation. No matter which of these tabs you use, the Slide pane will still be visible.

Do it!

Objective 1.1.2

A-3:   Observing views

Here's how	Here's why
1 In the left pane, click the **Outline** tab, as shown	
Observe the Outline tab	It displays an outline of all text in the presentation.
2 Click the **Slides** tab	In the left pane.
3 Click 🔲	(The Slide Sorter button is on the status bar.) To switch to Slide Sorter view. The slides now appear as thumbnails in the Slide pane. You can use this view to rearrange the slides.
4 Click 🖳	(The Slide Show button is on the status bar.) To run the slide show from the current slide.
5 Press (ESC)	To end the slide show.
6 Click 🔲	(The Normal button is on the status bar.) To switch to Normal view.
7 Click 📖	(The Reading View button is on the status bar.) To run the slide show from the current slide but with the status bar and the Windows taskbar still visible.
8 Return to Normal view	Click the Normal view button.

Adjusting magnification

Explanation

You can change the magnification of a slide in Normal view by changing the zoom level. To do so, use the zoom controls on the status bar, shown in Exhibit 1-3.

Objective 1.1.2

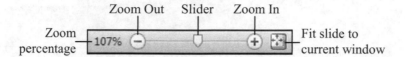

Exhibit 1-3: The zoom controls

To quickly increase the magnification level of the slide, click the Zoom In button, drag the slider to the right, or click the zoom percentage to open the Zoom dialog box. In the dialog box, set a higher zoom percentage and click OK.

To zoom out on a slide, click the Zoom Out button, drag the slider to the left, or click the zoom percentage to open the Zoom dialog box. Change the zoom to a lower percentage and click OK.

Do it!

A-4:   Zooming in and out on a slide

Here's how	Here's why
1 Observe the zoom controls	On the right side of the status bar.
2 Point to the slider	You'll use the slider to quickly zoom out.
Drag to the left	(Without releasing the mouse button.) To decrease the slide view, making it smaller.
Drag to the right	(Without releasing the mouse button.) To increase the slide view, making it bigger.
Release the mouse button	To change the slide view magnification.
3 Click the Zoom Out button twice	To decrease the zoom level by increments of 10%.
4 Click the Zoom In button twice	To increase the zoom level by increments of 10%.
5 Click the zoom percentage	To open the Zoom dialog box.
Observe the dialog box	

Under Zoom to, you select a zoom level, or in the Percent box, you enter the desired zoom level.

Under Zoom to, select **33%**	To reduce the zoom level.
Click **OK**	To close the dialog box and view the slide at 33%.
6 Click ⊕	(The "Fit the slide to current window" button.) To return the slide view to the default percentage.

Multiple presentation windows

Explanation

Objective 1.2.1

When you have more than one presentation open at the same time, each one is represented on the Windows 7 taskbar as an individual instance of PowerPoint 2010. To switch between open presentations, point to the stacked PowerPoint taskbar buttons, as shown in Exhibit 1-4, and select the desired presentation.

Exhibit 1-4: Working with multiple presentations

Closing a presentation and PowerPoint

You can close a PowerPoint presentation by clicking the File tab and clicking Close, or by pressing Ctrl+W.

There are several ways to close the PowerPoint program:

- Click the File tab and then click Exit.
- At the right edge of the title bar, click the Close button, shown in Exhibit 1-5. If multiple files are open, this button closes the active file. If one or no files are open, this button closes the program.
- Press Alt+F4.

Exhibit 1-5: The Close button

Do it!

A-5: Closing a presentation and closing PowerPoint

Here's how	Here's why
1 Click the **File** tab	To display Backstage view.
2 Click **Close**	(If prompted to save your changes, click No.) To close the presentation.
3 On the File tab, click **Exit**	To close PowerPoint.

Topic B: Getting help

Explanation

You can use the Help system to access program information and instructions as you work. To access Help, click the Microsoft Office PowerPoint Help icon in the top-right corner of the document window. (If your system is connected to the Internet, you can access online Help information as well.)

In the PowerPoint Help window, shown in Exhibit 1-6, click the Home button to browse Help topics. Help works like a Web browser—each topic is a hyperlink that, when clicked, displays information about that topic. You can display a table of contents by clicking the Show Table of Contents button. In addition, you can enter a word or phrase in the Search box to locate Help articles containing that word or phrase.

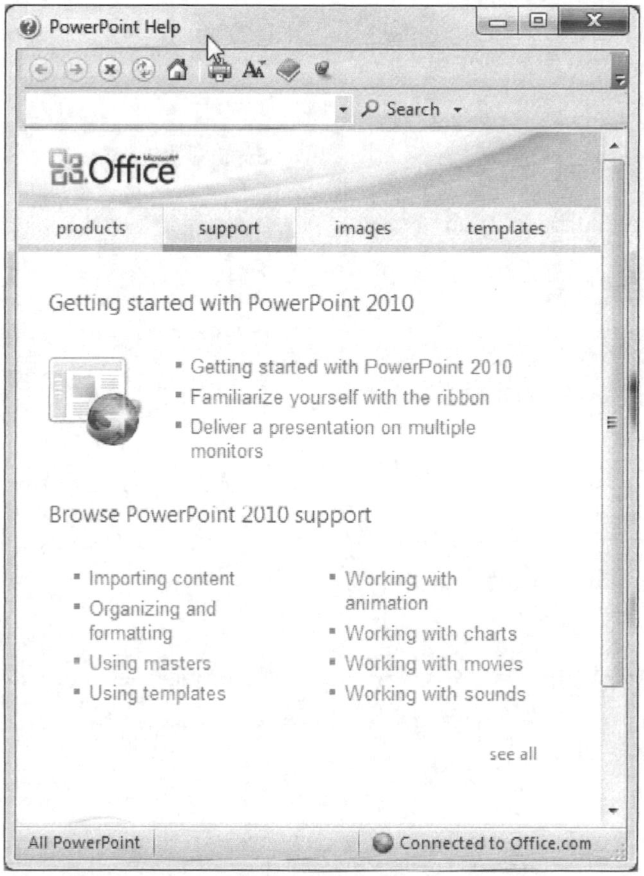

Exhibit 1-6: PowerPoint Help

B-1: Using PowerPoint Help

Here's how	Here's why
1 Start PowerPoint	(Click Start and choose All Programs, Microsoft Office, Microsoft PowerPoint 2010.) A blank presentation opens.
2 In the top-right corner of the document window, click ❓	(The Microsoft Office PowerPoint Help icon.) To open PowerPoint Help.
3 Click **Getting started with PowerPoint 2010**	To display a list of topics describing changes in PowerPoint 2010.
4 Click **What's new in PowerPoint 2010?**	To display an article describing the application's new features and enhancements.
5 Click 🏠	(The Home button.) To return to the initial Help content categories.
6 In the Search box, type **video**	[video ▾ 🔍 Search ▾]
Click **Search**	To search for Help topics containing the term "video."
7 Click **Trim a video**	To display information about that topic. You can make simple edits in a video in PowerPoint.
8 Click 📖	(The Show Table of Contents button.) To show the table of contents in a pane to the left.
9 Scroll up in the Table of Contents pane	If necessary.
10 Click **Working with text**	To display the articles in that category.
Click any article	*Table of Contents* ✕ — File management — Getting started with PowerPoint — Working with text — Add alternative text to a shape, picture, — Add bullets or numbers to text — **Add text to a slide** — Add, copy, or delete a text box — Adjust the indent in a bulleted or number — Change the color of text — Change the look, position, or function of — Wrap text around an object in PowerPoin — Spelling, grammar, and thesaurus
11 Click 📖	(The Hide Table of Contents button.) To hide the Table of Contents pane.
12 Close PowerPoint Help	Click the Close button.

Unit summary: Getting started

Topic A   In this topic, you opened a presentation and viewed it as a **slide show**. You also examined the PowerPoint environment and switched among Normal, Slide Sorter, Reading, and Slide Show views. You also adjusted **magnification** in Normal view.

Topic B   In this topic, you used **PowerPoint Help** to locate information on various PowerPoint topics.

Independent practice activity

In this activity, you'll open a presentation, switch views, change the magnification, and close the presentation.

The files for this activity are in Student Data folder **Unit 1\Unit summary**.

1 Start PowerPoint, if necessary.

2 Open Training.

3 Switch to Slide Sorter view.

4 Switch to Slide Show view. View each slide, and then end the slide show.

5 In Normal view, change the zoom percentage to 21%.

6 Switch to Reading view. View each slide and return to Normal view

7 Close the presentation and PowerPoint (you don't need to save changes).

Review questions

1 One way to run a slide show is to click the Slide Show tab and then click what button in the Start Slide Show group?

   Click the From Beginning button to begin playing the slide show from the first slide.

2 List the methods you can use to advance slides manually when running a slide show.

   Click the mouse; right-click the slide and choose Next from the shortcut menu; or press Page Down.

3 In Slide Show view, which key can you press to end the slide show at any time?

   Press Esc.

4 What is the Quick Access toolbar?

   A toolbar that contains buttons for frequently used commands, such as Save, Undo, and Repeat/Redo. It can be customized to include buttons for other commands as well.

5 What does the Live Preview feature do?

   When you move the pointer over options in a gallery or list that uses Live Preview, each option is previewed on the current slide.

6 List the four views you can use to look at a presentation.

   Normal, Slide Sorter, Reading, and Slide Show

Unit 2

New presentations

Unit time: 40 minutes

Complete this unit, and you'll know how to:

A Create a basic presentation by adding slides and inserting text on each slide.

B Save a presentation by using the Save and Save As commands.

C Rearrange and delete slides by using options in Normal view and Slide Sorter view.

D Insert slides by using slides from another presentation.

Topic A: Creating presentations

This topic covers the following Microsoft Office Specialist exam objectives for PowerPoint 2010.

#	Objective
2.3	**Add and remove slides**
	2.3.2 Reuse slides from a saved presentation
2.4	**Format slides**
	2.4.3 Switch to a different slide layout
2.5	**Enter and format text**
	2.5.4 Enter text in a placeholder text box
3.1	**Manipulate graphical elements**
	3.1.3 Resize graphical elements

Using Backstage view to create presentations

Explanation

To create a presentation in PowerPoint 2010, you'll use the File tab, which displays Backstage view. On the File tab, click New to display the Available Templates and Themes page, shown in Exhibit 2-1. Then select one of the options displayed. When you select a template or theme, PowerPoint will open a dialog box, display other options, or display a preview on the right side of the window.

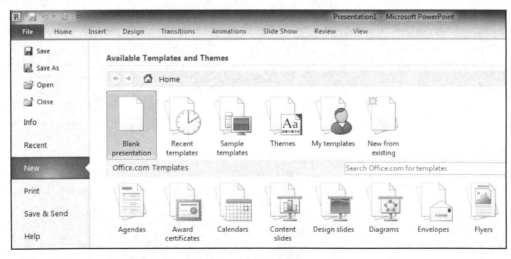

Exhibit 2-1: The Available Templates and Themes page

Basing new presentations on existing presentations

Objective 2.3.2

You might want to create a new presentation that includes much of the same content and formatting as an existing presentation. To save yourself some time, you can create the new presentation based on the existing one, and then modify the new one as needed. Here's how:

1 Click the File tab and then click New to display the Available Templates and Themes page.

2 Under Home, click "New from existing" to open the New from Existing Presentation dialog box.

3 Select the desired presentation and click Create New. The new presentation will be identical to the presentation on which it was based.

4 Save the new presentation with a new name.

Do it!

A-1:   Creating a presentation from an existing presentation

The files for this activity are in Student Data folder **Unit 2\Topic A**.

Objective 2.3.2

Here's how	Here's why
1 Start Microsoft PowerPoint 2010	(Click Start and choose All Programs, Microsoft Office, Microsoft PowerPoint 2010). A new, blank presentation opens.
Close the blank presentation	Click the File tab and click Close.
2 On the File tab, click **New**	To display the Available Templates and Themes page.
3 Under Home, click **New from existing**	To open the New from Existing Presentation dialog box.
Select **Training session**	In the current topic folder.
Click **Create New**	To create a new presentation based on the Training session presentation. You'll now save and name the new presentation.
4 On the Quick Access toolbar, click 🖫	(The Save button.) To open the Save As dialog box.
5 Edit the File name box to read **My training**	
Navigate to the current topic folder	If necessary.
Click **Save**	The new presentation is identical to the Training session presentation. You could now customize the My training presentation.
6 Close the My training presentation	On the File tab, click Close

Make sure students open this file from the current topic folder.

New blank presentations

If you want to create a presentation that starts out without any content, you should create a new blank presentation. Here's how:

1   On the File tab, click New.

2   Under Home, select Blank presentation, if necessary. On the far right, a preview of the blank presentation is displayed. (Because the presentation is blank, the preview is blank.)

3   Under the preview, click Create.

Slide layouts

A new blank presentation contains one slide by default. That slide uses the Title Slide layout, but you can select a different layout from the Layout gallery, which is available in the Home tab's Slides group. There are nine built-in layouts to choose from, as shown in Exhibit 2-2. These layouts are described in the following table.

Layout	Contains...
Title Slide	A title placeholder and a subtitle placeholder.
Title and Content	A title placeholder and one content placeholder. (This is the default slide layout.) Type text in the content placeholder, or click one of the icons at its center to specify other types of content, such as tables, charts, or pictures.
Section Header	A text placeholder above a title placeholder.
Two Content	A title placeholder and two content placeholders.
Comparison	A title placeholder, and two content placeholders with text placeholders for adding labels.
Title Only	A slide title placeholder.
Blank	No placeholders.
Content with Caption	A content placeholder, along with two text placeholders for adding text to accompany the slide content.
Picture with Caption	A picture placeholder, along with two text placeholders for adding text to accompany the picture.

Objective 2.4.3

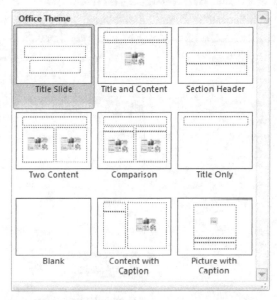

Exhibit 2-2: The nine layout options in the Layout gallery

A-2:   Creating a new blank presentation

Here's how	Here's why
1 On the File tab, click **New**	To display the Available Templates and Themes page.
2 Under Home, verify that **Blank presentation** is selected, as shown	
3 Observe the preview	(On the right side of the window.) Because the presentation is blank, the preview is also blank.
Click **Create**	(Under the preview.) To create a presentation that contains a single slide by default.
4 On the Home tab, in the Slides group, point to **Layout**, as shown	
Click once	To display a gallery of slide layouts, as shown in Exhibit 2-2.
5 Observe the first layout	Its name is "Title Slide." This is the layout that is automatically applied to the first slide in each presentation.
Observe the name of each layout	In the gallery.
Click **Layout** again	To close the gallery.

Entering text on slides

Explanation

Objective 2.5.4

After you select a slide layout, you can enter text on the slide. The Title Slide layout contains two placeholders for text: one for the title, and one for the subtitle. To enter text, click the placeholder text and begin typing.

Do it!

Objective 2.5.4

A-3: Entering text on a slide

Here's how	Here's why
1 Point to the text in the title placeholder, as shown	Click to add title Click to add subtitle The pointer's shape changes when you point to the placeholder text.
Click the title placeholder text	("Click to add title.") To place the insertion point in the title placeholder.
2 Type **Outlander Spices**	This will be the slide's title.
3 Click the subtitle placeholder text	(Below the title placeholder.) To place the insertion point.
Type **New Website Launch**	
4 Click the slide anywhere outside the placeholder	To deselect it.

Adding and editing slides

Explanation

Objective 2.4.3

After creating a new, blank presentation that has only one slide, you'll want to add more slides. To add a slide to a presentation, click the Home tab on the Ribbon. Then do either of the following:

- To add a slide with the default layout (Title and Content), click the New Slide button in the Slides group. You can also press Ctrl+M.
- To add a slide with a different layout, click the arrow on the New Slide button and then click the desired layout in the gallery.

Adding bulleted text to a slide

The most commonly used slide layout is the Title and Content layout. It has two placeholders: one for the title and a second for the content. You can use this layout to add several types of content, but one of the most typical uses is to add bulleted text.

Objective 2.5.4

To insert bulleted text in the content placeholder:

1 Click the text in the content placeholder.
2 Type the text for the first bullet.
3 Press Enter to display a second bullet.
4 Type the text for the second bullet, and press Enter.
5 Continue this process to add text for additional bullets.
6 When your list is complete, click outside the placeholder to deselect it.

Modifying a slide layout

Objectives 2.5.4, 3.1.3

You can modify a slide's layout by changing its placeholders. You can format, move, resize, and delete placeholders.

Deleting text and placeholders

To delete some of the text in a placeholder, select the text you want to remove and press Delete or Backspace. To delete all text in a placeholder, select the placeholder itself and press Delete. To select the placeholder, rather than the text within it, point to the edge of the placeholder (the mouse pointer changes to a four-headed arrow) and click.

After deleting the text you've added to a placeholder, you might want to delete the placeholder itself. When a placeholder displays its default placeholder text, you can select the placeholder and press Delete or Backspace to remove it from the slide.

Moving and resizing placeholders

You can move a placeholder by dragging it. Point to any edge of a placeholder so that a four-headed arrow appears; then drag the placeholder to the new position.

To change the size of a placeholder:

1 Click the edge of the placeholder so that sizing handles appear at each corner and along each edge.
2 Point to any of the sizing handles so that the mouse pointer becomes a two-headed arrow.
3 Drag the sizing handle to resize the placeholder.

Do it!   **A-4: Adding and editing slides**

Here's how	Here's why
1 Click the top portion of the New Slide button, as shown

(In the Slides group.) To add a new slide to the presentation. |
| Observe the new slide |

Click to add title

• Click to add text

By default, it has the Title and Content slide layout applied to it. It has two placeholders: one for the slide's title and another for the content. |
| Observe the Slides tab on the left | It shows that the presentation has two slides. |

Objective 2.5.4

2 Click the title placeholder text	(On the new slide.) To place the insertion point.
Type **Redesign Website**	To specify the slide's title.
3 Add a new slide	Click the New Slide button to add slide 3.
4 In the title placeholder, enter **Launch Plan**	Click in the placeholder and type.

⚠ *Be sure students click the bulleted text to place the insertion point.*

5 Click the bulleted-text placeholder	(Click the text in the content placeholder; don't click the icons at the center.) To place the insertion point in the placeholder. You are ready to enter text for the first bullet item.
6 Type **Go live next Monday**	To create the first bullet item. The icons for adding other types of content disappear, because by typing, you've specified that this placeholder will contain text.

Tell students they must press Enter only when the insertion point is at the end of the typed text.

Press (↵ ENTER)	To add a second bullet.

	7 Type **Press Kits**	To specify text for the second bullet.
	Observe the slide	It contains a title and a bulleted list with two items.
	8 Triple-click **Press**	To select the bullet item.
	Press (DELETE)	To remove the text from the slide.
Tell students they can also click the Undo button.	9 Press (CTRL) + (Z)	To undo the last step. The bullet point is restored.
Objective 3.1.3	10 Point as shown	

(Point to the placeholder box edge, but not to a sizing handle.) A four-headed arrow appears at the tip of the mouse pointer.

	Click the mouse button	To select the placeholder box.
	11 Press (DELETE)	To remove all of the text from the placeholder. The placeholder is still on the slide but it's empty, and it displays the content icons again.
	12 Select the placeholder box again	Point to an edge of it so that the pointer appears with the four-headed arrow, and click.
	Press (DELETE)	To remove the placeholder from the slide.
	13 Press (CTRL) + (Z) twice	To undo the last two steps: deleting the placeholder and deleting the text from the placeholder.
	14 Select the placeholder	
	Point to the bottom-left sizing handle, as shown	

You'll decrease the height and width of the placeholder. You can use the sizing handles on any of the corners to increase or decrease the height and width simultaneously.

15	Drag up and to the right	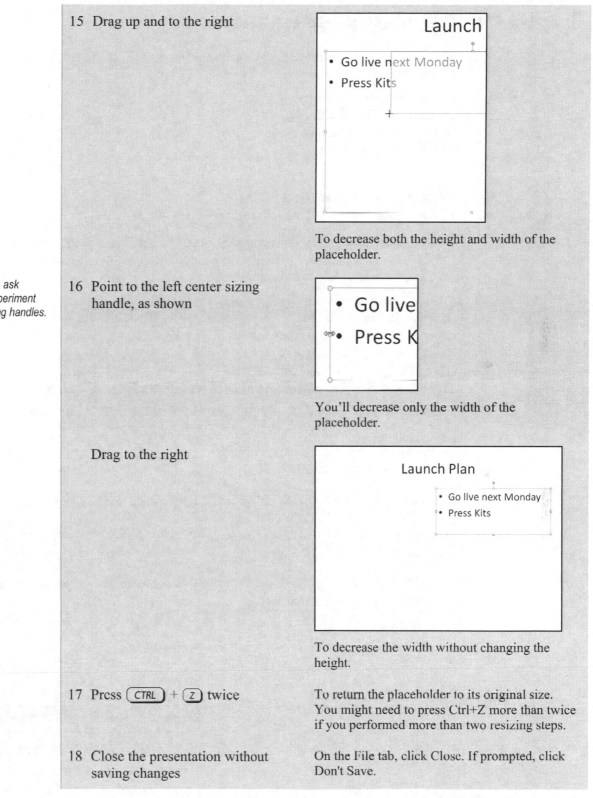
		To decrease both the height and width of the placeholder.
16	Point to the left center sizing handle, as shown	
		You'll decrease only the width of the placeholder.
	Drag to the right	
		To decrease the width without changing the height.
17	Press (CTRL) + (Z) twice	To return the placeholder to its original size. You might need to press Ctrl+Z more than twice if you performed more than two resizing steps.
18	Close the presentation without saving changes	On the File tab, click Close. If prompted, click Don't Save.

If time permits, ask students to experiment with other sizing handles.

Topic B: Saving presentations

This topic covers the following Microsoft Office Specialist exam objective for PowerPoint 2010.

#	Objective
7.1	Save a presentation

The Save command

Explanation

As you create presentations, it's important to save your work frequently. By saving your work, you ensure that any text, graphics, or other elements in your presentation are written to your computer's hard disk and stored for future use. You save a presentation by using the Save and Save As commands.

Objective 7.1

To save a presentation for the first time, you open the Save As dialog box by clicking the Save button on the Quick Access toolbar or the Save command on the File tab. Next, navigate to the desired location, edit the File name box to give your presentation a name, and then click Save.

Do it!

B-1: Saving a presentation in an existing folder

The files for this activity are in Student Data folder **Unit 2\Topic B**.

Objective 7.1

Here's how	Here's why
1 Open Draft presentation	From the current topic folder.
2 On the File tab, click **Save As**	To open the Save As dialog box.
3 Navigate to the current topic folder	(Unit 2\Topic B.) You'll save your presentation in an existing folder.
4 Edit the File name box to read **My draft presentation**	This will be the new presentation name.
Observe the Save as type box	By default, PowerPoint shows the type as PowerPoint Presentation.
Click **Save**	To save the presentation.
Observe the title bar	My draft presentation - Microsoft PowerPoint
	The file name appears in the title bar.

Help students navigate to the current topic folder.

Updating presentations

You have to specify a name and storage location for a presentation only when you save it for the first time. Each subsequent time you save a presentation, PowerPoint updates the file with your latest changes.

To update the presentation, you can do any of the following:

- On the File tab, click Save.
- Click the Save button on the Quick Access toolbar.
- Press Ctrl+S.

B-2: Updating a presentation

Here's how	Here's why
1 Move to the third slide	
Place the insertion point at the end of the second bullet item	You'll add more bullet items to the slide.
2 Press (↵ ENTER)	To add a third bullet to the slide.
3 Type **Advertising**	
Press (↵ ENTER)	
4 Type **Customer e-mail lists**	
Click outside the content placeholder	To deselect it.
5 Click 💾	(The Save button is on the Quick Access toolbar.) To save the changes.

The Save As command

Explanation

After you've saved a presentation, you can save a copy of it with a different name or in a different location. To do so, use the Save As command.

Objective 7.1

To save a presentation in a new folder:

1 On the File tab, click Save As to open the Save As dialog box.
2 Navigate to the appropriate location.
3 Click the New folder button to open the New Folder dialog box.
4 In the Name box, type a folder name. Click OK.
5 Verify that the Save in list displays the name of the new folder.
6 In the File name box, type a name for this copy of the presentation.
7 Click Save.

Compatibility with older versions of PowerPoint

Objective 7.1

Starting with PowerPoint 2007 presentations and continuing with PowerPoint 2010, presentations are saved with the extension ".pptx." Older versions of PowerPoint used the ".ppt" extension. Therefore, in order for older versions of PowerPoint to be able to open and read files created in PowerPoint 2010, you have to save them with the ".ppt" extension. To do so:

1 On the File tab, click Save & Send.
2 Under File Types, select Change File Type to display the Change File Type options on the right side of the window, as shown in Exhibit 2-3.
3 Under Presentation File Types, select PowerPoint 97-2003 Presentation to open the Save As dialog box. In the Save as type list, PowerPoint 97-2003 is already selected.
4 Click Save.

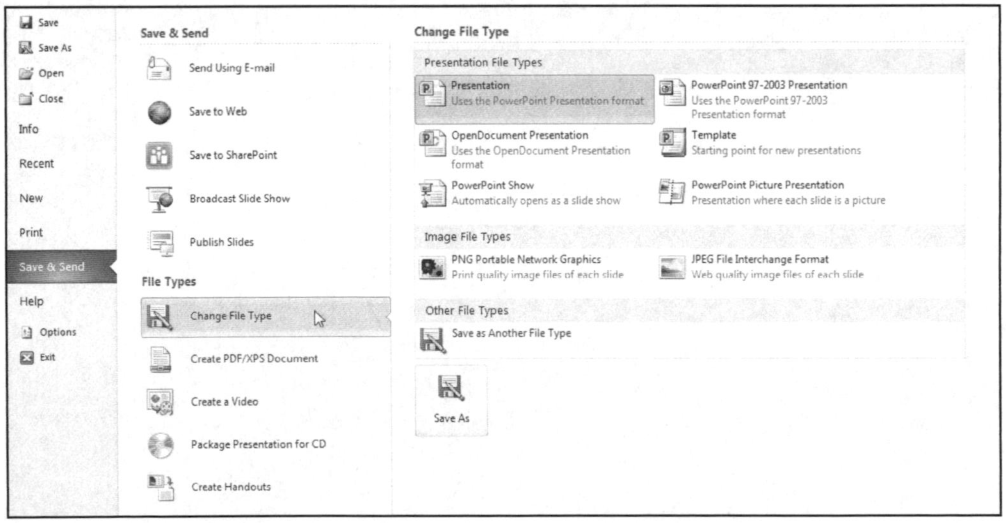

Exhibit 2-3: The Change File Type options

If you are consistently saving presentations in the old .ppt format, then you can change PowerPoint's settings so that this is the default. To do so:

1   On the File tab, click Options to open the PowerPoint Options dialog box.

2   In the left pane, click Save.

3   From the "Save files in this format" list, select PowerPoint Presentation 97-2003.

4   Click OK.

XML

Objective 7.1

Beginning with Office 2007 and continuing with Office 2010, all PowerPoint presentations use the Open XML format. This format makes it easier to use external data sources in PowerPoint files, makes the content of presentations easier to access in other applications, reduces file sizes, and improves data recovery. As explained previously, you can still save your presentations in the previous format to make them compatible with older versions of PowerPoint. In addition, updates to older versions of PowerPoint will enable those versions to use the new XML format. Finally, Microsoft will make converters available to use with previous versions of PowerPoint.

The OpenDocument format

Objective 7.1.5

Another XML-based file format option is OpenDocument Presentation, which uses the .odp file extension. Using PowerPoint 2010, you can save a presentation in this format or open an ODP file.

To save a presentation as an OpenDocument Presentation:

1   Open the Save As dialog box.

2   In the File name box, type a name.

3   From the Save as type list, select OpenDocument Presentation.

4   Click Save.

To open an OpenDocument Presentation:

1   Open the Open dialog box.

2   Navigate to the desired folder.

3   In the File of type list, verify that All PowerPoint Presentations is selected, or you can select OpenDocument Presentation.

4   Select the file and click Open.

When you save a PowerPoint 2010 file as an OpenDocument Presentation, you will lose some formatting and settings that are not compatible. For a complete list of these differences, open PowerPoint Help and search for "Differences between the OpenDocument and PowerPoint formats."

B-3:   Saving a presentation in a new folder

The files for this activity are in Student Data folder **Unit 2\Topic B**.

Here's how	Here's why
1 On the File tab, click **Save As**	To open the Save As dialog box.
2 Navigate to the current topic folder	(If necessary.) You'll create a folder within the current unit folder to save your presentation.
3 Click New folder	(In the Save As dialog box.) To create a folder with the name selected.
4 Type **My folder**	
Press ⏎ ENTER	To accept the name change. The "My folder" folder now appears as a subfolder of the Topic B folder.
5 Double-click **My folder**	To open it. This is where you will save the presentation.
6 Edit the File name box to read **My first presentation**	
7 Display the Save as type list	Click the down-arrow to the right of the list.
Observe the list	(Scroll through and read each line.) The list contains all the formats you can use to save a presentation.
Click the down-arrow	To close the list.
Verify that **PowerPoint Presentation** is selected	This is the default file format.
8 Click **Save**	To save the presentation in the folder My folder.
Close the presentation	On the File tab, click Close.

Topic C: Rearranging and deleting slides

This topic covers the following Microsoft Office Specialist exam objective for PowerPoint 2010.

#	Objective
2.3	**Add and remove slides**
	2.3.5 Delete multiple slides simultaneously
	2.3.4 Duplicate selected slides.
	2.3.6 Include non-contiguous slides in a presentation

Reordering and removing slides

Explanation

After you've added slides and text to your presentation, you might need to change the order of slides or remove a slide. You can rearrange and remove slides in both Normal view and Slide Sorter view. However, it is typically easier to rearrange slides in Slide Sorter view.

Moving slides in Normal view

In Normal view, you can use the Slides tab on the left side of the window to rearrange slides by dragging a slide thumbnail. As you drag, the insertion point shows you where the slide will appear when you release the mouse button. You can also move slides in Normal view by cutting or copying a slide and pasting it.

To cut or copy a slide and paste it in Normal view:

1   On the Slides tab, click a slide icon to select it.

2   On the Home tab, click the Cut or Copy button.

3   On the Slides tab, click above or below a slide icon to indicate the location where you want to paste the slide.

4   On the Home tab, click the Paste button.

Do it!

C-1: Rearranging slides in Normal view

The files for this activity are in Student Data folder **Unit 2\Topic C**.

Here's how	Here's why
1 Open OS Website redesign	From the current topic folder.
Save the presentation as **My OS Website redesign**	
2 Observe the slide thumbnails	On the Slides tab, on the left side of the window.
Scroll down	To view the last slide thumbnail.
Click the third thumbnail	You'll move slide 3 to a new location.

Tell students not to release the mouse button until instructed to do so.

3 Drag the slide thumbnail as shown

As you drag the slide up, the Slide tab will scroll up as well.

Observe the pointer and the line	A gray box appears as part of the mouse pointer. When you drag the mouse, a line appears to mark the slide's new position.
Release the mouse	To place the slide in the new position.
4 Observe the slides	The slide numbers have been changed automatically. Slide 3 has become slide 2.
5 Update the presentation	

Using Slide Sorter view

Explanation

In Slide Sorter view, you can see many slides at the same time, as shown in Exhibit 2-4. You can add, delete, and move slides in this view. You switch to Slide Sorter view by clicking the Slide Sorter button in the status bar. Because you can view many slides in Slide Sorter view, this is the easiest place to rearrange them in any order you want. You move a slide by dragging it to a new location in the presentation.

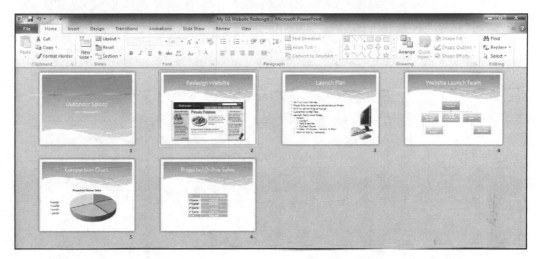

Exhibit 2-4: Slide Sorter view

C-2: Rearranging slides in Slide Sorter view

Here's how	Here's why
1 In the status bar, click ⊞	To switch to Slide Sorter view.
Observe the screen	You'll see thumbnail versions of all of the slides in the presentation.
2 Observe the border around slide 2	You were working on this slide when you switched to Slide Sorter view. A border appears around the active slide, as shown in Exhibit 2-4.
3 Select the fourth slide	You'll move this slide.
Drag the slide until it is after the sixth slide	(At the end of the presentation.) A vertical line indicates where the slide will appear.
Release the mouse	To place the slide in its new position. Slide 4 has become slide 6.
4 Move slide 4 to after slide 5	Select slide 4 and drag it to the space between slides 5 and 6.
5 Observe the slides	The slides have been rearranged, and the slide numbers reflect the new order.
6 Update the presentation	Click the Save button on the Quick Access toolbar.

Deleting and duplicating slides

Explanation

In addition to using Normal view and Slide Sorter view to rearrange slides, you can use these views to delete and duplicate slides.

Deleting slides

Objective 2.3.5

To delete slides in Normal view:

1   On the Slides tab, select the slide you want to remove.
2   Press Delete.

To delete slides in Slide Sorter view, either select the thumbnail for the slide you want to delete and press Delete; or right-click the slide and choose Delete Slide.

Deleting multiple slides

Objective 2.3.6

To delete multiple slides simultaneously in Slide Sorter view:

1   Select the first slide you want to delete.
2   Do one of the following:

   - If the slides you want to delete are in order, press and hold Shift, and click the last slide you want to remove. The first slide, the last side, and all slides in between are now selected.

   - If the slides you want to delete are not in order, press and hold Ctrl, and click each slide to select all of the slides you want to remove.

3   Press Delete.

The same steps work in Normal view. The only difference is that you select the thumbnail slide you want to remove on the Slides tab and then press Delete.

Duplicating slides

Objective 2.3.4

To duplicate a slide in either Normal view or Slide Sorter view, start by selecting the desired slide. Then do any of the following:

   - Click the Home tab. In the Clipboard group, click the Copy arrow and choose Duplicate from the menu.

   - Right-click a slide and choose Duplicate.

   - Press Ctrl+D.

C-3:   Deleting a slide in Slide Sorter view

Tell students that slides can also be hidden. (That is covered elsewhere in the course.)

Here's how	Here's why
1 Select the fifth slide	(In Slide Sorter view.) You'll delete this slide because the audience you will be showing the presentation to doesn't need this information.
2 Press (DELETE)	(Or right-click the slide and choose Delete Slide.) To delete the slide.
Observe the presentation	There are only five slides now.
3 Delete the fifth slide	
4 Switch to Normal view	(Click the Normal button in the status bar.) The presentation now contains only four slides.
5 Update the presentation	
Close the presentation	

Topic D: Using slides from other presentations

This topic covers the following Microsoft Office Specialist exam objectives for PowerPoint 2010.

#	Objective
2.3	**Add and remove slides**
	2.3.2 Reuse slides from a saved presentation
	2.3.3 Reuse slides from a slide library
2.4	**Format slides**
	2.4.3 Switch to a different slide layout

Reusing slides

Explanation

You can copy slides from one presentation to another. When you insert a slide from one presentation into another, the default setting causes the inserted slide to adopt the color and design theme of the presentation you insert it into. You can insert slides individually, or you can insert multiple slides simultaneously.

To insert a slide from another presentation:

Objective 2.3.2

1   In the Slides group on the Home tab, click the down-arrow on the New Slide button to display the gallery.

2   At the bottom of the gallery, click Reuse Slides to display the Reuse Slides pane on the right side of the application window.

3   In the Reuse Slides pane, click Browse and choose Browse File to open the Browse dialog box.

4   Navigate to the desired folder, select the presentation, and click Open. Each slide in the selected presentation is displayed in the Reuse Slides pane.

5   At the bottom of the Reuse Slides pane, verify that "Keep source formatting" is cleared if you want to apply the current presentation's slide masters to any inserted slides. Check the checkbox if you want the inserted slides to retain their slide masters.

6   In the Reuse Slides pane, click a slide to add it to the current presentation.

Changing the slide layouts

Objective 2.4.3

If you want to use a different layout for a slide, you can apply another layout style. To do so, select the slide and click the Home tab. In the Slides group, click the Layout button to display the Layout gallery. Click the desired layout to apply it.

Slide libraries

Objective 2.3.3

Another way to reuse or share slides is to store them in a slide library on a server running Office SharePoint Server 2007 or 2010. Once the slides are stored on the server, anyone who has access to the slide library can perform the following tasks, as long as he or she has PowerPoint 2007 or 2010 installed:

- Add and edit slides
- Reuse the stored slides
- Sort the slides
- Track changes, the latest version of a slide, and the history of a slide's use

When you store a presentation in a slide library, each individual slide is saved as a file, but the files maintain links to the original presentation.

Do it!

D-1: Inserting slides from another presentation

Objective 2.3.2

Outlander Spices wants to give the sales force an update on the expansion project.

Here's how	Here's why
1 Create a new, blank presentation	On the File tab, click New. Select Blank presentation and click Create.
2 Click the title placeholder	To place the insertion point so you can enter a title.
Type **Sales Update**	As the title for the slide.
3 In the subtitle placeholder, type **Corporate Plans**	Click the subtitle placeholder text, and type to add the subtitle.
4 Click the **New Slide** arrow	(In the Slides group.) To display the gallery.
At the bottom of the gallery, choose **Reuse Slides...**	To display the Reuse Slide pane on the right side of the application window.
5 In the Reuse Slides pane, click **Browse** as shown	You'll navigate to the presentation containing the slides you want to insert.
Choose **Browse File...**	To open the Browse dialog box.
6 Navigate to the current topic folder	
Select **Outlander Spices website redesign**	
Click **Open**	To display the slides in the selected presentation. They are added to the Reuse Slides pane.

7	Verify that "Keep source formatting" is cleared	(At the bottom of the Reuse Slides pane.) The slides you insert will take on the background and text formats of the current presentation.
8	Point to each slide in the Reuse Slides pane	(Point to each slide thumbnail, not the text next to it.) Notice that when you do, the slide is enlarged.
9	Click slide 4	(In the Reuse Slides pane.) To insert the "Projected Online Sales" slide as slide 2.
	Click slide 5	To insert the "Comparison Chart" slide as slide 3.
10	Observe the presentation	The two slides are now part of the new presentation. The content is the same, but the formatting is different because the inserted slides now use the formatting from the current presentation's slide master.
11	In the Reuse Slides pane, click the Close button	 To close the pane.
12	Save the presentation as **My sales update**	In the current topic folder.
	Close the presentation	

Unit summary: New presentations

Topic A   In this topic, you created a new, blank presentation. You also **added slides** to the presentation, **entered text** on a slide, and edited the text.

Topic B   In this topic, you used the Save As dialog box to **save** a presentation. Next, you updated a presentation by using the Save command. Then, you used the Save As dialog box to save a presentation in a new location.

Topic C   In this topic, you **moved slides** in both Normal view and Slide Sorter view. Then you **deleted slides** in Slide Sorter view.

Topic D   In this topic, you **inserted slides** from another presentation into the current presentation.

Independent practice activity

In this activity, you'll create a presentation, add slides and text, rearrange slides, and save the presentation.

The files for this activity are in Student Data folder **Unit 2\Unit summary**.

1 Create a new, blank presentation.

2 On the title slide, enter **My Company** as the title.

3 Using the Title and Content slide layout, add a new slide. Enter **New Locations In Major US Cities** as the title. Enter **New York**, **Los Angeles**, and **Dallas** as a bulleted list.

4 Save the presentation as **My practice presentation** in the Unit summary folder.

5 Add another Title and Content slide, and enter **Current Locations in Major US Cities** as the title. Enter **Chicago**, **Miami**, and **Las Vegas** as a bulleted list.

6 Update the presentation.

7 Switch to Slide Sorter view.

8 Move slide 3 before slide 2.

9 Update and close the presentation.

Review questions

1 Name the nine slide layouts available in the Layout gallery.

Title Slide, Title and Content, Section Header, Two Content, Comparison, Title Only, Blank, Content with Caption, and Picture with Caption

2 How do you enter text on a title slide?

Click the placeholder text and begin typing.

3 To add a slide with the default layout to a presentation, you click the Home tab and then click which button in the Slides group?

New Slide

4 How do you add a new slide with a layout other than the default layout?

Click the New Slide button's down-arrow to display a gallery, and click the desired layout to add a new slide with that layout applied.

5   How would you insert bulleted text in the content placeholder of a Title and Content slide?

   a   *Click the placeholder text in the content placeholder.*

   b   *Type the text for the first bullet.*

   c   *Press Enter to display a second bullet.*

   d   *Type the text for the second bullet and press Enter.*

   e   *Continue this process to add text for additional bullets.*

   f   *When you're done, click outside the placeholder to deselect it.*

6   To delete some of the text in a placeholder, you first select the text you want to remove. Then what do you do?

   Press Delete or Backspace

7   To save a copy of a presentation, what command do you use?

   Save As

8   What views can you use to change the order of slides?

   Normal and Slide Sorter views

9   How can you delete slides in Slide Sorter view?

   Select the thumbnail for the slide you want to delete and then press Delete; or right-click the slide and choose Delete Slide.

10   When you're inserting slides from another presentation, what task pane do you use?

   The Reuse Slides pane

11   How can you apply a different layout to an existing slide?

   Select the slide and click the Home tab. In the Slides group, click Layout to display the Layout gallery. Click a layout to apply it.

U n i t   3

Formatting slides

Unit time: 45 minutes

Complete this unit, and you'll know how to:

A Apply formatting to text and bulleted lists by using options on the Mini toolbar and in the Font and Paragraph groups.

B Search for, replace, move, and copy text.

C Change the alignment of text by using options on the Mini toolbar and in the Font and Paragraph groups.

Topic A: Formatting text

This topic covers the following Microsoft Office Specialist exam objectives for PowerPoint 2010.

#	Objective
2.5	**Enter and format text**
	2.5.2 Change text formats
	2.5.3 Change the formatting of bulleted and numbered lists
	2.5.8 Use Format Painter

Character and paragraph formatting

Explanation

Objective 2.5.2

After you add text to a slide, you can select the text and apply formatting to it. There are two types of formatting you can apply: character formatting and paragraph formatting.

Character formatting is any formatting that you can apply to individual characters. It includes changing the font, font size, and typestyle (boldface, italics, and underlining). *Paragraph formatting* is any formatting that can be applied only to whole paragraphs. It includes text alignment, line spacing, and bulleted and numbered lists.

The best way to understand the difference between the two types of formatting is to focus on what happens to the selected text. For example, when you select a specific section of text and apply character formatting, the formatting is applied to only the selected text. In contrast, when applying paragraph formatting, you can select entire paragraphs, select part of one or more paragraphs, or just place the insertion point in a paragraph. When you then apply the paragraph formatting, any paragraph that is partly or fully selected or that has the insertion point in it will have the formatting applied to all of it.

The Font group and the Mini toolbar

After the text is selected, there are two main ways to apply character formatting. You can use the buttons and options in the Font group on the Home tab, or use the Mini toolbar.

The Font group, shown in Exhibit 3-1, includes the Font and Font Size lists, various buttons, and the Dialog Box Launcher (in the bottom-right corner). The buttons include Bold, Italic, Underline, and Shadow.

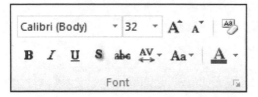

Exhibit 3-1: The Font group on the Ribbon

The *Mini toolbar* is a floating palette that appears immediately after you select text on a slide. The Mini toolbar contains some of the formatting options available in the Font and Paragraph groups. When it first appears, the Mini toolbar is almost transparent; you activate it by pointing to it. When you do, you have access to the most commonly used features based on your selection. Exhibit 3-2 shows the options on the Mini toolbar when text on a slide is selected.

Exhibit 3-2: The Mini toolbar

The Mini toolbar will disappear if you move the pointer too far away from it after making the selection. You can display the Mini toolbar at any time by right-clicking the selected text.

Selecting text

You can use several techniques to select text on PowerPoint slides. The following table describes these techniques.

Technique	Description
Drag across text	Point next to the first word you want to select, and drag across one or more words to select them.
Double-click a word	Point to a word and click two times quickly, without moving the pointer, to select the word.
Triple-click a word	Point to a word and click three times quickly to select the entire paragraph.
Press Ctrl+A	Click within a text placeholder to place the insertion point; then press Ctrl+A to select all of the text in the placeholder.
Shift+click	Place the insertion point where you want to begin the selection; then point to where you want to end the selection, press Shift, and click. The text between the two locations is selected.

Do it!

A-1:   Applying bold and italic formatting

The files for this activity are in Student Data folder **Unit 3\Topic A**.

Objective 2.5.2

If necessary, help students navigate to the current topic folder.

Here's how	Here's why
1 Open Project phase one	(From the current topic folder.) You'll format the text in this presentation.
Save the presentation as **My project phase one**	
2 Zoom to fit the slide the current window	(On the Status bar, click the Fit slide to current window button.) If necessary.
3 Double-click **Outlander**	(In the title placeholder.) To select the word. You'll format the title of the first slide.
4 On the Ribbon, click [B]	(The Bold button is in the Font group.) To apply bold formatting to the selected word.
5 Select **Spices**	Double-click the word, but don't move the mouse pointer.
Observe the slide	Near the selection, there is a floating toolbar that is almost completely transparent.
Point to the Mini toolbar	To activate it.
Click the **Bold** button, as shown	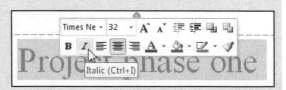
	To apply bold formatting to the selection.
6 Triple-click **Project**	(In the subtitle placeholder.) To select all three words in the subtitle. You'll italicize this text.
Activate the Mini toolbar	(Point to it.) If you can't see the Mini toolbar, select the text again.
Click the **Italic** button, as shown	Times Ne ▼ 32 ▼ A˄ A˅ ⁝ ⁝ ◨ ◨ B *I* ≣ ≣ ≣ A ▼ ◇ ▼ ☑ ▼ ✦ Proje̶c̶t̶ ̶p̶hase one Italic (Ctrl+I)
	To italicize the text.
7 Update the presentation	

⚠ *If students don't see the Mini toolbar, have them reselect the word but keep the pointer completely still after making the selection.*

TIPS ✔ *Tell students they can also click the Italic button in the Font group.*

Changing the font, size, and color of text

Explanation

In addition to applying bold and italic formatting, you can format text by specifying a different font, size, and color.

To change the font:

Objective 2.5.2

1   Select the text.
2   Using either the Font group or the Mini toolbar, click the Font arrow to display the font list.
3   As you point to a font name, a Live Preview of the font is temporarily applied to the selected text.
4   When you decide which font you want to apply, select it.

To change the font size:

Objective 2.5.2

1   Select the text.
2   Using either the Font group or the Mini toolbar, click the Font Size arrow to display the font size list.
3   As you point to a font size, a Live Preview of the font size is temporarily applied to the selected text.
4   Select the font size you want to apply.

To change the font color, select the text. Then, in the Font group or on the Mini toolbar, click the Font Color arrow to display the Font Color gallery. When you select a color, it's applied to the selected text, and the gallery closes. Also, the horizontal line at the bottom of the Font Color button displays the color you just applied. You can apply the indicated color to additional text by clicking the button itself, rather than clicking its arrow.

A-2:   Changing the font, font size, and font color

Here's how	Here's why
1 Triple-click **Outlander**	To select the text "Outlander Spices." You'll make the title larger.

2 In the Font group, click the **Font** button's arrow, as shown	

Times New Roman ▾ 44 ▾

B *I* <u>U</u> **S** ~~abc~~ AV ↔

Font

To display a list of fonts.

Point to a font	A Live Preview of the font is temporarily applied to the selected text.
Select **Arial Black**	To change the font.
3 Select **Project phase one**	Triple-click any word in the subtitle text.
Activate the Mini toolbar	Point to it.
From the Font list, select **Arial**	To apply the font to the selected text.
4 In the Font group, click the **Font Size** arrow, as shown	

Arial ▾ 32 ▾ A˄ A˅ ▯▯ ▯▯ ▯ ▯

B *I* ≡ ≡   Font Size   ▾ ▯ ▾ ▯

(The subtitle text should still be selected.) To display a list of font sizes.

Select **40**	To increase the size of the subtitle text.
5 Go to slide 2	(In the Slides tab on the left side of the screen, click the thumbnail for the second slide.) You'll format the slide title.
6 Apply the font **Arial Black** and a font size of **54** to the slide title	Triple-click the slide title text to select it, and use the Font list and Font Size list in the Font group.
7 Verify that **Outlander Spices** is selected	

8 Click the **Font Color** arrow, as shown

(The Font Color button is in the Font group.) To display the Font Color gallery.

Under Standard Colors, select the green color

(Select the color with the ScreenTip that says "Green," not "Light Green.") To apply the color and close the gallery.

9 Deselect the text

The text color has changed from black to green.

Observe the Font Color button

The button shows the last color you selected. You can click the button to apply that color without opening the color gallery.

10 Go to slide 1

In the Slides tab on the left side of the screen, click the thumbnail for the first slide.

11 Select **Outlander Spices**

In the Font group, click [**A** ▾]

(Click the Font Color button, not its arrow.) To apply the green color that you used most recently.

12 Update the presentation

The Format Painter

Explanation

You can use the Format Painter button to create consistent text formatting throughout a presentation. The Format Painter copies the formatting of the selected text, and you can apply this formatting to other text simply by selecting it. This button saves you time because it can apply complex formatting options in a single step.

To format text by using the Format Painter:

1 Select the text that contains the formatting you want to copy.

2 Click the Format Painter button (in the Clipboard group or on the Mini toolbar). Notice that the button is locked in the down position and the pointer has changed shape. This occurs because the pointer is "loaded" with the copied formats.

3 Select the text that you want to apply the copied formatting to. The Format Painter button and the mouse pointer return to their normal states.

Objective 2.5.8

Using the Format Painter multiple times

If you want to use the Format Painter to copy selected formatting multiple times, then double-click the Format Painter button, rather than clicking it once. The Format Painter button remains locked in the down position and the pointer remains "loaded" so you can continue selecting text to apply the copied formatting. To turn off the Format Painter, click the Format Painter button again or press Escape.

Do it!

A-3:   Using the Format Painter to copy text formatting

Objective 2.5.8

Here's how	Here's why
1 Go to slide 2	
2 Select **Outlander Spices**	The title of the slide.
3 In the Clipboard group, point to [Format Painter]	To display the ScreenTip for this button.
Read the ScreenTip	It tells you how to use the Format Painter.
4 Click [Format Painter]	You'll apply the formatting of the selected text to text on another slide.
Observe the Format Painter button	It remains locked in the down position, indicating that it is active.
5 Press (PAGE DOWN)	To move to the next slide.
6 Point to the slide	The mouse pointer has changed to an I-beam with a paintbrush next to it.

Depending on screen resolution, icons on the Ribbon may have different sizes and appearances. Help students find the Format Painter, if necessary.

7 Point to the beginning of the word **Project**

(On the third slide.) You'll drag across the text that you want to format.

Drag to select the words **Project justification**

To apply the copied formatting.

8 Observe the selected text

The formatting from the first slide's title is applied to the selected text.

Observe the Format Painter button

It has returned to its normal state, indicating that it is not active.

Deselect the text

(Click outside of the placeholder.) The pointer has returned to its normal shape.

9 Select **Project justification**

You'll access the Format Painter from the Mini toolbar this time.

Activate the Mini toolbar

Double-click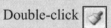

(On the Mini toolbar.) To lock the Format Painter so you can format text multiple times. You'll apply the formatting of the selected text to the title text on multiple slides.

10 Move to the next slide

Select **Cost of expansion**

(Drag across the text.) To apply the formatting. The pointer is still an I-beam with a paintbrush next to it.

11 Apply the formatting to the title text on the remaining slides

12 Click **Format Painter**

(In the Clipboard group or on the Mini toolbar.) To turn off the feature.

13 Update the presentation

Changing the bullet style

Explanation

Objective 2.5.3

If you want to emphasize a bulleted slide or make a two-level bulleted list stand out, you can change the bullet styles. To do so, select the text next to the bullet or bullets that you want to change. In the Paragraph group or on the Mini toolbar, click the Bullets down-arrow to display the Bullets gallery. Click one of the bullet styles to apply it and close the gallery.

If you want to remove or apply bullet formatting, you can select the text and click the Bullets button in the Paragraph group on the Home tab. If you want to demote bulleted or numbered text to a sub-list, you can select the text and do either of the following:

- Press Tab.
- Click the Increase List Level button in the Paragraph group.

When you demote bulleted text, the text is indented to the right, the text size is reduced, and the bullet character changes. When you demote numbered text, the text is indented to the right, the text size is reduced, and the numbering starts over at 1.

If you want to promote bulleted or numbered text to a higher level, select the text and do either of the following:

- Press Shift+Tab.
- Click the Decrease List Level button in the Paragraph group.

Do it!

A-4:   Changing bullet styles

Objective 2.5.3

Here's how	Here's why
1 Go to slide 2	
2 Select the text as shown	 (Point to the left of "Project" and drag down and to the right.) You'll change the bullet style.
3 In the Paragraph group, click the **Bullets** arrow, as shown	 (Or use the Mini toolbar.) To display the Bullets gallery.
Observe the gallery	By default, the previously applied bullet style is selected.

TIPS *Tell students they can also use the Mini toolbar.*

4	Select the Checkmark Bullets style, as shown	
		To apply the new bullet style.
5	Observe the slide	The bullet style changes.
6	Go to slide 3	The two items below "Provide high-quality merchandise" should be indented because they are a sub-list.
7	Select the third and fourth items	The items that begin with "Work" and "Purchase."
8	Press TAB	
		To demote the selected items to indicate a sub-list within the larger list.
9	Update the presentation	

Numbered lists

Explanation

Similar to applying bullets to text, you can also apply automatic numbering to a list. When you do, any item you add to the list is numbered sequentially according to the previous number.

Objective 2.5.3

To apply numbered list formatting with the default numbering style, select the text and click the Numbering button. To apply a specific numbering style:

1 Select the text.

2 In the Paragraph group, click the Numbering button's down-arrow to display the Numbering gallery.

3 Click one of the numbering styles to apply it and close the gallery.

Do it!

A-5: Creating a numbered list

Objective 2.5.3

Here's how	Here's why
1 Move to the seventh slide	
2 Click within the bulleted text	To place the insertion point.
Press CTRL + A	To select all of the text in the placeholder.
3 In the Paragraph group, click	(Click the Numbering button, not its arrow.) To apply the default numbering style.
Observe the slide	The bulleted list has changed into a numbered list. You'll specify a different numbering style.
4 Click the **Numbering** arrow, as shown	 To open the Numbering gallery.
5 Click the indicated style	

⚠ *Tell students to click the button, not the arrow.*

Next, you'll add another item to the list.

6	Place the insertion point at the end of the fifth line	Click after the word "program."
	Press (↵ ENTER)	To create a new line.
7	Observe the slide	The new line is numbered accordingly.
8	Type **New employees**	You'll add another item to the list.
	Press (↵ ENTER) and type **Training**	To add a seventh item.
9	Select the sixth numbered item	Triple-click "New employees."
	Press (DELETE)	To delete this item from the list.
	Observe the list	The numbering has adjusted automatically.
10	Delete the last numbered item	(Triple-click "Training" and press Delete.) The numbered list now has five items in it.
11	Update the presentation and close it	

⚠ *Be sure that students triple-click the item before pressing Delete so they delete the entire line.*

Topic B: Modifying text

This topic covers the following Microsoft Office Specialist exam objective for PowerPoint 2010.

#	Objective
2.5	**Enter and format text**
	2.5.6 Copy and paste text
	2.5.7 Use Paste Special

Editing efficiently

Explanation

You can move and copy text and objects from one slide to another or from one presentation to another. This can be a significant time saver as you reorganize a presentation. It's also useful if you want to use only a portion of a slide in another presentation.

The Find and Replace commands

You can search for all instances of specific text within a presentation and change that text by using the Find and Replace commands. You'll save time because you don't need to read through the entire set of slides to find that text.

To find and replace text:

1. On the Home tab, in the Editing group, click Find to open the Find dialog box.
2. In the Find what box, type the text you want to find.
3. Click Replace to change the dialog box to the Replace dialog box.
4. In the Replace with box, type the text you want to use.
5. Click Find Next to start the search. PowerPoint will highlight the first occurrence of the found text.
6. Click Replace if you want to change a single occurrence, or click Replace All if you want to change all occurrences of that specific text.

Do it!

B-1:   Finding and replacing text

The files for this activity are in Student Data folder **Unit 3\Topic B**.

Here's how	Here's why
1 Open OS project	From the current topic folder.
Save the presentation as **My OS project**	
2 Zoom to fit the slide the current window	(On the status bar, click the "Fit slide to current window" button.) If necessary.
3 Verify the first slide is selected	
4 On the Home tab, in the Editing group, click **Find**	To open the Find dialog box. The insertion point appears in the Find what box.
5 In the Find what box, type **merchandise**	You'll replace "merchandise" with "products."
6 Verify that "Match case" is cleared	To ensure that the search locates the word whether or not it is capitalized.
7 Click **Replace**	To change the dialog box to the Replace dialog box, which includes the Replace with box.
8 In the Replace with box, type **products**	
9 Click **Find Next**	The first instance of "merchandise" is highlighted in the presentation.
10 Click **Replace**	To change the selected word to "products." The next instance of "merchandise" is selected.
11 Click **Replace**	To replace the second instance of "merchandise" with "products." A message box appears, stating that the search is complete.
Click **OK**	To close the message box.
12 Click **Close**	To close the Replace dialog box.
13 Update the presentation	

The Cut and Paste commands

Explanation

Objective 2.5.6

When you want to move text or an object from one location to another, you use the Cut command. The Cut command removes the text or object from its original location so you can paste it elsewhere. When the Cut command removes text or an object from a slide, it places it on the Clipboard.

The Clipboard

When you cut or copy text or objects, PowerPoint places the selected text or object on the Clipboard. The *Clipboard* is a temporary storage area that holds the cut or copied item until you specify where to place it in a document. The Windows Clipboard can hold only one item at a time and is cleared when you shut down your computer. You can overcome this limitation by using the Clipboard task pane, which can hold up to 24 individual items.

After you use the Cut command to move text or an object to the Clipboard, you can place the text or object in a new location on the same slide, on another slide, or in a different presentation. To place an item, you use the Paste command. The Paste command takes the text or object from the Clipboard and inserts a copy of it wherever the insertion point is positioned.

To move text or an object:

1   Select the text or object that you want to move.

2   In the Clipboard group, click the Cut button, or press Ctrl+X.

3   Place the insertion point wherever you want to insert the text or object.

4   In the Clipboard group, click the Paste button, or press Ctrl+V.

The Paste Special command

Objective 2.5.7

When you copy text from one slide to another, the text appears on the new slide with the formatting it displayed on the original slide. However, you can use the Paste Special command to specify that the text be pasted as unformatted text, so that it takes on the formatting of the new slide. Here's how:

1   Place the insertion point where you want to paste the text.

2   In the Clipboard group, click the Paste button's down-arrow.

3   At the bottom of the gallery, choose Paste Special to open the Paste Special dialog box.

4   In the As list, select Unformatted Text. Click OK.

Instead of using the Paste Special dialog box, you can paste unformatted text by displaying the Paste Special gallery and clicking the Keep Text Only icon.

Drag and drop

You can also move text by using drag and drop (usually called just "dragging"). To drag text to a new location:

1   Select the text you want to move.

2   Point to the selected text. The pointer appears as an arrow.

3   Press and hold the mouse button, and drag to move the text to a new location on the slide.

4   Release the mouse button.

Do it!

Objective 2.5.6

B-2:   Cutting and dragging text

Here's how	Here's why
1 Go to slide 6	The last item in the list on this slide has not yet been accomplished, so you'll move it to the "Outstanding issues" slide. You're moving a bulleted item to a numbered list, so you must be careful to select only the text, and not the entire paragraph, which includes the bullet formatting.
2 Point just before **Specifications** and click	To place the insertion point to the left of the word. You'll use the Shift+click method to select the text.
Point just after **initiative**	(Point to the right of the letter "e" at the end of the word so that the pointer touches the "e.") Be sure not to select any space after the word.
Press (SHIFT) and click	To select the text without including any space after it. Selecting the space to the right of the last word would cause the entire line to be selected, including the bullet character formatting.
3 In the Clipboard group, click [✂ Cut]	To remove the text from the slide and place it on the Clipboard.
4 Press (← BACKSPACE) twice	To remove the leftover bullet character and blank line.
5 Go to the last slide	
6 Click at the end of the last line	To place the insertion point.
Press (↵ ENTER)	To add a sixth item to the list.
7 In the Clipboard group, click as shown	
	(Click the top portion of the Paste button, not the arrow.) To paste the text from the Clipboard into the numbered list. The text is pasted with its blue formatting. You'll undo this step and use Paste Special to paste the text without its original formatting.
8 Click [↻ ▾]	(The Undo button is on the Quick Access toolbar.) To undo the paste step.

9	Click the **Paste** arrow	To display the Paste menu.
	Select **Keep Text Only**, as shown	
		You can also choose the Paste Special command at the bottom of the gallery to open the Paste Special dialog box; then select Unformatted Text and click OK.
10	Press ⏎ ENTER	To add a blank line below the item you just pasted. You'll move the third item to the end of the list by dragging it.
11	Triple-click **Building**	To select "Building a Website."
12	Point to the selected text	The pointer appears as a white arrow, indicating that you can drag to move the text.
13	Press and hold the mouse button and drag to the empty line	To move the selected text to the end of the list. The item numbering is updated automatically.
14	Update the presentation	

The Copy command

Explanation

When you want to copy text or an object from one location to another, you use the Copy command. As you'd expect, it places a copy of the selected text or object on the Clipboard, and the item you're copying remains in its original location.

To copy text or an object:

Objective 2.5.6

1 Select the text or object that you want to copy.

2 In the Clipboard group, click the Copy button or press Ctrl+C.

3 Place the insertion point wherever you want to insert the text or object. This can be on the same slide, on another slide, or in another presentation.

4 Click the Paste button or press Ctrl+V.

The Paste Options button

The text you paste might be formatted differently than the text in the location where you want to paste it. You can choose whether the text should keep its formatting or inherit the formatting of the destination paragraph. To do so, click the Paste Options button, which appears to the right of any text you've pasted, and then choose an option from the drop-down menu.

Do it!

Objective 2.5.6

B-3: Copying text to another slide

The files for this activity are in Student Data folder **Unit 3\Topic B**.

Here's how	Here's why
1 At the end of the presentation, insert a new slide	Move to the last slide and click the New Slide button. Verify that the Title and Content slide layout is applied.
2 Go to slide 2	
Select **Outlander Spices**	Triple-click the text to select the entire line.
3 In the Clipboard group, click [Copy]	To copy the title to the Clipboard. The text also remains in its original location.
Go to the last slide	
4 Click the title placeholder	To place the insertion point.
Click the top portion of the Paste button	(Not the arrow.) To paste the text from the Clipboard into the title placeholder.
5 Observe the slide	The title text has been inserted from the Clipboard. The Paste Options button appears on the slide.
6 Click the **Paste Options** button, as shown	[(Ctrl) ▾] To display the Paste Options menu.
Select the **Keep Source Formatting** icon	The pasted text has the same formatting as the source text.
7 Deselect the title placeholder	Next, you'll copy text from one slide and paste it on a slide in another presentation.
8 Go to slide 5	
9 Copy the text in the left text box	(Click the left text box, press Ctrl+A, and click the Copy button.) You'll paste the text in a new presentation.
10 Create a blank new presentation	On the File tab, click New. Select Blank presentation and click Create.
11 Create a new slide	Click the top portion of the New Slide button.

TIPS ✓ *Tell students that they need to point to the button to see the arrow.*

12	Click within the content placeholder	To place the insertion point.
	Paste the text	Click the top portion of the Paste button, or press Ctrl+V.
13	Save the presentation as **My pasted text**	In the current topic folder.
14	Close the presentation	To return to the My OS project presentation.
15	Update the My OS project presentation	

The Clipboard pane

Explanation

Objective 2.5.6

In addition to the standard Windows Clipboard, you can also use the Clipboard task pane (an Office feature). These features differ in that the Clipboard pane can store multiple items and is integrated across all Office programs. Because of this expanded capacity, you can use it to copy multiple items in succession and then paste them, one at a time or simultaneously, into the preferred location(s) in a presentation. This procedure is called *collect and paste*. Because this tool is integrated across Office 2010, you can use it in any Office program, including Word, Excel, Outlook, Access, and PowerPoint.

To use the collect-and-paste procedure, you must use the Clipboard pane, which you can display by clicking the Dialog Box Launcher in the bottom-right corner of the Clipboard group.

Using collect and paste

When you collect and paste multiple items, they can come from any program with a Copy command. After copying the items, you can paste them into your other Office 2010 documents by using the Clipboard pane. For example, you can copy a chart in Excel, switch to Word and copy part of a document, switch to Internet Explorer and copy some text, and then switch to PowerPoint and paste the collected items in any order.

To copy an item to the Office Clipboard, select the item and then click the Copy button or press Ctrl+C, just as you'd copy something to the regular Clipboard.

Using the Clipboard pane

The objects that you copy by using the Office Clipboard appear in the Clipboard pane. The Clipboard pane can contain a maximum of 24 copied (or cut) items. The contents of the Clipboard pane are not cleared when you close the pane. To clear the contents of the task pane, click the Clear All button.

The following table describes the options on the Clipboard pane.

Option	Description
Paste All	Pastes all of the collected items simultaneously at the insertion point. The items are pasted in the order in which they were collected.
Clear All	Clears the contents of the Clipboard pane.
Paste	Pastes the selected item at the insertion point.
Delete	Clears the selected item from the Clipboard pane.

Do it!

B-4:   Using the Clipboard pane

Here's how	Here's why
1 At the end of the presentation, insert a new slide	Use the default Title and Content layout.
2 Type **Summary** as the title of the new slide	
3 In the Clipboard group, click the Dialog Box Launcher, as shown

To display the Clipboard pane. It contains the text that you pasted into the new presentation. |
4 Click [✗ Clear All]	(In the Clipboard pane.) To clear the Clipboard.
5 Move to the third slide	You'll copy items from this slide.
6 Copy the first two items from the bullet list	(Drag to select the two items; then click the Copy button.) The Clipboard pane now contains the copied text and shows that this text is the first item out of 24 items that you can copy.
7 Move to the sixth slide	
8 Copy the first two items from the bullet list	The Clipboard pane now contains both instances of copied text. The most recently copied text becomes the first item in the Clipboard pane's list. The Clipboard pane also shows that this is the second out of 24 items you can copy.
9 Move to the last slide	The slide you just created.
10 Place the insertion point in the content placeholder	
11 In the Clipboard pane, point to the top item	(Do not click.) To display the item's arrow. You can click the arrow to display a short menu (choose Paste or Delete). You can also paste an item by clicking it.
12 Click the top item	(In the Clipboard pane.) The slide now contains the bullet items copied from the sixth slide.
Press [↵ ENTER]	(If necessary.) To create a blank bulleted line below the two items you pasted.
13 Paste the second item from the Clipboard pane	Point to the second item in the Clipboard pane, click the arrow, and choose Paste.

14	Clear the contents of the Clipboard pane	Click the Clear All button.
	Click as shown	

Clipboard ▼ ✕

🗐 Paste All   🗙 Clear All

Click an item to paste:

To close the Clipboard pane.

15	Press (← BACKSPACE) twice	(If necessary.) To remove the extra bullet and line.
16	Apply a black color to all of the text	Press Ctrl+A, click the Font Color arrow, and select a black swatch.
17	Update and close the presentation	

Topic C: Formatting paragraphs

This topic covers the following Microsoft Office Specialist exam objectives for PowerPoint 2010.

#	Objective
2.5	**Enter and format text**
	2.5.2 Change text formats
2.6	**Format a text box**
	2.6.5 Set the alignment

Text alignment

Explanation

Text alignment, text spacing, and indentation are considered paragraph formats because they always apply to an entire paragraph. To adjust any type of paragraph formatting, you can select any part of a paragraph, or you can simply place the insertion point in the paragraph.

When text uses *Align Text Left* formatting, the lines of text are aligned along the left side of the text placeholder, and the right side of the paragraph appears ragged. With *Align Text Right* formatting, the lines of text are aligned along the right side of the text placeholder, and the left side looks ragged. You can *Justify* text so that the lines end evenly at the left and right sides of the placeholder.

Objectives 2.5.2, 2.6.5

To align text, place the insertion point in a line of text or select multiple paragraphs. In the Paragraph group on the Home tab, click the Align Left, Center, Align Right, or Justify button. You can also use the alignment buttons on the Mini toolbar and specify alignment settings in the Paragraph dialog box.

Line spacing

Objectives 2.5.2, 2.6.5

To change line spacing (the amount of space between lines of text), place the insertion point in a line of text or select multiple paragraphs, click the Line Spacing button in the Paragraph group, and choose a line spacing value. Line spacing values are measured in lines (such as 1.5 lines).

You can also add space before or after a paragraph. To do so:

1 Open the Paragraph dialog box by using either of these techniques:
   - In the Paragraph group, click the Dialog Box Launcher.
   - Click the Line Spacing button and choose Line Spacing Options.
2 Under Spacing, enter a value in the Before or After box. (You can set line spacing in this dialog box, too.)
3 Click OK.

Indentation

Objectives 2.5.2, 2.6.5

You can also use the Paragraph dialog box to specify paragraph indentation. To indent the left side of all lines of a paragraph, enter a value in the Before box. You can also specify a first-line indent value or a hanging-indent value. If you don't want a first-line indent or a hanging indent, select "(none)" from the list of indenting styles. After specifying text indent settings, click OK.

Do it!

C-1: Applying paragraph formatting

The files for this activity are in Student Data folder **Unit 3\Topic C**.

Objectives 2.5.2, 2.6.5

Here's how	Here's why
1 Open OS project phase one	From the current topic folder.
Save the presentation as **My OS project phase one**	
2 Zoom to fit the slide the current window	(On the Status bar, click the Fit slide to current window button.) If necessary.
3 Move to the fifth slide in the presentation	The slide titled "Performance."
Select the left-side text	The text on the left is in its own placeholder. You'll change the alignment of the entire left side of the slide.
4 Click ▤	(The Align Text Right button is in the Paragraph group.) To align the text to the right.
Deselect and observe the text	

Help students select all text on the left side.

Performance

Our pricing typically undercuts our competitors', yet still provides a large margin of profit for distributors.

Our products are manufactured for quality, and have earned end-user loyalty resulting in repeat sales.

Our products move! Inventory typically turns over 50% faster than competitive products.

Our customers have saved up to 14% of inventory cost while improving productivity and cash flow.

Sales to restaurants have never been better.

The left-side text is aligned to the right, and the right-side text is still aligned to the left.

5 Select the left-side text again	
6 Activate the Mini toolbar	Right-click the selected text to display the Mini toolbar.
Click ▤	(The Center button.) To center the selected text.

7 Align the right-side text to the center	Select the text and click the Center button (on the Mini toolbar or on the Ribbon).
Deselect the text	
8 Observe the slide	

Performance

Our pricing typically undercuts our competitors', yet still provides a large margin of profit for distributors.	Our products move! Inventory typically turns over 50% faster than competitive products.
Our products are manufactured for quality, and have earned end user loyalty resulting in repeat sales.	Our customers have saved up to 14% of inventory cost while improving productivity and cash flow.
	Sales to restaurants have never been better.

Both text blocks have centered text.

9 Align the left-side text to the left	
Align the right-side text to the lcft	Next, you'll increase the line spacing. To format both text boxes at the same time, you'll select them both.
10 Click the left text box	To select it.
Press and hold (SHIFT) and click the right text box	To select both text boxes.
11 Click ⬆≡▾	The Line Spacing button is in the Paragraph group.
Choose **1.5**	To increase the line spacing.
12 Go to slide 3	
13 Select the two items in the sub-list	You'll increase the left indent for the sub-list.
14 In the Paragraph group, click the Dialog Box Launcher	To open the Paragraph dialog box.
15 Under Indentation, in the Before text box, enter **1**	To specify a left indent of 1 inch.
Click **OK**	To close the Paragraph dialog box.
16 Update and close the presentation	

Unit summary: Formatting slides

Topic A   In this topic, you applied **character formatting** to selected text by using commands in the Font group and on the Mini toolbar. You changed the font, size, and color of text, and you used the **Format Painter** to repeat text formatting. Then, you changed bullet styles and applied a numbered **list** format.

Topic B   In this topic, you used the Find dialog box to search for specific text, and you used the Replace dialog box to **replace text**. Next, you used the Cut, Copy, and Paste commands to **move and copy text** to another slide in the same presentation and to another presentation. You also dragged text to move it. Finally, you used the **Clipboard pane** to copy and paste multiple items.

Topic C   In this topic, you applied **paragraph formats** such as text alignment, line spacing, and indentation.

Independent practice activity

In this activity, you'll search for specific text and replace it. You'll apply formatting to text and use the Format Painter to repeat that formatting.

The files for this activity are in Student Data folder **Unit 3\Unit summary**.

1 Open New activities practice.

2 Save the presentation as **My new activities practice**.

3 Find the text **Creating** and replace it with the word **Developing**.

4 Find the phrase **Markets in the East** and replace it with the phrase **Markets in the North**.

5 Apply bold formatting to the first slide's title, and increase the font size to 60.

6 On the second slide, format the title as Trebuchet MS, Bold, and apply a red color. Align the title to the left.

7 Using the Format Painter, apply this formatting to the titles of the remaining slides. (*Hint:* After applying the formatting, remember to disable the Format Painter.)

8 On the second slide, apply a new bullet style. Using the Format Painter, apply this change to the other bulleted lists in the presentation.

9 Update and close the presentation.

Review questions

1 What is the difference between character formatting and paragraph formatting?

Character formatting is any formatting you can apply to individual characters. Examples are font, font size, and typestyle. Paragraph formatting is any formatting you can apply only to whole paragraphs. Examples are text alignment, line spacing, and bulleted and numbered lists.

2 List the buttons in the Font group.

Font, Font Size, Increase Font Size, Decrease Font Size, Clear Formatting, Bold, Italic, Underline, Strikethrough, Text Shadow, Character Spacing, Change Case, and Font Color.

3 What is the Mini toolbar?

The Mini toolbar is a floating palette that appears when you make a selection. It is almost transparent until you activate it by pointing to it. When you do, you have access to the most commonly used features based on your selection.

4 List the steps you would use to apply a new font to slide text.

a *Select the text.*

b *In the Font group or on the Mini toolbar, display the Font list.*

c *Select the font you want to apply.*

5 You can use the Format _____ button to copy the formatting of selected text and apply it to other text.

Painter

6 How can you change the bullet style for a selected bullet list on a slide?

In the Paragraph group or on the Mini toolbar, click the Bullets arrow to display the Bullets gallery. Click a bullet style to apply it and close the gallery.

7 What is the Clipboard?

The Clipboard is a temporary storage area that holds a cut or copied object or text until you specify where to place it in a document. The Windows Clipboard can hold only one selection at a time and is cleared when you shut down your computer.

8 How do you open the Find dialog box?

On the Home tab, click the Find button.

9 What do the Cut and Paste commands do?

The Cut command removes the selected text or object from the current slide and places it on the Clipboard. The Paste command takes the text or object from the Clipboard and inserts a copy of it wherever the insertion point is positioned.

10 How does the Clipboard pane differ from the Clipboard?

The Clipboard pane can store multiple items, and the Windows Clipboard holds only one item at a time.

11 You select one entire paragraph and part of another, and then click the Center button. What happens to the text?

Both paragraphs are centered.

Unit 4

Using drawing objects

Unit time: 60 minutes

Complete this unit, and you'll know how to:

A Draw objects by using tools in the Drawing group.

B Format, modify, move, rotate, and delete drawn objects by using tools on the Drawing Tools | Format tab.

C Add text to drawn objects and to text boxes.

Topic A: Adding shapes

This topic covers the following Microsoft Office Specialist exam objectives for PowerPoint 2010.

#	Objective
2.6	Format a text box
	2.6.3 Change the shape of the text box
3.1	Manipulate graphical elements

Drawing shapes

Explanation

Objective 3.1

You can make your presentations more appealing by adding drawn objects, such as rectangles, ovals, lines, arrows, and other shapes. The tools needed to draw objects are located on the Insert tab and the Drawing Tools | Format tab, which is context sensitive.

To create an object on a slide:

1   In the Drawing group on the Home tab, scroll through the Shapes list, as shown in Exhibit 4-1, or click the More button (at the bottom of the list's scrollbar). You can also display the shapes gallery by clicking the Shapes button in the Illustrations group on the Insert tab.

2   Select one of the tools, such as the Rectangle tool.

3   Point to the location where you want to begin drawing. The pointer changes to a crosshair.

4   Click and then drag until the drawing object reaches the size and shape you want.

5   Release the mouse button. The new object is automatically selected.

Another way to create an object is to select a tool and click the slide. The specified shape is automatically drawn at a default size.

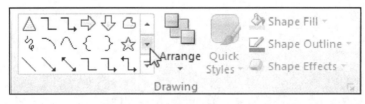

Exhibit 4-1: Scrolling through the Shapes list in the Drawing group on the Home tab

Exhibit 4-2 shows a selected drawn object and its handles. You use the rotation handle to change the rotation angle and use the sizing handles to resize the object.

Objective 3.1

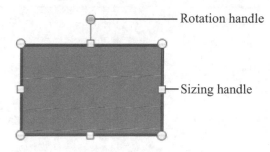

Exhibit 4-2: A drawn object

Polygons

When you select a polygon, it might display one or more yellow *adjustment handles* in addition to the rotation handle and sizing handles. You can drag an adjustment handle to reshape the polygon. When you point to an adjustment handle, the pointer appears as a white arrowhead, as shown in Exhibit 4-3.

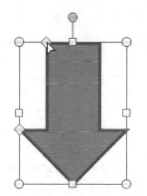

Exhibit 4-3: The pointer as it appears when pointing to an adjustment handle

The Drawing Tools | Format tab

When you select a drawn object, the Drawing Tools | Format tab is added to the Ribbon, as shown in Exhibit 4-4. This tab contains the options you'll need to format the object.

Exhibit 4-4: The Drawing Tools | Format tab

The Microsoft Office 2010 contextual-tabs feature will automatically display the appropriate tab when you insert a picture, create a text box, draw a chart, or draw a diagram. You can then click the tab to access the commands and options on it.

A-1:   Using the drawing tools

Here's how	Here's why
1 Create a new blank presentation	On the File tab, click New. Verify that New presentation is selected and click Create.
2 In the title placeholder, enter **Drawing Practice**	To give the presentation a name.
3 Click the **New Slide** arrow	(In the Slides group.) To display the slide layout gallery.
4 Select the **Blank** layout	(Scroll down in the slide layout gallery, and click Blank.) To create a blank slide.
5 Save the presentation as **My drawing practice**	In Student Data folder Unit 4\Topic A.
6 Click **Shapes** and click as shown	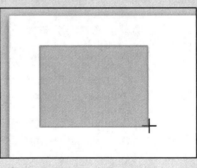 (On the Home tab, in the Drawing group.) To select the Rectangle tool.
Point to the slide	
Observe the pointer	It appears as a crosshair.
7 Drag to create a rectangle, as shown	

![A rectangle being drawn on a slide with a crosshair pointer]

The rectangle should be roughly one quarter the width of the slide.

Release the mouse button	To complete the rectangle.

8 Observe the rectangle

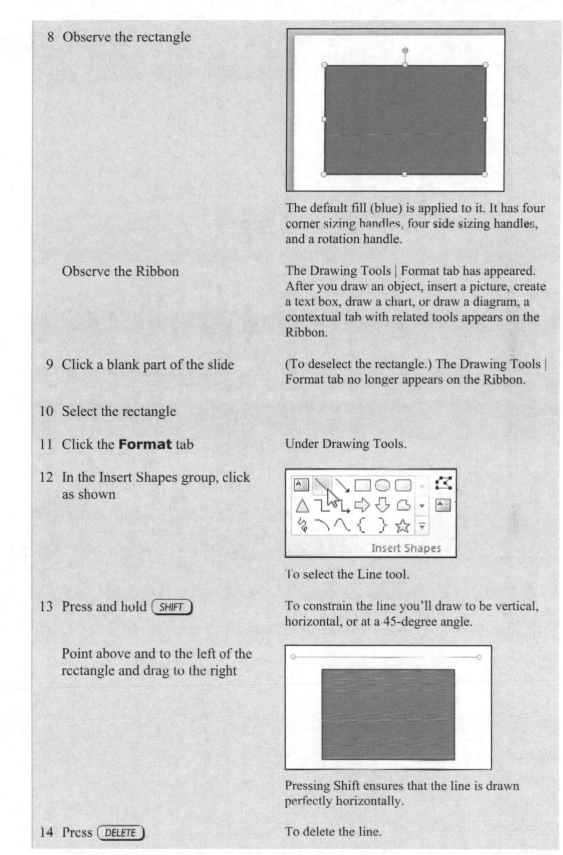

The default fill (blue) is applied to it. It has four corner sizing handles, four side sizing handles, and a rotation handle.

Observe the Ribbon

The Drawing Tools | Format tab has appeared. After you draw an object, insert a picture, create a text box, draw a chart, or draw a diagram, a contextual tab with related tools appears on the Ribbon.

9 Click a blank part of the slide

(To deselect the rectangle.) The Drawing Tools | Format tab no longer appears on the Ribbon.

10 Select the rectangle

11 Click the **Format** tab

Under Drawing Tools.

12 In the Insert Shapes group, click as shown

To select the Line tool.

13 Press and hold (SHIFT)

To constrain the line you'll draw to be vertical, horizontal, or at a 45-degree angle.

Point above and to the left of the rectangle and drag to the right

Pressing Shift ensures that the line is drawn perfectly horizontally.

14 Press (DELETE)

To delete the line.

15 Below the rectangle, draw an arrow that points to the rectangle

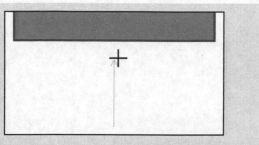

On the Home tab, in the Drawing group, select the Arrow tool from the Shapes list. Point below the rectangle, press and hold Shift, and drag up. Click a blank area to deselect the arrow.

16 Delete the arrow

(Select it and press Delete.) You'll draw a block arrow.

17 Select the **Up Arrow** tool

Scroll down the Shapes list and select the Up Arrow tool.

18 Point below the rectangle, and begin dragging up and to the right

(Don't release the mouse button.) Dragging horizontally changes the shape's width, and dragging vertically changes its height.

Drag to draw the arrow as shown

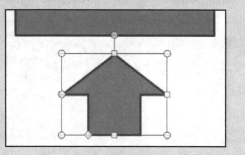

When the arrow has the correct proportions and is the right size, release the mouse button.

19 Delete the shape

Press Delete.

20 Update the presentation

Changing object shapes

Explanation

Objective 2.6.3

After you draw an object, you can change it to a different shape. For example, after drawing a rectangle, you can change it to an oval. To change an object to another shape:

1 Select the shape you want to change.

2 Verify that the Drawing Tools | Format tab is active.

3 In the Insert Shapes group, click the Edit Shape button and point to Change Shape to display the gallery.

4 Select the shape you want to use. The new shape replaces the old one, but retains any formatting you had applied to the old shape.

Do it!

Objective 3.1

A-2:   Changing an object's shape

Here's how	Here's why
1 Select the rectangle	You'll change the rectangle to an oval.
2 Click the **Format** tab	Under Drawing Tools.
3 In the Insert Shapes group, click **Edit Shape**	To display the Edit Shape menu.
4 Point to **Change Shape**	To display the gallery.
5 Under Basic Shapes, select the Oval shape	To change the shape of the rectangle to an oval.
6 Update the presentation and close it	

Topic B: Modifying objects

This topic covers the following Microsoft Office Specialist exam objectives for PowerPoint 2010.

#	Objective
2.6	**Format a text box**
	2.6.2 Change the outline of a text box
3.1	**Manipulate graphical elements**
	3.1.1 Arrange graphical elements
	3.1.2 Position graphical elements
	3.1.3 Resize graphical elements
	3.1.4 Apply effects to graphical elements
	3.1.5 Apply styles to graphical elements
	3.1.6 Apply borders to graphical elements
3.3	**Modify WordArt and shapes**
	3.3.1 Set the formatting of the current shape as the default for future shapes
	3.3.2 Change the fill color or texture

Working with shapes

Explanation

When you create objects, you can change fill colors, outline colors, and effects. You can make the changes quickly by using options in the Shape Styles group. You can also duplicate, move, resize, rotate, and change shapes. If you no longer need a drawn object, you can delete it.

Shape styles

Objective 3.1.5

The Drawing Tools | Format tab includes the Shape Styles group. It contains the Shape Fill, Shape Outline, and Shape Effects buttons, which you can use to modify an object manually. It also provides shape styles that you can use to quickly apply a complete set of formats (fill color, outline color, and effects). When you point to one of the styles, a Live Preview is displayed on the selected object(s). To display a gallery of shape styles, click the More button. Point to one of the styles to see the Live Preview, or select it to apply that style.

Shape fills

Objective 3.3.2

To change an object's fill color, select the object and click the Drawing Tools | Format tab. In the Shape Styles group, click the Shape Fill arrow to display a gallery; then select a color.

The following table describes the options in the Shape Fill gallery.

Option	Description
Theme Colors	Contains ten main colors and five tints under each main color (for a total of 60 color swatches).
Standard Colors	Contains the ten regular colors that span the color spectrum: Dark Red, Red, Orange, Yellow, Light Green, Green, Light Blue, Blue, Dark Blue, and Purple
No Fill	Removes the fill completely.
More Fill Colors	Opens the Colors dialog box, which contains two tabs: the Standard tab and the Custom tab. On the Custom tab, you can change the color model, change the color tint, change the transparency, and select any of the millions of colors that are available.
Picture	Opens the Insert Picture dialog box, which you can use to add an image file as a fill.
Gradient	Opens a gallery of gradients divided into two categories, Light Variations and Dark Variations.
Texture	Opens a gallery of 24 textured fills.

Shape outlines

Objectives 2.6.2, 3.1.6

To change an object's outline color, select the object. In the Shape Styles group, click the Shape Outlines arrow to display a gallery. Select a color, or choose one of the other options, such as No Outline, More Outline Colors, Weight, Dashes, or Arrows.

Shape effects

Objective 3.1.4

To change the effects applied to a shape, select the object. In the Shape Styles group, click the Shape Effects button to display a menu. You can use the Preset, Shadow, Reflection, Glow, Soft Edges, Bevel, and 3-D Rotation submenus to display the respective galleries. From the desired gallery, select an effect to apply.

Default shape settings

Objective 3.3.1

Once you've finished formatting a shape, you can set that formatting as the new default. To do so:

1   Verify that the desired shape is selected. This shape uses the fill, outline, and effects that you want to set as the new default.

2   Right-click the selected shape and choose Set as Default Shape.

When you draw the next shape in the presentation, it will automatically be formatted with the default fill, outline, and effects you've defined. Note that this new default shape applies to only the open presentation.

Do it!

B-1:   Applying formatting to objects

The files for this activity are in Student Data folder **Unit 4\Topic B**.

Here's how	Here's why
1 Open Drawing practice2	From the current topic folder.
Save the presentation as **My drawing practice2**	
2 On slide 2, select the oval	
Click the **Format** tab	Under Drawing Tools.

Objective 3.1.5

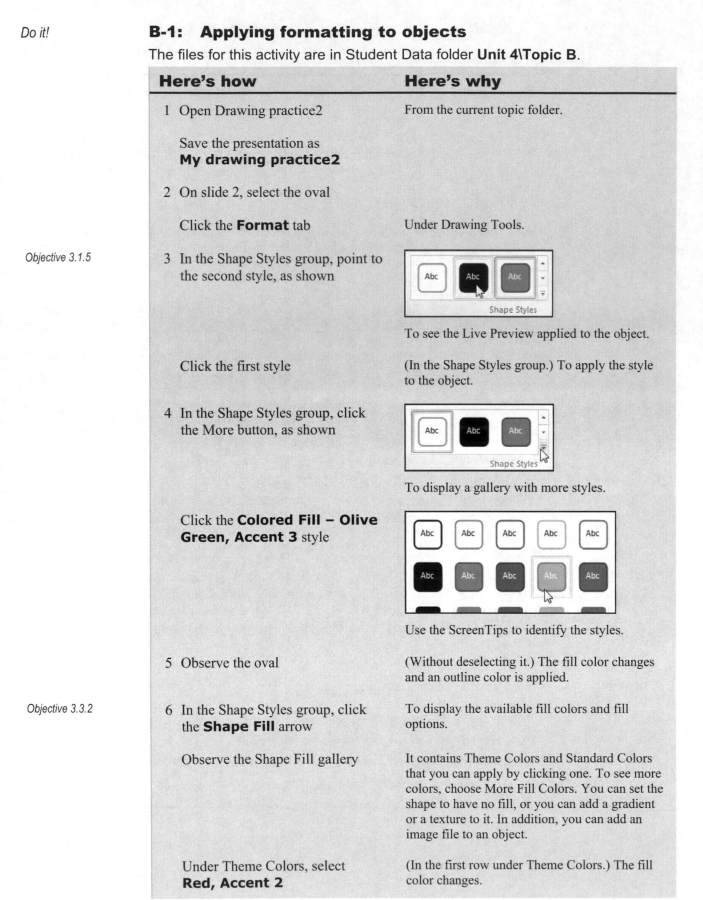

3 In the Shape Styles group, point to the second style, as shown	To see the Live Preview applied to the object.
Click the first style	(In the Shape Styles group.) To apply the style to the object.
4 In the Shape Styles group, click the More button, as shown	To display a gallery with more styles.
Click the **Colored Fill – Olive Green, Accent 3** style	Use the ScreenTips to identify the styles.
5 Observe the oval	(Without deselecting it.) The fill color changes and an outline color is applied.

Objective 3.3.2

6 In the Shape Styles group, click the **Shape Fill** arrow	To display the available fill colors and fill options.
Observe the Shape Fill gallery	It contains Theme Colors and Standard Colors that you can apply by clicking one. To see more colors, choose More Fill Colors. You can set the shape to have no fill, or you can add a gradient or a texture to it. In addition, you can add an image file to an object.
Under Theme Colors, select **Red, Accent 2**	(In the first row under Theme Colors.) The fill color changes.

Objective 3.1.6	7 Click the **Shape Outline** arrow	To display the outline colors and options.
	Observe the Shape Outline gallery	You can apply a color quickly to the shape outline by clicking one of the Theme Colors or Standard Colors. To see more colors, choose More Outline Colors. You can set the shape to have no outline, change the line weight, apply dashes, and add an arrow or two.
	Click the **Shape Outline** arrow	To close the gallery without changing the shape outline.
Objective 3.1.4	8 Click **Shape Effects**	To display the Shape Effects menu.
	Point to each effect submenu	To see the galleries.
	Point to **Preset**	To display the gallery of options. Currently, no 3-D effect is applied.
	Under Presets, select **Preset 2**	(The second item in the first row.) To apply the new effect.
	9 Update the presentation	

Duplicating objects

Explanation

After you create an object, you can duplicate it. Creating duplicates ensures that similar objects have a uniform size and shape in your presentation. For example, if your presentation contains multiple oval objects, you can make them all the same by creating duplicates of the original oval.

To duplicate an object:

1 Select the object.

2 Click the Home tab.

3 In the Clipboard group, click the Copy button's arrow and choose Duplicate.

You can also press Ctrl+D to duplicate a selected object.

Deleting objects

To remove an object that is no longer needed, select it and press Delete.

Moving objects

After an object is drawn or duplicated, you'll probably want to move it. To do so:

Objective 3.1.2

1 Select the object. The rotation handle and sizing handles appear around it.

2 Point to the object:

- If the object has a fill applied to it, point anywhere on the object; the mouse pointer displays a four-headed arrow.

- If the object doesn't have a fill (no color and completely empty), point to the edge of the selected object but not to any of the sizing handles. The mouse pointer displays a four-headed arrow.

3 Drag the object to move it to a new position; then release the mouse button.

Smart guides

When there are multiple objects on the slide and you're moving one of them, you'll notice that a dotted line will appear when the selected object is aligned (either vertically or horizontally) with the stationary object. This dotted line is called a *smart guide*.

For example, you have two rectangles on the slide and both are exactly the same size. They are near each other, as shown on the left side of Exhibit 4-5. You've selected the bottom rectangle and are moving it up and to the right of the other rectangle. As you do, you'll see the smart guide indicating that the two objects are aligned horizontally, as shown on the right side of Exhibit 4-5. Once the smart guide appears and doesn't go away, release the mouse to complete the move. The two rectangles are now horizontally aligned.

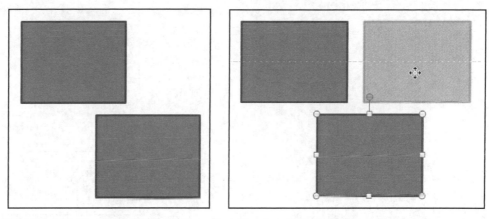

Exhibit 4-5: On the left, two rectangles. On the right, a smart guide appears as you move the bottom rectangle up and to the right to align it with the top rectangle.

Do it!

Objective 3.1.2

B-2: Duplicating, deleting, and moving objects

Here's how	Here's why
1 Verify that the oval is selected	
Click the **Home** tab	If necessary.
2 Copy the oval to the Clipboard	Click the Copy button or press Ctrl+C.
3 Paste the oval	Click the Paste button or press Ctrl+V.
Observe the ovals	The original is deselected. The pasted copy is offset to the right and down a bit.
4 Verify that the new oval is selected	
Press (DELETE)	To delete the oval. No objects are selected.
5 Click the **Copy** arrow	You can't because no items are selected.
6 Select the oval	The Drawing Tools | Format tab is visible but not active.
Click the **Copy** arrow	To display a menu.
Choose **Duplicate**	To create a duplicate of the oval.

TIPS
✓ *You can also press Ctrl+D.*

7 Point to the oval

The pointer changes to include a four-headed arrow, which you'll use to move the oval.

TIPS
Tell students that a Smart Guide appears when the oval being moved is aligned with the original oval.

Press and hold the mouse button, and drag the oval to the right

A transparent preview of the oval moves with the pointer. Notice the smart guide—the dotted line—that appears.

Release the mouse button

To complete the move.

8 With the oval selected, press `CTRL` + `D`

To duplicate it.

Move the third oval to the right

(If necessary.) The three ovals are now in a line.

9 Verify that the third oval is selected

10 Click the **Format** tab

Under Drawing Tools.

In the Shape Styles group, click the More button

To display more styles.

Select the second style

(Colored Outline – Blue, Accent 1.) To change the style applied to the object. The fill has been changed to white, and a blue outline has been added.

11 Drag the selected oval to the left

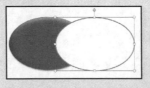

So that it partially overlaps the oval next to it. You can see the oval's white fill covering the other oval where they overlap.

12 Click the **Shape Fill** arrow	You will remove the white fill from the oval.
Choose **No Fill**	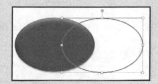
	To remove the fill from the object.
13 Point within the selected oval	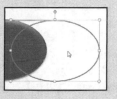
	Because there is no longer a fill applied to the object, you can't move it by dragging from within the object.
Point to the oval's outline	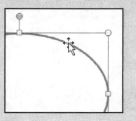
	The pointer changes shape to indicate that you can now move the object.
14 Drag to the right and release the mouse button	To move the oval so that it no longer overlaps the other oval.
15 Update the presentation	

Resizing objects

Explanation

Objective 3.1.3

After drawing an object, you can change its size at any time. To resize an object:

1   Select the object. The rotation handle and sizing handles appear.

2   Do one of the following:

- Point to a corner sizing handle if you want adjust the object's width and height at the same time. The pointer changes to a diagonal double-headed arrow.
- Point to a side sizing handle if you want to increase or decrease only the object's width. The pointer changes to a horizontal double-headed arrow.
- Point to the top or bottom sizing handle if you want to adjust only the object's height. The pointer changes to a vertical double-headed arrow.

3   Drag the sizing handle until the object reaches the size you want; then release the mouse button.

If you want to resize an object to specific dimensions, you can enter numeric values in the Height and Width boxes in the Size group on the Drawing Tools | Format tab.

If you want to maintain the object's proportions as you resize it, point to a corner handle, press and hold Shift, and drag to resize the object.

Do it!

Objective 3.1.3

B-3: Resizing an object

Here's how	Here's why
1 Click the **Home** tab	
2 Click the **New Slide** arrow	To display the gallery.
Click **Title Only**	To add a new slide with the Title Only layout.
3 In the title placeholder, enter **Monthly Sales Awards**	You'll create star shapes to contain the names of several employees.
4 In the Drawing group, click the More button for the Shapes list	To display the Shapes gallery.
5 Under Stars and Banners, select the **16-Point Star**	You'll use this tool to draw a star object.

Tell students that they can press and hold Shift while dragging to draw a star proportionally.

6 Drag as shown

To draw a star of any size.

Tell students that the star size isn't important because they will resize it.

Release the mouse button

To finish drawing the star. The star is selected, and the Drawing Tools | Format tab appears.

7 Point to the bottom-right corner sizing handle, as shown

The pointer changes to a diagonal two-way arrow, indicating that you can use it to change the object's width and height.

Drag down and to the right about an inch

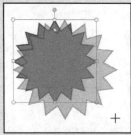

To change the object's height and width.

Release the mouse button

To finish resizing.

8   Point to the bottom-center sizing
    handle, as shown

The pointer changes to a vertical two-headed
arrow, indicating that you can change the
object's height.

    Drag up about half an inch

(Release the mouse button when done.) To
reduce the height of the star about half an inch.

9   Point to the center-right sizing
    handle, as shown

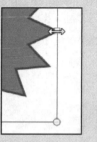

    Drag to the left about half an inch

To reduce the width of the star about half an
inch.

10 On the Drawing Tools | Format
    tab, observe the Size group

You'll use tools in this group to resize the star
using exact measurements. The Height and
Width numbers will vary based on how you've
drawn and resized the star.

11 Point to the Shape Height box

The Shape Height box is at the top of the Size
group.

    Click the current value

To select the value in the Shape Height box.

    Type **2.5** and press (↵ ENTER)

To change the height to 2.5 inches.

12 Select the value in the Shape
    Width box

    Type **2.5** and press (↵ ENTER)

To change the width to 2.5 inches.

13 Update the presentation

Rotating objects

Explanation

Objective 3.1.2

You can change the rotation angle of an object. To rotate an object:

1 Select the object. The rotation handle and sizing handles appear.

2 Point to the rotation handle. The pointer changes to a black circle with an arrow, indicating a rotating motion.

3 Drag in a clockwise or counterclockwise motion; release the mouse button when you have the angle you want.

If you want to rotate an object to a specific angle, select the object and verify that the Drawing Tools | Format tab is active. In the Size group, click the Dialog Box Launcher to open the Format Shape dialog box with the Size tab active. Under "Size and rotate," enter the desired angle in the Rotation box; then click Close.

Do it!

Objective 3.1.2

B-4:   Rotating an object

Here's how	Here's why
1 Point to the rotation handle, as shown	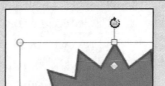
	The pointer changes to a black circle with an arrow, indicating a rotating motion.
Drag down and to the right, as shown	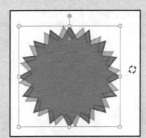
	To rotate the star to the right.
2 Observe the star	
	The star and the selection box are rotated to the right. The rotation handle is at the same angle that the pointer was when you released the mouse button.
3 In the Size group, click the Dialog Box Launcher	(On the Drawing Tools | Format tab.) To open the Format Shape dialog box with the Size tab active.
Observe the Rotation box	Size Size and rotate Height: 2.5″ Rotation: 79°
	It shows the shape's current angle of rotation. The number in the box will differ based on where you stopped rotating the object.
In the Rotation box, enter **0**	To return the star to its original rotation.
Click **Close**	To apply the rotation and close the dialog box.
4 Update the presentation	

Aligning objects

Explanation

Objective 3.1.1

When placing multiple objects on a slide, you can use the Align menu to align them in relation to one another and to evenly space them. To align objects:

1 Select one of the objects that you want to align.

2 Press Ctrl or Shift, and select the other objects.

3 Click the Drawing Tools | Format tab.

4 In the Arrange group, click the Align button and choose an option.

The following table describes the options in the Align menu.

Option	Description
Align Left	Aligns the selected objects with the left side of the leftmost object.
Align Center	Aligns the selected objects at their centers.
Align Right	Aligns the selected objects with the right side of the rightmost object.
Align Top	Aligns the selected objects with the top of the topmost object.
Align Middle	Aligns the selected objects at their middles.
Align Bottom	Aligns the selected objects with the bottom of the bottommost object.
Distribute Horizontally	Evenly distributes the horizontal space between the selected objects.
Distribute Vertically	Evenly distributes the vertical space between the selected objects.
Align to Slide	When this option is checked, the Align commands align objects with the slide, rather than with one another.
Align selected objects	When this option is checked, the Align commands align objects with one another, rather than with the slide.
View Gridlines	Displays the default gridlines on the slide.
Grid Settings	Opens the Grid and Guidelines dialog box.

Grids and guides

When moving objects on a slide, you can use gridlines and guides to place them in exactly the right place. A *grid* is a set of intersecting lines that appear on a slide, as shown in Exhibit 4-6. To display the grid on a slide, verify that the Drawing Tools | Format tab is active. In the Arrange group, click the Align button and choose View Gridlines.

A *guide* is a pair of horizontal and vertical nonprinting lines that intersect the middle of the slide by default. They are movable, and you can use them to position objects at specific locations on a slide or to place objects in relation to other objects.

To display and use the guides:

1   In the Arrange group on the Drawing Tools | Format tab, click the Align button and choose Grid Settings to open the Grid and Guides dialog box.

2   Under Guide settings, check "Display drawing guides on screen."

3   Click OK.

4   Drag the guide to a position where you want to align the object.

5   Drag the object near the guide so that the object's center or edge aligns with the guide automatically.

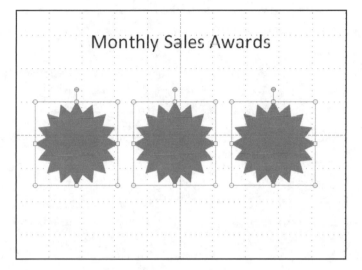

Exhibit 4-6: A slide with a grid and guides

Smart guides

As you've already discovered, you can quickly and easily align objects with one another by using smart guides. To turn smart guides on and off:

1   Select an object and click the Drawing Tools | Format tab.

2   In the Arrange group, click Align and choose Grid Settings to open the Grid and Guides dialog box.

3   Under Guide settings, check "Display smart guides when shapes are aligned" to turn the feature on, or clear it to turn the feature off.

4   Click OK.

B-5: Aligning objects

Here's how	Here's why
1 Select the star object	If necessary.
2 Duplicate the object twice	Press Ctrl+D twice to create two copies.
Move the stars as shown	

Here's how	Here's why
3 Press and hold CTRL and select the other two star objects	All three objects are now selected.
Release CTRL	
4 Click the **Format** tab	(Under Drawing Tools.) If necessary.
5 Click ⌷ Align ▾	(In the Arrange group.) To display the Align menu.
Choose **Align to Slide**	(If necessary.) You want to align the objects with the slide.
6 Click **Align** and choose **Distribute Horizontally**	To evenly distribute the horizontal space between the objects.
7 Click **Align** and choose **Align Middle**	To center the objects horizontally.
8 Click **Align** and choose **Grid Settings...**	To open the Grid and Guides dialog box.
Check **Display grid on screen**	Under Grid settings.
Check **Display drawing guides on screen**	Under Guide settings.
Click **OK**	To turn on the grid and guides and close the dialog box.
9 Observe the slide	The grid and guides are displayed. The three objects are evenly distributed and centered on the slide.

10	Verify that all three shapes are selected	
	Press ⬆ multiple times	To position the three star objects just above the center of the slide. Use the grid and guides as references to determine the slide's center.
11	Click **Align** and choose **View Gridlines**	To hide the gridlines.
12	Open the Grid and Guides dialog box	Click Align and choose Grid Settings.
	Clear **Display drawing guides on screen**	
	Click **OK**	To remove the guides from the slide and close the dialog box.
13	Deselect the objects	Click the slide.
14	Update and close the presentation	

Topic C: Using text in objects

This topic covers the following Microsoft Office Specialist exam objectives for PowerPoint 2010.

#	Objective
2.5	**Enter and format text**
	2.5.2 Change text formats
	2.5.3 Change the formatting of bulleted and numbered lists
	2.5.4 Enter text in a placeholder text box
2.6	**Format a text box**
	2.6.1 Apply formatting to a text box
	2.6.2 Change the outline of a text box
	2.6.3 Change the shape of the text box
	2.6.4 Apply effects
	2.6.6 Create columns in a text box
	2.6.7 Set internal margins
	2.6.8 Set the current text box formatting as the default for new text boxes
	2.6.10 Use AutoFit

Adding text to objects

Explanation

Objects by themselves can enhance the overall message you want to convey in a presentation, but in some cases, adding descriptive text to objects makes your message much more effective. When you add text to an object, the text becomes part of the object and moves along with it on a slide. However, if you resize the object, the text is not automatically resized.

Objective 2.5.4

To add text to an object, simply select the object and type the text. By default, the text is centered in the object. However, you can change the alignment of the text relative to the object.

Do it!

Objective 2.5.4

C-1: Adding text to an object

The files for this activity are in Student Data folder **Unit 4\Topic C**.

Here's how	Here's why
1 Open Monthly sales awards	
Save the presentation as **My Monthly sales awards**	
2 On slide 2, select the center star object	
3 Type **Morgan O.**	To add the text within the shape.
4 Observe the star	The text is centered within the star and is white.
5 Select the left star	
6 Type **Peyton J.**	
7 Select the right star and type **Michele C.**	
8 Update the presentation	

Formatting text in objects

Explanation

You can format text in objects just as you would format any other text. To do so, select the text or the object containing the text, and use the options on the Mini toolbar or in the Font group on the Home tab. You can change the font, size, and color of the text, and make it bold, italic, underlined, or shadowed.

Do it!

C-2: Formatting text in an object

Objectives 2.5.2, 2.6.1

Here's how	Here's why
1 Point to the "Peyton J." text	(In the left star.) The mouse pointer changes to an I-beam.
Click once	To place the insertion point in the text.
Press CTRL + A	To select all of the text in the object.
2 Observe the selection	
	There is a white box around the text, indicating that it is selected.
3 Click the **Home** tab	If necessary.
4 From the Font list, select **Arial Black**	
From the Font Size list, select **20**	Next, you'll format the text in the other two stars simultaneously.
5 Select the other two stars	Click the star containing "Morgan O."; then press Ctrl and click the star containing "Michele G."
Change the font to **Arial Black** and the font size to **20**	When you do, the first names become too large for the objects.
6 Select all three stars	
7 Click the **Format** tab	Under Drawing Tools.
8 Using the Size group, change both the Height and Width to **2.8**	To enlarge the star objects to fit the text within them.
9 Click **Align** and choose **Distribute Horizontally**	To redistribute the space between the three objects.
Click **Align** and choose **Align Middle**	To center the three objects on the slide.
10 Update the presentation	

Drawing text boxes

Explanation

By default, when you select an object and type text, PowerPoint automatically creates a text box. You can also draw a text box on a slide and then enter text in it. As you add text to a text box, its width remains constant but the height adjusts to fit the text.

To create a text box and add text:

Objectives 2.5.2, 2.6.1

1   Click the Text Box button in any of these groups:
    - The Drawing group on the Home tab
    - The Text group on the Insert tab
    - The Insert Shapes group on the Drawing Tools | Format tab
2   Drag the mouse pointer to create a text box.
3   Type the text you want to add.
4   Resize and move the text box as needed.

To resize a text box, click it so that selection handles appear along the edges and on the corners; then drag a selection handle. To delete a text box, point to an edge of it and click (to select the text box); then press Delete.

Text formatting and orientation

Objectives 2.5.2, 2.6.1

You can format the text in a text box by using the same techniques you use to format other slide text. You can also specify the orientation for the text in a text box. For example, you can rotate the text 90 degrees or 270 degrees within the text box. To change the orientation of text within a text box:

1   Click the Home tab.
2   In the Paragraph group, click the Text Direction button and choose a text direction.
3   Resize and move the text box as necessary.

Do it!

Objectives 2.5.2, 2.6.1

C-3: Creating text boxes

Here's how	Here's why
1 Create a new blank slide	You'll add text listing new kiosk locations.
2 Click the **Insert** tab	You'll create a text box displaying vertical text for the slide's title.
3 Click **Text Box**	In the Text group.
4 Drag to draw the text box as shown	

5 Type **New kiosk locations**	
Format the text as Arial Black, 40 pt	
6 Click [Text Direction ▾]	(In the Paragraph group.) To display the Text Direction menu.
Choose **Rotate all text 270°**	The text is rotated but looks jumbled within the text box. You'll resize the text box.
7 Point to the bottom-right handle on the text box, as shown	
	The pointer changes to a two-headed arrow.
Drag down and to the left, as shown	
	(To the bottom-left corner of the slide.) To resize the text box so that the text fits vertically on one line.

8   Point to an edge of the text box

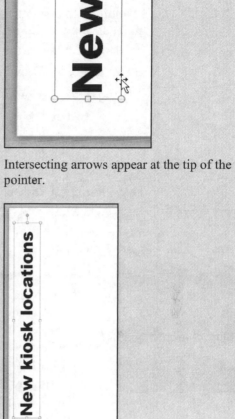

Intersecting arrows appear at the tip of the pointer.

Drag to move the text box as shown

Move it near the left edge of the slide, and center it vertically on the slide.

Formatting text boxes

Explanation

In addition to formatting the text within a text box, you can format the text box itself. You can apply a fill, border, and effects. Here's how:

Objectives 2.5.2, 2.6.1, 2.6.2

1 Select the text box.

2 Click the Drawing Tools | Format tab.

3 Apply formatting by using options in the Shape Styles group:

- Click Shape Fill and choose a fill color.
- Click Shape Outline and choose an outline color, weight, and style.
- Click Shape Effects and choose an effect.

Text alignment and margins

Objectives 2.5.2, 2.6.1

You might want to change the alignment of text within a text box, or change the internal margin settings for the text box. You can do so by using options in the Home tab's Paragraph group:

- Click a horizontal alignment button to specify horizontal alignment.
- Click the Align Text button and choose Top, Middle, or Bottom to specify vertical alignment within the text box. You can also choose More Options to open the Format Text Effects dialog box with the Text Box tab active, and then specify:

Objectives 2.6.7, 2.6.10

  – Autofit options — The default is "Do not Autofit," but you can change the setting by selecting "Shrink text on overflow" or "Resize shape to fit text."
  – Internal margin settings — Use these text boxes to set the space between the shape outline and the text. By default, "Wrap text in shape" is checked.

Bullet formatting

Objective 2.5.3

You can use bulleted lists in text boxes. To apply bulleted list formatting, first select the text. Then either click the Bullets button to apply the default bullet style, or click the Bullets arrow and select a bullet style.

Columns in text boxes

Objective 2.6.6

You can format a text box to display its text in columns. To do so, select the text box. Then, in the Paragraph group on the Home tab, click the Columns button and choose the number of columns you want.

You can also click the Columns button and choose More Columns to open the Columns dialog box. Specify the number of columns and a spacing value between columns, and then click OK.

Default text box settings

Objective 2.6.8

After you have formatted a text box, you can define its settings as the new defaults. To do so:

1 Verify that the desired text box is selected. If the text box has no fill, you'll need to select the edge.

2 Right-click the selected text box and choose Set as Default Text Box.

Changing the shape of a text box

As with other objects, you can change the shape of a text box to another shape. Here's how:

Objective 2.6.3

1 Select the text box you want to change.

2 Verify that the Drawing Tools | Format tab is active.

3 In the Insert Shapes group, click the Edit Shape button and point to Change Shape to display the gallery.

4 Select the shape you want to use. The new shape replaces the old one, but retains any formatting you had applied to the old shape.

Do it!

C-4: Formatting text boxes

Objectives 2.5.2, 2.6.1

Here's how	Here's why
1 Click the **Format** tab	(Under Drawing Tools.) The text box must be selected for this tab to appear.
2 Click the **Shape Fill** arrow and choose a light blue color	To apply the fill color to the text box.
3 Click the **Shape Outline** arrow and choose a dark blue color	To apply the outline color to the text box.
4 Click the **Shape Outline** arrow and choose **Weight, 3 pt**	To increase the outline's weight (thickness).
Objective 2.6.4 5 Click **Shape Effects**, point to **Bevel**, and click the Cool Slant bevel effect, as shown	 To apply a bevel effect.
6 Click the **Home** tab	You'll change the text box's margin settings.
7 Click [Align Text ▾] and choose **More Options...**	(In the Paragraph group.) To open the Format Text Effects dialog box.
8 Under Internal margin, change the Left and Right values to **0.2**	To increase the left and right margins in the text box, thereby increasing the box's width, too.
9 Verify that the Top and Bottom values are set to **0.05**	
Click **Close**	The text might be forced to two lines. You'll change the text box's height.
10 Set the text box's height to **7.2** inches	Click the Drawing Tools	Format tab. In the Size group, enter 7.2 in the Shape Height box.
11 Set the text box's width to **1.1** inches	

12 Move the text box up   If necessary.

    Center align the text

13 Create another text box as shown

                                          Click the Insert tab, click Text Box, and drag to
                                          draw the text box.

14 Type **Dale** and press (↵ ENTER)

15 Enter the remaining cities as
   shown

Dale
Denver
Fresno
Portland
Seattle
Tucson

16 Format the city names as Times
   New Roman, 44 pt

Objective 2.5.3   17 Click ⟨bullets icon⟩   (The Bullets button is in the Paragraph group.)
                                          To apply bullet formatting to the selected items.

                                          You'll display the city names in two columns.

Objective 2.6.6   18 Click ⟨columns icon⟩   (The Columns button is in the Paragraph group.)
                                          To display the Columns list.

    Choose **Two Columns**

19 Resize the text box as shown

• Dale   • Portland
• Denver   • Seattle
• Fresno   • Tucson

                                          (Point to the bottom-right sizing handle and drag
                                          up.) The text is displayed in two columns.

20 Update and close the presentation

Unit summary: Using drawing objects

Topic A   In this topic, you used the drawing tools to create **basic shapes**.

Topic B   In this topic, you applied formatting to selected objects. Next, you **duplicated**, deleted, and **moved objects**. Then, you **modified objects** by resizing and rotating them. Finally, you aligned multiple objects with one another.

Topic C   In this topic, you added **text** to an object, formatted text in an object, and created and formatted **text boxes**.

Independent practice activity

In this activity, you'll draw an object, add text to it, apply formatting, and rotate it. Then you'll create a text box, and position both the object and text box on the slide.

1 Create a new presentation. Change the slide layout for the first slide to Blank.

2 On the Home tab, in the Drawing group, display the Shapes gallery and click the Horizontal Scroll shape (located under Stars and Banners).

3 Drag to draw the shape across the slide.

4 Apply the shape style of your choice. Apply a fill color, an outline color, and effects of your choosing. (*Hint:* Use the Drawing Tools | Format tab.)

5 Add the text **Employee of the Month** to the banner object. Apply the formatting of your choice to the text. Resize the banner object to display all of the text on one line, if necessary.

6 Draw a text box at the bottom of the slide, add the text **Award**, and apply the formatting of your choice.

7 Use the rotation handle to rotate the banner object slightly.

8 Align the banner object with the center of the slide. (*Hint:* On the Drawing Tools | Format tab, click Align and choose Align Center and Align Middle.)

9 Move the Award text box near the banner. Compare your slide to Exhibit 4-7.

10 Save the presentation as **My employee presentation** in the current unit summary folder.

11 Close the presentation.

Exhibit 4-7: Employee of the Month banner object and Award text box.

Review questions

1 To draw a shape on a slide, which tab do you use?

   A Home

   B Design

   C Animations

   D Slide Show

2 After an object is drawn, how can you change its shape?

   Select the object. Click the Drawing Tools | Format tab. Click the Edit Shape button, choose Change Shape, and select the desired shape.

3 To change fill colors and outline colors and apply effects to a selected shape, you use the commands in which group?

   A Insert Shapes

   B Shape Styles

   C Design

   D Formatting

4 List the two methods you can use to duplicate an object (without using Copy and Paste).

   In the Home tab's Clipboard group, click Copy and choose Duplicate, or press Ctrl+D.

5   When you select an object, the _____ handle and _____ handles appear around it.

rotation, sizing

6   List the steps you would perform to change the height and width of an object by dragging.

a   *Select the object.*

b   *Point to one of the corner sizing handles.*

c   *Drag the sizing handle until the object reaches the size you want; then release the mouse button.*

7   To rotate an object to a specific angle, you select the object and then do which of the following?

A   In the Size group, place the insertion point in the Rotate box, enter the desired angle, and press Enter.

B   In the Shape Styles gallery, select the angle you want.

C   Click the Align button and choose Rotate. In the Rotate dialog box, enter the desired angle in the Rotation box and click Close.

D   In the Size group, click the Dialog Box Launcher to open the Format Shape dialog box with the Size tab active. Enter the desired angle in the Rotation box, and click Close.

8   What is the difference between a grid and guides?

A grid is a set of intersecting lines that appear on a slide and are not movable. Guides are a pair of horizontal and vertical lines that are movable.

9   How do you add text to an object?

Select the object and begin typing.

10   List the steps you use to draw a text box on a slide.

a   *Click the Text Box button in the Home tab's Drawing group, the Insert tab's Text group, or the Drawing Tools | Format tab's Insert Shapes group.*

b   *Drag the mouse pointer to create a text box.*

c   *Type the text you want to add.*

d   *Resize and move the text box as necessary.*

Unit 5

Working with graphics

Unit time: 45 minutes

Complete this unit, and you'll know how to:

A Create visually appealing text objects by using WordArt.

B Add images to a slide and modify the images by using options on the Picture Tools | Format tab.

C Add clip art images to a slide by using the Clip Art task pane, and modify the clip art images.

Topic A: WordArt

This topic covers the following Microsoft Office Specialist exam objectives for PowerPoint 2010.

#	Objective
2.5	**Enter and format text**
	2.5.1 Use text effects
3.1	**Manipulate graphical elements**
	3.1.3 Resize graphical elements
	3.1.4 Apply effects to graphical elements
	3.1.5 Apply styles to graphical elements
3.3	**Modify WordArt and shapes**
	3.3.3 Change the WordArt

Working with WordArt

Explanation

You can use WordArt to create text that has special formatting applied to it. *WordArt* is a text object that has predefined effects that are applied when you create the object. Exhibit 5-1 shows an example of WordArt.

Exhibit 5-1: An example of WordArt

Adding and editing WordArt

To add a WordArt object:

1   Click the Insert tab.
2   In the Text group, click WordArt to display the WordArt gallery.
3   Select a WordArt style to add a WordArt object in the center of the slide. The text is selected and ready for you to type.
4   Type to enter text in the WordArt object.

You edit the text in a WordArt object just as you would edit text in any other text placeholder. Click it to place the insertion point in the WordArt object, and then start editing. For example, you can type to add text, drag to select the desired text, or press Ctrl+A to select all of the text.

Resizing and rotating WordArt

Objective 3.1.3

You can resize and rotate WordArt just as you would a graphic or any other drawn object. Select the object to display the rotation handle and sizing handles, and then do any of the following:

- Drag a corner sizing handle to change the object's height and width, causing the text to re-flow within the object.
- Drag a sizing handle on the left or right side of the object to change only the width.
- Drag a sizing handle on the top or bottom of the object to change only the height.
- Drag the rotation handle to change the angle of the object.

A-1:   Adding and modifying WordArt

Here's how	Here's why
1 Create a new, blank presentation	
Save the presentation as **My website announcement**	In Student Data folder Unit 5\Topic A.
2 In the title placeholder, enter **Outlander Spices**	
In the subtitle placeholder, enter **New Website Launch**	You are creating a presentation that will introduce Outlander Spices' new Web site.
3 Add a new slide with the Title Only layout	
4 In the title placeholder, enter **Redesigned Website**	To give the slide a title.
5 Click the **Insert** tab	
Observe the Text group	It contains the WordArt button.
6 Click **WordArt**	To display the WordArt gallery.
Observe the WordArt gallery	It contains a variety of WordArt styles.
Select the **Fill – White, Outline – Accent 1** style	(Located in the top row, fourth from the left.) To insert a WordArt object, formatted with WordArt Style 1, on the center of the slide.
7 Observe the WordArt object	The placeholder text is selected and formatted with the desired style. As soon as you begin typing, the text will be replaced.
8 Type **Launches**	To replace the placeholder text.

9   Verify that the insertion point is at the end of the line

As long as you haven't deselected the object, the insertion point should still be in place. If it isn't, click the text and use the arrow keys to place the insertion point at the end of the line.

10 Press (SPACEBAR) and type **Next Week!**

To add more text to the WordArt object. The object might extend off the slide's right edge.

11 Point to any edge of the WordArt object

(Don't point to a handle.) The pointer changes to include a four-headed arrow.

Drag to the left

To move the WordArt object near the edge of the slide.

12 Use the rotation handle to drag counterclockwise, as shown

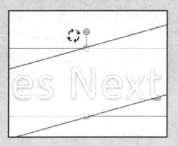

To rotate the object at a slight angle.

13 Deselect the object

14 Update the presentation

Formatting WordArt

Explanation

After you've created a WordArt object, you can edit it, change the WordArt style, and customize it with other formatting.

Selecting WordArt text

Before you apply a new WordArt style, make sure you have selected the text correctly. If you just place the insertion point in the WordArt text and change the WordArt style, the style will be applied to only part of the text, not necessarily to all of it. Instead, you have to select all of the text (drag to select or press Ctrl+A), or select the entire object (point to the edge of the WordArt object, and click when the insertion point changes to include a four-headed arrow).

Using the WordArt Styles group

Objectives 3.1.4, 3.1.5, 3.3.3

After the WordArt object is selected (or the text in the WordArt object is selected), the Drawing Tools | Format tab appears. In the WordArt Styles group, click Quick Styles to display a gallery of WordArt styles. Then point to a style to see the Live Preview, or select a style to apply it.

The WordArt Styles group includes the Text Fill, Text Outline, and Text Effects buttons. The following table describes them.

Button	Description
A Text Fill ▾	Click the button's arrow to display a gallery. Use this gallery to change the text's fill color, remove the fill, or add a gradient or a texture.
Text Outline ▾	Click the button's arrow to display a gallery. Use this gallery to change the text's outline color and other options.
A Text Effects ▾	Click the button to display a menu. Each menu item displays a gallery that you can use to apply specific effects, such as Shadow, Reflection, Glow, Bevel, 3-D Rotation, and Transform.

Objective 2.5.1 (for Text Effects row)

Applying WordArt to text

Objective 2.5.1

Besides creating WordArt by using the WordArt button, you can also apply a WordArt style to existing text, such as the text in a title placeholder. To do so, select the text; in the WordArt Styles group on the Drawing Tools | Format tab, click Quick Styles and select a style.

After the WordArt style is applied, you can change it or add other formatting by changing the font color or the outline color or by applying additional effects.

Do it! **A-2: Applying WordArt styles**

Here's how	Here's why
1 In the WordArt object, place the insertion point in the word **Next**	You'll change the formatting by using the commands in the WordArt Styles group.
Click the **Format** tab	(Under Drawing Tools.) If necessary.
Objective 3.3.3 2 In the WordArt Styles group, click the More button	To display the gallery.
Under Applies to Selected Text, click the **Fill – Olive Green, Accent 3, Outline – Text 2** style	(The last style in the top row.) To apply the style to the object.
3 Observe the WordArt object	
	Because you placed the insertion point in a single word, instead of selecting all of the text (Ctrl+A) or selecting the object (clicking the edge of the object), the formatting was applied to only the one word.
4 Point to the edge of the WordArt object	The pointer changes to include a four-pointed arrow.
Click once	To select the WordArt object. You could also drag to select all the text in the object.
Apply the **Fill – Olive Green, Accent 3, Outline – Text 2** style	All of the text is formatted.
Objectives 3.1.4, 3.1.5 5 Display the Text Fill gallery	(In the WordArt Styles group, click the Text Fill arrow.) You use this gallery to apply a font fill.
Display the Text Outline gallery	(In the WordArt Styles group, click the Text Outline arrow.) You use this gallery to specify the outline color and other outline formatting.
Objective 2.5.1 Display the Text Effects menu	(In the WordArt Styles group, click Text Effects.) Each submenu contains a gallery that you can use to apply specific effects.

6	Point to **Glow**	(In the Text Effects menu.) You are going to add a glow effect to the WordArt object.
	Under Glow Variations, in the third column, click the first glow variation	The Olive Green, 5 pt glow, Accent color 3 style.
7	Deselect the WordArt object	
8	Select **Redesigned Website**	(Triple-click the text in the title placeholder.) The Drawing Tools Format group is still active. You'll apply a Word Art Style to this text.
9	Apply the WordArt style **Fill – Tan, Text 2, Outline – Background 2**	(The first style in the top row.) In the WordArt Styles group, click Quick Styles and select the style.
10	Click **Text Effects** and point to **Shadow**	To display the Shadow effects gallery.
	Select the **Offset Diagonal Bottom Right** effect	(The first shadow effect under Outer.) To apply a shadow to the "Redesign Website" text.
11	Click the **Text Fill** arrow and select **Olive Green, Accent 3**	The Olive Green, Accent 3 swatch is a green color in the first row under Theme colors. It is the seventh swatch from the left.
12	Deselect the text	
13	Update and close the presentation	

Topic B: Pictures

This topic covers the following Microsoft Office Specialist exam objectives for PowerPoint 2010.

#	Objective
3.1	**Manipulate graphical elements**
	3.1.1 Arrange graphical elements
3.2	**Manipulate images**
	3.2.1 Apply color adjustments
	3.2.2 Apply image corrections
	3.2.3 Add artistic effects to an image
	3.2.4 Remove a background
	3.2.5 Crop a picture
	3.2.6 Compress selected pictures or all pictures
	3.2.7 Change a picture
	3.2.8 Reset a picture
7.2	**Share a presentation**
	7.2.4 Compress media

Using images in a presentation

Explanation

You can use images to convey ideas and information that can be difficult to express in words. With that in mind, it's a good idea to add images to a presentation whenever they will be useful. After you insert an image on a slide, you might be able to increase the visual appeal of that image by modifying it.

Inserting pictures

To insert a picture file:

1 Click the Insert tab.

2 In the Images group, click the Picture button to open the Insert Picture dialog box.

3 Navigate to the appropriate folder and select the desired file.

4 Click Insert.

You can also use a slide layout to insert a picture. Here's how:

1 Insert a new slide with the Title and Content, Two Content, Comparison, Content with Caption, or Picture with Caption layout, or change the layout of an existing slide to one of those layout styles. In those layouts, the middle of the slide has an icon you can click to insert a picture, as well as icons for other inserting other types of content.

2 On the slide, click the Picture icon to open the Insert Picture dialog box.

3 Locate and select the desired file.

4 Click Insert.

After you insert a picture, it is selected automatically. A frame surrounds it, as shown in Exhibit 5-2, and sizing handles appear at each corner.

Exhibit 5-2: A selected picture

Do it! **B-1: Inserting a picture**

The files for this activity are in Student Data folder **Unit 5\Topic B**.

Here's how	Here's why
1 Open Website announcement	In the current topic folder.
Save the presentation as **My website announcement**	
2 Move to slide 2	
3 Click the **Insert** tab	
4 In the Images group, click **Picture**	To open the Insert Picture dialog box.
Navigate to the current topic folder and select **Website**	This is a JPEG file provided by the IT department. They've completed the updated version of the Outlander Spices Web site.
5 Click **Insert**	To insert the picture on the slide.
6 Observe the slide	The slide title is visible, but the "Launch Next Month!" WordArt object is under the picture.
7 Observe the picture	The picture is selected and displays a rotation handle and sizing handles.
8 Observe the Ribbon	The Picture Tools | Format tab is active. This is a contextual tab that appears when you select a placed picture file.
9 Update the presentation	

Working with pictures

Explanation

Office 2010 offers many features that you can use to modify pictures. These features are found on the Picture Tools | Format tab, shown in Exhibit 5-3, and are divided among the Adjust, Picture Styles, Arrange, and Size groups.

Exhibit 5-3: The Picture Tools | Format tab (shown in two overlapping parts)

The Adjust group

The Adjust group contains most of the tools you'll use to edit the selected image, including Remove Background, Corrections, Color, Artistic Effects, Compress Pictures, Change Picture, and Reset Picture.

Remove Background

Objective 3.2.4

The Remove Background tool is used to edit out portions of the selected image. Click this button to display the Background Removal tab on the Ribbon (it's context-sensitive) and to automatically select portions of the image. Use the active selection box to indicate what you want to edit. When you're finished adjusting the selection, click either the Mark Areas to Keep button or the Mark Areas to Remove button. Then click Keep Changes to accept the edits, or click Discard All Changes to reject the edits.

Corrections

Objective 3.2.2

To change a picture's brightness, contrast, or sharpness, select the image and click Corrections to display the gallery. Point to one of the Sharpen and Soften presets or one of the Brightness and Contrast presets to see the settings applied to the selected picture using Live Preview. Click the desired preset to apply it. After you've selected a Sharpen and Soften preset, you can open the gallery again and select one of the Brightness and Contrast presets, and both will be applied.

If you want to avoid the presets and make custom corrections, display the Corrections gallery and choose Picture Corrections Options to open the Format Picture dialog box with the Picture Corrections tab active. As you change various settings, you can see them applied to the selected image via Live Preview. Click Close to accept the changes.

Color

Objective 3.2.1

When you insert an image onto a slide, it's important that the picture match the presentation's theme, but sometimes the two color schemes will clash. To overcome this obstacle, select the picture and click Color. In the gallery, select one of the Color Saturation, Color Tone, or Recolor presets. You can apply one preset from each of the three categories.

To apply custom colorization, select the picture, display the Color gallery, and choose either More Variations or Picture Color Options. The More Variations submenu opens a gallery of colors you can use to tint the selection. The Picture Color Options command opens the Format Picture dialog box with the Picture Color tab active. Specify your settings, and click Close to accept the changes.

To set one color in the selected picture as transparent, select the image, display the Color gallery, and choose Set Transparent Color. The mouse pointer changes to indicate that you can now click a color within the selected image. After you click, that color is removed from the picture, and the mouse pointer returns to its normal state.

Artistic Effects

Objective 3.2.3

An interesting new feature in PowerPoint 2010 is the Artistic Effects tool, which contains 22 presets you can use to alter an image. Select the picture and click Artistic Effects to display the gallery. Then, using Live Preview, point to each preset to see what the image would look like if it were drawn in pencil, sketched with chalk, photocopied, and so on. Once you've decided on a preset, click to apply it to the picture.

Compress Pictures

Objectives 3.2.6, 7.2.4

Images can be an integral part of a slide show, but adding them will increase the presentation's file size. To minimize this disadvantage, you can use the Compress Pictures tool to reduce the file size while maintaining image quality. Select the picture(s) and click the Compress Pictures button to open the Compress Pictures dialog box. Specify compression and output settings, and click OK.

Change Picture

Objective 3.2.7

Let's say you've taken the time to resize an image and apply formatting to it. You have it just the way you want it, but now you've been asked to replace the picture with another. In this scenario, you can use the Change Picture tool to quickly replace the image while maintaining the size and formatting. Select the image and click the Change Picture button to open the Insert Picture dialog box. Navigate to and select the desired file, and click Insert.

Reset Picture

Objective 3.2.8

To remove the formatting applied to an image, select the picture and click the Reset Picture button. The image returns to its original state.

The Picture Styles, Arrange, and Size groups

The following table describes some of the options in the Picture Styles, Arrange, and Size groups on the Picture Tools | Format tab.

Button	Group	Description
Picture Border	Picture Styles	Displays the Picture Border gallery, used to apply a border to the selected picture. Select a border color, change the border, or remove the border.
Picture Effects	Picture Styles	Displays the Picture Effects gallery, used to add effects to a picture, such as shadow, reflection, glow, soft edges, and 3-D rotation effects.
Bring Forward	Arrange	Brings the selected object forward one position in the stacking order. Click the down-arrow and choose Bring to Front to bring the selected object in front of all other objects on the slide.
Send Backward	Arrange	Sends the selected object back one position in the stacking order. Click the down-arrow and choose Send to Back to send the selected object behind all other objects on the slide.
Selection Pane	Arrange	Displays the Selection pane, which you can use to select objects, change their stacking order, or hide or show objects.
Crop	Size	Used to hide part of an image. Click the tool to activate it; the mouse pointer changes to include the crop icon. Point to the edge of a picture and drag to hide a portion of it.

Objective 3.2.5

The Picture Tools | Format tab's Arrange group also includes Align, Group, and Rotate buttons, which each display a menu of options for working with pictures.

Do it!

B-2:   Adjusting pictures

Here's how	Here's why
1 Verify that the picture is selected and the Picture Tools | Format tab is active	
2 In the Adjust group, click **Corrections**	To display the Corrections gallery.
Point to each preset	(In the gallery.) To see the Live Preview applied to the picture.
Under Sharpen and Soften, click **Sharpen: 25%**	To increase the sharpness applied to the picture.
3 Display the Corrections gallery	Click Corrections.
Under Brightness and Contrast, select **Brightness: 0% (Normal) Contrast: –20%**	Under Brightness and Contrast, click the preset in the second row, third from the left to reduce the contrast by 20%.
4 Display the Corrections gallery and choose **Picture Corrections Options...**	To open the Format Picture dialog box with the Picture Corrections tab active. You'll apply a custom picture correction.
5 Under Sharpen and Soften, drag the slider to the left, as shown	To change the Sharpen value to 10%.
Under Brightness and Contrast, change the Contrast to **–10%**	
Click **Close**	To accept the changes.
6 Click **Picture Effects** and point to **Shadow**	(In the Picture Styles group.) To display the Shadow gallery.
Click the **Offset Right** effect, as shown	To apply a shadow to the picture.

Objective 3.2.2

7 Click **Picture Effects** and point to **Bevel**

To display the Bevel gallery.

Click **Cool Slant**

(Under Bevel, click the fourth preset in the first row.) To give the picture's edge more definition.

8 Deselect and observe the picture

You've increased the sharpness, reduced the contrast, added a shadow, and applied a beveled edge to the image.

Next, you'll add a picture of a spice container.

At the last minute, it has been decided that each page of the Web site will contain pictures of Outlander Spices bottles. There isn't time to get a new screen shot for your presentation, so the Marketing department wants you to add a spice bottle to the picture you already have.

9 Insert the **Spice bottle** image

On the Insert tab, click Picture. In the current topic folder, click Spice bottle, and click Insert.

10 In the Adjust group, click **Color** and choose **Set Transparent Color**

11 Point to the slide

The pointer changes to indicate that you can now click a color within the picture to set that color to transparent.

Objective 3.2.1

12 Point to the white area behind the bottle

Click the white area

To make it transparent. The image behind the bottle is now visible through the area that you set to transparent. However, a white fringe appears around the bottle.

13 Move the bottle to a white area on the slide

You'll make some additional changes.

14 In the Size group, change the Height to **0.75** and press `↵ ENTER`

Height: 0.75"
Crop Width: 0.36"
Size

When you press Enter, the width value is changed to keep the image proportional.

15 Zoom in

(Use the Zoom In button on the status bar.) To view the image.

16 Rotate the bottle as shown

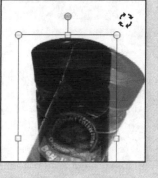

17 Move the bottle as shown

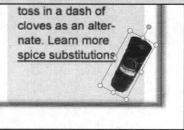

toss in a dash of cloves as an alternate. Learn more spice substitutions

Place the bottle in the bottom-right corner of the Website image.

18 Deselect all images

19 View the entire slide

On the status bar, click the "Fit slide to current window" button.

20 Update the presentation

Arranging and grouping items

Explanation

Objective 3.1.1

When a slide contains several items, you might need to arrange them so that they overlap one another the way you want. In addition, you might want to group items so that you can select them as a single item.

Adjusting the stacking order

By default, newer items you add to a slide appear in front of older items where they overlap. The order in which items overlap one another is called the *stacking order*. To modify the stacking order, select the item whose stacking order you want to change, and select an option from the Arrange group, which appears on several tabs. You can click the Bring Forward or Send Backward buttons to move an object, or you can click either button's arrow to display a list with additional options for adjusting the stacking order.

Grouping items

If you position several items on a slide, and you want them to maintain their positions relative to one another, you can group them. In this way, you can select them as a single item and move them together. To group items, select them, click the Group button, and choose Group. You can ungroup selected items by clicking the Group button and choosing Ungroup.

Do it!

Objective 3.1.1

B-3:   Arranging and grouping overlapping items

Here's how	Here's why
1 Select the WordArt object	You'll move this object in front of the other items.
Click the **Format** tab	(Under Drawing Tools.) If necessary.
2 In the Arrange group, click **Bring Forward**	(Not the arrow.) To move the item forward one place in the stacking order.
3 In the Arrange group, click **Selection Pane**	To display the Selection and Visibility pane.
Observe the stacking order	The bottle is at the top of the stacking order, followed by the WordArt object (which is selected), the Website picture, and the slide title.
Close the Selection and Visibility pane	Click the pane's Close button.
4 Verify that the WordArt object is selected	Click the edge of the placeholder, if necessary.
Set the font size to **66**	
5 Move the WordArt object over the center of the Website picture, as shown	
	(Point to the WordArt object's border and drag.) Putting the WordArt over the picture may look odd now, but after you add animation to the slide, it will make more sense when you're playing the slide show for your audience.
6 Select the Website picture and the bottle	With only the Website picture selected, press Ctrl and click the bottle image.
Click the **Format** tab	(Under Picture Tools.) If necessary.
7 In the Arrange group, click [⊡ Group ▾]	To display the Group menu.
Choose **Group**	To combine the Website picture and bottle into one selection. The picture frame has changed. Both the Drawing Tools	Format and Picture Tools	Format tabs are now available. Because the bottle was at the top of the stacking order, the group is above the WordArt object.

This slide will have animation applied to it, so the slide appears with just the Website picture. Then the WordArt object will be animated to appear for a short time.

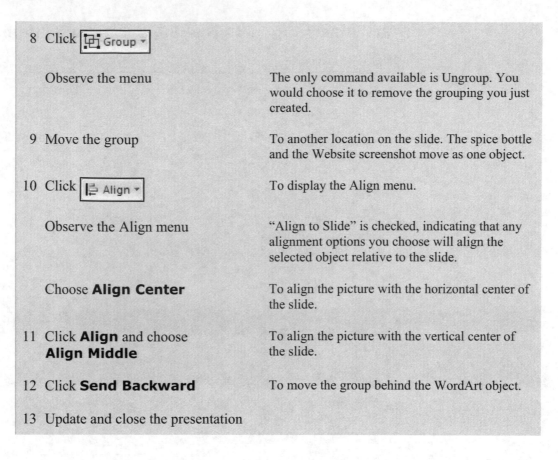

8 Click [Group ▾]

   Observe the menu

The only command available is Ungroup. You would choose it to remove the grouping you just created.

9 Move the group

To another location on the slide. The spice bottle and the Website screenshot move as one object.

10 Click [Align ▾]

To display the Align menu.

   Observe the Align menu

"Align to Slide" is checked, indicating that any alignment options you choose will align the selected object relative to the slide.

   Choose **Align Center**

To align the picture with the horizontal center of the slide.

11 Click **Align** and choose **Align Middle**

To align the picture with the vertical center of the slide.

12 Click **Send Backward**

To move the group behind the WordArt object.

13 Update and close the presentation

Topic C: Clip art

This topic covers the following Microsoft Office Specialist exam objective for PowerPoint 2010.

#	Objective
3.1	**Manipulate graphical elements**
	3.1.1 Arrange graphical elements
	3.1.2 Position graphical elements
	3.1.3 Resize graphical elements

Adding clip art

Explanation

In addition to purchasing or creating your own image files to add to your presentations, you can add clip art objects. Some clip art objects are included with the Office Suite and PowerPoint and are stored on your computer. Additional clip art objects are available on the Web.

To add clip art to a slide:

1 Insert a slide with the Title and Content, Two Content, Comparison, or Content with Caption layout, or change the layout of an existing slide to one of those layout styles. When you do, the middle of the slide will contain icons you can use to insert a table, chart, clip art, picture, SmartArt graphic, or movie.

2 Click the Clip Art icon to open the Clip Art pane.

3 In the Clip Art pane, display the "Results should be" list and check the media types you want to search for. Close the list.

4 In the Search for box, enter a description and click Go. The results of the search are displayed in the pane.

5 Insert the desired image on the slide by doing one of the following:

- Click the image.

- Drag the image onto the slide.

- Click the down-arrow and choose Insert.

You can also insert a clip art object on any slide by clicking the Insert tab and then clicking the Clip Art button in the Images group.

After you insert a clip art object, like the one shown in Exhibit 5-4, select it. Then you can resize and format it as you would a picture file or a drawn shape.

Exhibit 5-4: A slide with a clip art object added

Do it!

C-1: Inserting and modifying clip art

The files for this activity are in Student Data folder **Unit 5\Topic C**.

Here's how	Here's why
1 Open Launch plan	From the current topic folder.
Save the presentation as **My launch plan**	
2 Insert a new slide with the Title and Content layout	At the end of the presentation.
In the title placeholder, enter **Launch Plan**	
3 Observe the icons in the middle of the slide	There are six icons that you can use to add a table, chart, clip art, picture, SmartArt graphic, or movie.
4 Click the **Clip Art** icon, as shown	To display the Clip Art pane on the right side of the application window.

	5 In the Clip Art pane, display the **Results should be** list	(Click the arrow to the right of the list.) You can search for four types of media: Illustrations, Photographs, Videos, and Audio.
	Clear **Illustrations**, **Videos**, and **Audio**	Only Photographs is checked.
	Close the list	Click the arrow again.
If students do not check "Include Office.com content," their results will be limited.	6 Check **Include Office.com content**	(If necessary.) Under the "Results should be" list.
	7 In the Search for box, enter **computer wrapped in red bow**	You are looking for an image that goes with the "Launch Plan" slide.
	Click **Go**	(Or press Enter.) To search the Clip Art collections on your computer and at Office.com. The search results are displayed in the Clip Art pane.
	8 Point to the computer clip art image, as shown	
		If you click the image, it will appear on the slide, and the content placeholder will be removed. To add the clip art image and keep the placeholder for adding text later, you'll drag the clip art onto the slide.
	Drag the image onto the slide	To add the clip art to the slide without deleting the content placeholder.
	9 Close the Clip Art pane	Click the Close button.
⚠ *If the content placeholder is selected as well, have student deselect and then select the clip art image.*	10 Verify that the computer clip art is selected and the Picture Tools | Format tab is active	
	11 In the Size group, change the Height **4** inches	Select the number in the Height box and type 4.
Objective 3.1.3	Press ⏎ ENTER	To also change the width of the image and maintain proportions.
Objective 3.1.2	12 Move the image to the bottom-right corner of the content placeholder	

Computer wrapped in red bow
Provided By: iStockphoto
756 (w) x 1050 (h) pixels | 150 DPI | 264 KB | JPG

13 Place the insertion point in the content placeholder text	You'll finish the slide by adding text.

Enter the text shown

- Go live next Monday
- Press Kits to industry publications on Friday
- Online advertising campaign
- Customer e-mail lists
- Launch Party next Friday

14 Move the clip art image	(If necessary.) To show all of the text.
15 Double-click the clip art image	To select the image and activate the Picture Tools | Format tab.

Objective 3.1.1

16 In the Arrange group, click **Rotate**	To display the Rotate menu.
Choose **Flip Horizontal**	To flip the image left to right. The back of the computer now points to the edge of the slide.
17 Deselect the image	Compare your slide to Exhibit 5-4.

Update and close the presentation

Unit summary: Working with graphics

Topic A   In this topic, you added a **WordArt** object to a slide. Then you modified a WordArt object by applying different styles.

Topic B   In this topic, you inserted **pictures**. You also adjusted and modified pictures and grouped items together.

Topic C   In this topic, you inserted and modified a **clip art object**.

Independent practice activity

In this activity, you'll create and modify a WordArt object. Then, you'll add a slide, enter text, and insert a clip art image. Next, you'll add image files and modify them.

The files for this activity are in Student Data folder **Unit 5\Unit summary**.

1 Create a new presentation, starting with a blank slide.

2 Create a WordArt text object with the text **Keys To Our Success** and the WordArt style of your choice.

3 Make the WordArt text bigger, and move it to the center of the slide. Modify the WordArt style with the formatting of your choice.

4 Insert a new slide with the Title and Content layout.

5 In the title placeholder, type **Keys To Our Success**.

6 Insert clip art of your choice without removing the content placeholder. (*Hint:* Drag the clip art from the Clip Art pane onto the slide.)

7 In the bulleted list, enter five items, as shown in Exhibit 5-5.

8 Save the presentation as **My success** in the current Unit summary folder. Then close the presentation.

9 Open Practice images.

10 Save the presentation as **My practice images**.

11 On the second slide, insert the Bay Leaf image from the current Unit summary folder, and move the image to center it below the title. Using the Corrections tool, soften the image. Then change the Brightness and Contrast to hide the background.

12 On the third slide, insert the Black Pepper image. Center it below the title. Using the Color tool, change the saturation and tone. Then recolor the image.

13 On the fourth slide, insert the Cinnamon image. Center it below the title. Using the Artistic Effects tool, apply the Pastels Smooth preset.

14 On the fifth slide, insert the Garlic image. Move the image and modify it with the options of your choice.

15 On the sixth slide, insert the Nutmeg image. Move the image and modify it with the options of your choice.

16 On the seventh slide, insert the Red Chili Pepper image. Move the image and modify it with the options of your choice.

17 Update and close the presentation.

18 Close the Clip Art panel, if necessary.

Exhibit 5-5: The slide after Step 7

Review questions

1 Which Ribbon tab contains the WordArt button?

A Home

B Insert

C Design

D Animations

2 How do you edit WordArt text?

You edit the text in a WordArt object just as you would edit text in any other text placeholder. Click it to place the insertion point in the WordArt object, and then start editing.

3 What is a quick and easy way to apply a new set of formats to a WordArt object?

Select the WordArt object. On the Drawing Tools | Format tab, in the WordArt Styles group, click Quick Styles and select a style.

4 True or false? You can apply WordArt styles to existing text, such as a slide title.

True

5 How do you open the Insert Picture dialog box?

Click the Insert tab and click the Picture button in the Images group; or click the Picture icon in the middle of a slide.

6 How do you add a shadow to an imported picture?

Select the picture, and click the Picture Tools | Format tab. Click Picture Effects, point to Shadow, and click a shadow style to apply it.

7 True or false? After inserting a clip art image, you can't resize it but you can format it as you would a picture file or a drawn image.

False

8 True or false? You can use PowerPoint to search clip art collections stored on your computer, as well as collections on Office.com.

True

Unit 6

Using tables and charts

Unit time: 45 minutes

Complete this unit, and you'll know how to:

A Add a table to a presentation, enter text in the table, and format the table.

B Create and modify a chart by using the Insert Chart dialog box and the Chart Tools tabs.

C Create and modify SmartArt objects.

Topic A: Tables

This topic covers the following Microsoft Office Specialist exam objective for PowerPoint 2010.

#	Objective
4.1	**Construct and modify a table**
	4.1.3 Set table style options
	4.1.4 Add shading
	4.1.6 Add effects
	4.1.7 Manipulate columns and rows

Using tables

Explanation

You can add a table to any slide in your presentation. While working on a table, you can also modify it by inserting or deleting rows or columns.

A table consists of rows and columns. The intersection of a row and a column is called a *cell*. You can add text or numbers to a cell. Exhibit 6-1 shows the structure of a table.

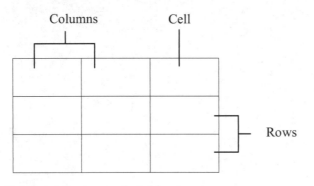

Exhibit 6-1: A sample table structure

Adding tables

There are several techniques you can use to add tables to a presentation. One way is to use one of the slide layouts that displays the Table icon, such as the Title and Content or the Two Content layouts. Click the Table icon to open the Insert Table dialog box. Enter the number of columns and rows you want, and click OK.

You can also add a table to a slide by using the Table button on the Insert tab:

1 Click the Insert tab.

2 In the Tables group, click Table to display the Table menu.

3 In the Table menu, point to indicate the number of rows and columns you want in the table. As you do, you'll see a Live Preview of the table on the slide.

4 When the table is the size you want, click to add it to the slide.

Another way to add a table to a slide is to specify values in the Insert Table dialog box. Here's how:

1 Click the Insert tab and click Table to display the Table menu.

2 Choose Insert Table to open the Insert Table dialog box.

3 Specify the number of columns and rows you want.

4 Click OK.

A third way to create a table is to draw it:

1 Click the Insert tab and click Table to display the Table menu.

2 Choose Draw Table.

3 Point to the slide and drag to draw the table. At first, it includes a single cell.

4 Drag within the table to create rows and columns.

The Table Tools tabs

After you add a table to a slide, the Table Tools tabs appear. These are the Design and Layout tabs, which you use to modify and format tables. Exhibit 6-2 shows the Table Tools | Design tab.

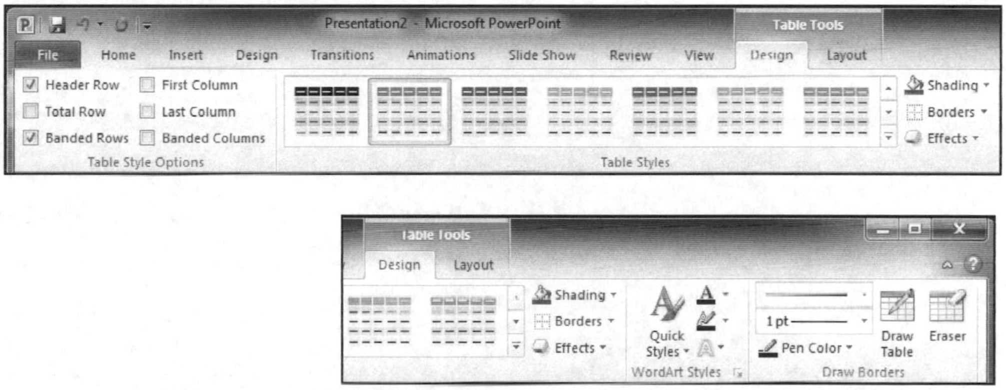

Exhibit 6-2: The Table Tools | Design tab (shown in two overlapping parts)

Adding text to tables

You add text to a table the same way you add text to any other object. Text or numbers are entered in a table's cell. You move from one cell to another by pressing Tab, pressing the arrow keys, or clicking a cell.

When the insertion point is in the last cell of the last row and you press Tab, a new row is added to the table.

Do it!

A-1:   Adding a table

The files for this activity are in Student Data folder **Unit 6\Topic A**.

Here's how	Here's why
1 Open Website announcement1 sales	(From the current topic folder.) You'll insert a table into this presentation.
Save the presentation as **My website announcement1**	
2 After slide 3, insert a new slide with the Title and Content layout	
3 In the title placeholder, enter **Projected Online Sales**	
4 In the content placeholder, click the Table icon, as shown	To open the Insert Table dialog box.
Observe the Insert Table dialog box	You can specify the number of columns and rows in the table.
5 In the Number of columns box, enter **2**	You will insert a table that contains two columns and four rows.
In the Number of rows box, enter **4**	
Click **OK**	The table appears on the slide, and the Table Tools | Design tab is active.
6 Observe the Table Tools tabs	Because a table is selected, the Table Tools tabs (Design and Layout) appear on the Ribbon.
Observe the Design tab	It contains the Table Style Options, Table Styles, WordArt Styles, and Draw Borders groups.
Click the **Layout** tab	It contains the Table, Rows & Columns, Merge, Cell Size, Alignment, Table Size, and Arrange groups.

TIPS *Tell students that they can also use the spin controls to specify the values.*

7   Type **2011**   To place the number in the first cell of the table.

8   Press TAB   To move to the next cell in the table.

    Observe the cell   The insertion point appears in the cell, indicating that you can add text to it.

9   Type **Projected Online Sales**

    Press TAB   To select the first cell in the second row.

10 Type **1st Quarter**

11 Complete the table as shown

2011	Projected Online Sales
1st Quarter	$100,000
2nd Quarter	$120,000
3rd Quarter	$150,000

12 Press TAB   To add a new row and select the first cell in the new row.

13 Type **4th Quarter** and move to the next cell

    Type **$175,000**

14 Update the presentation

Modifying tables

Explanation

While working on a table, you might have to increase or decrease the size and width of a row or column to fit the content. You do this by dragging the row or column boundaries. If you need to insert a new row or column, use the buttons in the Rows & Columns group on the Table Tools | Layout tab, shown in Exhibit 6-3.

Objective 4.1.7

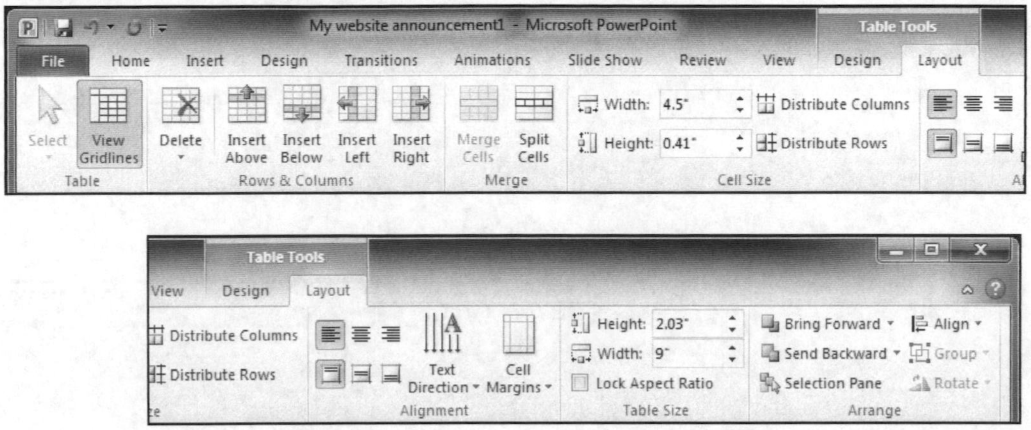

Exhibit 6-3: The Table Tools | Layout tab (shown in two overlapping parts)

The following table lists techniques for adding rows and columns by using the buttons in the Rows & Columns group.

Button	Select a cell and then...
Insert Above	Click Insert Above to insert a new row above the current row.
Insert Below	Click Insert Below to insert a new row below the current row.
Insert Left	Click Insert Left to insert a new column to the left of the current column.
Insert Right	Click Insert Right to insert a new column to the right of the current column.

Objective 4.1.7

To delete a row or a column, select the row or column that you want to delete. In the Rows & Columns group, click Delete to display a menu. Choose Delete Columns or Delete Rows.

A-2:   Modifying a table

Here's how	Here's why
1 Observe the table	Both columns are wider than necessary.
2 Point to the line separating the two columns, as shown	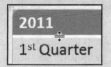
	The pointer changes to indicate that you can now drag to adjust the column width.
Drag the column boundary to the left, as shown	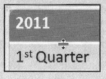
	The width of the second column increases, and the text in the first column fits better. Next, you'll increase the height of the top row.
3 Point to the bottom of the first row, as shown	2011 1ˢᵗ Quarter
	The pointer changes to indicate that you can now drag to adjust the row height.
Drag down slightly, as shown	2011 1ˢᵗ Quarter
	To increase the height of the first row.

4 Point just inside the right edge of the table, as shown

You'll resize the right column without resizing the left column. To resize the table so that both columns resize, you would drag from the right sizing handle.

Drag to the left as shown

2011	Projected Online Sales
1st Quarter	$100,000
2nd Quarter	$120,000
3rd Quarter	$150,000
4th Quarter	$175,000

To reduce the size of the second column and the entire table.

5 Verify that the insertion point is still in the last cell

You'll add a row above the last row.

Verify that the Table Tools | Layout tab is active

6 In the Rows & Columns group, click **Insert Above**

To insert a row above the current row. You won't need the new row, so you'll delete it.

Click **Delete** and choose **Delete Rows**

(In the Rows & Columns group.) To remove the row you just inserted. The first cell in the last row is now selected.

7 Click **Insert Left**

To insert a column to the left of the current column.

Click **Delete** and choose **Delete Columns**

To remove the column you just inserted.

8 Place the insertion point in the last cell

Click **Insert Below**

(Or press Tab.) To add a row at the bottom of the table.

9 Resize the table columns to fit the text

The text should fit on one line within each cell.

10 Add the text in the last row as shown

2011	Projected Online Sales
1st Quarter	$100,000
2nd Quarter	$120,000
3rd Quarter	$150,000
4th Quarter	$175,000
TOTAL	$545,000

11 Update the presentation

Formatting tables

Explanation

Before applying styles and other formatting, you have to be sure that the part of the table you want to format is selected. The following table describes three common selection techniques that you will use with tables.

Selection	Pointer shape	Method
Table		Point to the edge of the table; the mouse pointer changes to include a four-headed arrow. Click to select the entire table.
Row		Just outside the table (on the left or right side), point to a row; the pointer changes to a black arrow. Click to select the row, or click and drag to select multiple rows.
Column		Just outside the table (on the top or bottom), point to a column; the pointer changes to a black arrow. Click to select the column, or click and drag to select multiple columns.

Aligning text in a cell

You can change the horizontal and vertical alignment of text within a cell. To do so, select the desired cell(s), row(s), or columns(s). Click the Table Tools | Layout tab, and in the Alignment group, click the appropriate button. The following table describes the buttons.

Objective 4.1.7

Button Name	Description
Align Text Left	Aligns the selected text to the left side of the cell.
Align Text Right	Aligns the selected text to the right side of the cell.
Center	Aligns the selected text between the left and right edges of the cell.
Align Top	Aligns the selected text to the top of the cell.
Center Vertically	Aligns the selected text between the top and bottom edges of the cell.
Align Bottom	Aligns the selected text to the bottom of the cell.

In addition to changing the text alignment, you can use options in the Alignment group to change text orientation in a cell. In the Alignment group, click Text Direction and choose an option. For example, you can specify that the text in a cell be rotated 90 degrees.

The Table Tools | Design tab

Objective 4.1.3

Most formatting changes you will make in a selected table require you to use the Table Tools | Design tab. It contains several groups.

In the Table Style Options group, check the desired options and clear the ones you don't want. You will immediately see the changes applied to the selected table.

In the Table Styles group, point to a Quick Style to see its Live Preview, and click to apply it. You can also use the Shading, Borders, and Table Effects buttons to change colors and add more interesting formatting.

Do it!

A-3: Formatting a table

Objective 4.1.3

Here's how	Here's why
1 Point to the top of the right column, as shown	**Projected Online Sales** $100,000
Click once	To select the column.
2 Click the **Layout** tab	(Under Table Tools.) If necessary.
3 Click [≡]	(The Center button is in the Alignment group.) To center the text in the column.
4 Point as shown	**2011** 1st Quarter
Click once	To select the row.
5 Click [≡]	(The Center Vertically button is in the Alignment group.) To center the text between the top and bottom edges of the row.
6 Click the **Design** tab	Under Table Tools.
7 In the Table Style Options group, clear **Header Row**	To change the way the top row is formatted.
Experiment with the options	(In the Table Style Options group.) Check and clear each option to see the effect.
Set the options as shown	☑ Header Row ☐ First Column ☑ Total Row ☑ Last Column ☑ Banded Rows ☐ Banded Columns Table Style Options

8	In the Table Styles group, click any style	To apply a table style.

9	Click [🖳 Effects ▾]	(In the Table Styles group.) To display the Table Effects menu.
	Point to **Shadow**	To display the Shadow gallery.
	Select **Offset Diagonal Bottom Right**, as shownA	

Outer

Offset Diagonal Bottom Right

To apply a shadow effect to the table.

10	Click the edge of the table, as shown	

2011

1st Quarter

To select the table.

	Move the table to the slide's center	It doesn't have to be exact.
11	Deselect the table	To view the finished table.
12	Update and close the presentation	

Cell fill options

You can fill table cells with a solid color, a picture, a gradient, or a texture. A cell fill applies to the cell background, behind any text in the cell. You can add cell fills by using the Shading list on the Table Tools | Design tab.

To specify a cell fill, select the cell or cells you want to fill; then click the Shading button's arrow and select a fill type. For example, to add an image to a table cell, click the Shading button's arrow and choose Picture. In the Insert Picture dialog box, select a picture and click Insert. The picture fits to the cell's dimensions, and you can still type to add text in the cell, with the image in the background.

Do it!

Objective 4.1.4

A-4:   Adding images to a table

The files for this activity are in Student Data folder **Unit 6\Topic A**.

Here's how	Here's why
1 Open Spice pricing	In the current topic folder.
Save the presentation as **My spice pricing**	
2 Fit the slide to the current window	If necessary.
3 Go to slide 2	You'll add images to the cells in the first column.
4 Click in the cell below "Spice image"	Next to "Cinnamon."
5 Click the **Design** tab	Under Table Tools.
6 Click the **Shading** arrow, as shown	In the Table Styles group.
Choose **Picture...**	To open the Insert Picture dialog box.
7 Select **Cinnamon**	In the current topic folder.
Click **Insert**	
8 Press ↓	To move the insertion point to the cell below the cinnamon image.
9 Insert the Black Pepper image	Click the Shading arrow and choose Picture. Select Black Pepper and click Insert.
10 In the cell below, insert the Nutmeg image	
11 Update and close the presentation	

Be sure that students navigate to the current topic folder.

Spice image	Spice name	Cost per unit
	Cinnamon	$75
	Black Pepper	$125
	Nutmeg	$175

Topic B: Charts

This topic covers the following Microsoft Office Specialist exam objectives for PowerPoint 2010.

#	Objective
4.2	**Insert and modify a chart**
4.2.1	Select a chart type
4.2.2	Enter chart data
4.2.4	Change the chart layout
4.3	**Apply chart elements**
4.3.1	Use chart labels
4.5	**Manipulate chart elements**
4.5.5	Apply Quick Styles

Creating and modifying charts

Explanation

Charts are graphical representations of numerical data. PowerPoint includes several chart types for you to choose from and includes formatting options you can use to modify them.

Inserting charts

Objective 4.2.1

There are two methods you can use to create a chart: click the Chart icon on a content slide layout; or click the Chart button in the Illustrations group on the Insert tab. Both methods will open the Insert Chart dialog box. In this dialog box, select a chart type in the left pane. In the right pane, select the specific chart you want to create, and click OK. The chart is placed on the slide, and Microsoft Excel 2010 opens.

The sample numerical data is contained in the Excel worksheet, and the corresponding chart is displayed on the PowerPoint slide. Edit the data in Excel to customize the chart, and close Excel when you are done.

Do it!

B-1: Creating a chart

The files for this activity are in Student Data folder **Unit 6\Topic B**.

Objective 4.2.1

Here's how	Here's why
1 Open Website announcement2	
Save the presentation as **My Website announcement2**	
2 At the end of the presentation, insert a new slide with a Title and Content layout	
3 In the title placeholder, type **Comparison Chart**	
4 Click the Chart icon, as shown	
	To open the Insert Chart dialog box.

If students don't see the Insert Chart dialog box, they don't have Excel installed and this activity will not work as described.

Here's how	Here's why
5 In the left pane, select **Pie**	To view the available Pie charts.
Select the second pie chart, as shown	
Click **OK**	Microsoft Excel 2010 starts, and appears alongside the PowerPoint window.

Objective 4.2.2

Here's how	Here's why
6 In Excel, click as shown	
	To select the cell.
Type **Projected Sales**	To add a heading.
Press ⏎ ENTER	To select the cell below.
7 Type **$100**	This represents the $100,000 of revenue that the redesigned Web site is projected to produce in the first quarter.
Press ⏎ ENTER	To select the next cell below.

8 Type **$120**	To specify the value projected for the second quarter sales.
Press (↵ ENTER) and type **$150**	
Press (↵ ENTER) and type **$175**	
9 Click as shown	

	A	B
1	✥	Projected Q
2	1st Qtr	$100

(To select the cell.) Make sure you don't select a cell other than one of the cells that has text or numbers in it.

10 Observe the chart	(In the PowerPoint window.) The pie chart has four slices, plus a legend to the right identifying what each color represents.
11 Close Excel	(Click the Close button.) You're returned to PowerPoint; its window maximizes.
12 Update the presentation	

Changing the chart type

Explanation

Objective 4.2.1

If you want to change the chart type for a chart, click the Chart Tools | Design tab; then, in the Type group, click Change Chart Type. In the Change Chart Type dialog box that appears, specify a new chart type and click OK.

Do it!

Objective 4.2.1

B-2:   Changing the chart type

Here's how	Here's why
1 Verify that the chart is selected	On the slide.
Under Chart Tools, click the **Design** tab	(If necessary.) You'll change the chart type.
2 In the Type group, click **Change Chart Type**	To open the Change Chart Type dialog box.
3 Under Pie, click as shown	To select the "Exploded pie in 3-D" chart type.

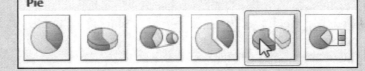

4 Click **OK**	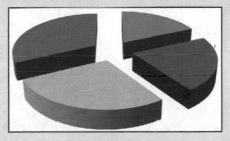

You can drag a slice toward the center to decrease the space between slices. |
| 5 Point to the bottom slice, and drag up |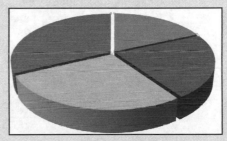

To decrease the space between slices. If a single slice is selected, only that slice will move. To select all slices when dragging, click outside the slices but within the chart's bounding box to deselect all slices; then begin dragging a slice. |
| 6 Update the presentation | |

Formatting charts

Explanation

After entering your data, you might want to modify the chart. You can change the chart formatting and apply styles. You can alter the graphical representation of your data so that it's easier for your audience to comprehend.

You can format each individual chart element or format the entire chart. The commands for formatting charts are found on the Chart Tools tabs, which are the Design, Layout, and Format tabs.

The Chart Tools | Format tab

The Chart Tools | Format tab contains five groups. The Current Selection group contains three options. You can use the Chart Elements list to select specific parts of the chart, or click a chart element and look at this list to identify the selected element. After you've selected a chart element, click the Format Selection button to open the Format dialog box and make the necessary changes.

As with other style groups, you use the Shape Styles group to apply styles, change a shape fill or outline, and apply an effect.

The Chart Tools | Layout tab

Objective 4.2.4

The Chart Tools | Layout tab contains six groups. Use the Insert group to add a shape, a text box, or a picture to the chart. You can use the other groups to add, remove, and edit chart elements.

The chart legend

Objective 4.2.4

When you create a chart, it typically displays a legend by default. However, you can hide or show a legend, and you can change its position. To add, remove, or position the chart legend, click the Chart Tools | Layout tab; in the Labels group, click Legend and choose an option.

Chart labels

Objective 4.3.1

You can add, remove, or position a chart title, along with other chart labels, by using the other options in the Labels group in the Chart Tools | Layout tab. For example, to add, remove, or reposition a chart's title, click the Chart Tools | Layout tab, click Chart Title in the Labels group, and choose an option.

Do it!

B-3: Formatting a chart

Here's how	Here's why
1 Observe the Chart Tools tabs	There are three Chart Tools tabs—Design, Layout, and Format. The Chart Tools | Design tab is selected by default
Objective 4.5.5 2 In the Chart Styles group, click the More button	To display the gallery of layouts.
Click **Style 5**	

3 On the slide, click the Chart Title text	To select the placeholder.
Click the Chart Title text again	
	To place the insertion point in the placeholder.
Edit the text to read **Projected Online Sales**	
4 Click the edge of the chart frame	To deselect the chart title.
5 Click the **Layout** tab	Under Chart Tools. You'll hide the legend.
6 In the Labels group, click **Legend**	To display the Legend list.
Choose **None**	To remove the legend. You'll add the legend, but in a different location.
7 Click **Legend** and choose **Show Legend at Left**	To add the Legend to the left of the chart.
8 Click **Chart Title** and choose **None**	(In the Labels group.) To remove the chart title.
9 Click **Chart Title** and choose **Above Chart**	The chart title returns, but appears as the original title, rather than the version you edited. Next, you'll format an individual pie slice.
10 Click the top-left slice	All slices are selected.
Click the same slice again	To select that slice individually.
11 Click the **Format** tab	Under Chart Tools.
12 Click the **Shape Fill** arrow and select the **Red, Accent 2** color	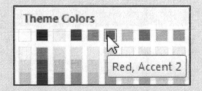
	To change the slice to red.
13 Update and close the presentation	

Objective 4.2.4

Topic C: Diagrams

This topic covers the following Microsoft Office Specialist exam objective for PowerPoint 2010.

#	Objective
3.4	**Manipulate SmartArt**
	3.4.1 Add and remove shapes
	3.4.2 Change SmartArt styles
	3.4.3 Change the SmartArt layout
	3.4.4 Reorder shapes
	3.4.7 Make shapes larger or smaller
	3.4.8 Promote bullet levels
	3.4.9 Demote bullet levels

Creating and modifying SmartArt

Explanation

You can use PowerPoint to create diagrams, such as organization charts, that visually represent relationships or processes.

Diagram types

You insert a diagram by using the Choose a SmartArt Graphic dialog box, shown in Exhibit 6-4. From this dialog box, you can choose from some of the commonly used standard diagrams, such as organization charts, cycle diagrams, or Venn diagrams.

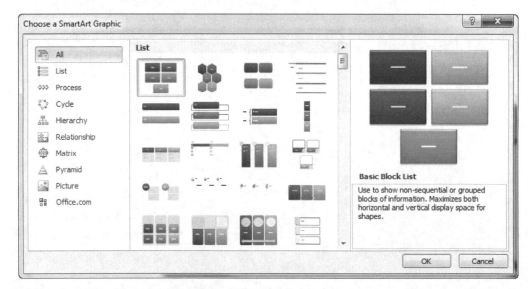

Exhibit 6-4: The Choose a SmartArt Graphic dialog box

The Choose a SmartArt Graphic dialog box divides the diagrams into seven categories, which are described in the following table.

Diagram	Description
List	Shows non-sequential blocks of information, grouped blocks of information, or sequential steps in a task, process, or workflow. For example, use this diagram to show three sales teams that each contain several employees.
Process	Shows steps leading toward a goal. For example, use this diagram to show the steps involved in hiring a new employee.
Cycle	Shows the steps of a cyclical process. For example, use this diagram to describe the process of developing a product, marketing it, and reinvesting profit in further development.
Hierarchy	Shows the hierarchical relationships among elements. For example, use an organization chart to represent the positions in an organization.
Relationship	Shows the relationships among items. For example, use a Venn diagram to show company resources used by two departments, differentiating among shared resources and resources used only in a given department.
Matrix	Shows the relationship of components to a whole in quadrants. For example, use this diagram to display the names of four departments within a division.
Pyramid	Shows containment, foundation-based, hierarchical, interconnected, overlapping, or proportional relationships. For example, use this diagram to display the food groups, arranged from those you should eat often to those you should eat sparingly.

Objective 3.4.3

Creating a hierarchy chart

You can display the hierarchical details of your company by using an organization chart, which is a type of hierarchy chart. After a chart is created, you can add different levels to it, edit it, and change the formatting.

Adding a hierarchy chart

To add a hierarchy chart to a presentation, either add a slide with a content slide layout and click the SmartArt icon, or click the Insert tab and click the SmartArt button in the Illustrations group. When you do, the Choose a SmartArt Graphic dialog box opens. In the left pane, select the chart type, and in the right pane, select a specific chart. Click OK to insert the chart.

The SmartArt Tools tabs

After you insert a diagram, it is selected, a Text Pane is displayed to the left of it, and the SmartArt Tools | Design tab is active, as shown in Exhibit 6-5. There is also a SmartArt Tools | Format tab.

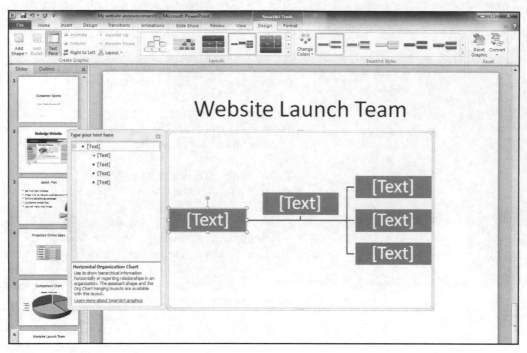

Exhibit 6-5: A hierarchy chart added to a slide

Adding text to a diagram

Objective 3.4.1

To use the Text Pane to add text, click the top bullet item to place the insertion point in that line, and then type to add the text. Click the next bullet item and type to complete that one. Repeat until all the chart boxes are full. The indent level of each item in the Text Pane corresponds to each item's position in the chart. The further an item is indented in the Text Pane, the lower it appears in the chart's hierarchy.

To add another box below a specific box by using the Text Pane:

1 In the Text Pane, place the insertion point to the right of the text corresponding to the box below which you want to add a new item. Press Enter to add another box at the same level.

2 Press Tab to demote the item so its box appears below the initial box in the chart.

3 Type to insert text in the new box.

Objectives 3.4.8, 3.4.9

You can promote an item by clicking its name in the Text Pane and pressing Shift+Tab. To demote an item, place the insertion point in the item's name and press Tab.

If you don't want to use the Text Pane, you can close it by clicking the Text Pane button in the Create Graphics group on the SmartArt Tools | Design tab. You can then select a chart box and type to add text. In addition, you can use the Create Graphic group's options to add, promote, and demote items.

Do it!   ## C-1:   Adding a hierarchy chart

The files for this activity are in Student Data folder **Unit 6\Topic C**.

Here's how	Here's why
1 Open Website announcement3	
Save the presentation as **My Website announcement3**	
2 After slide 5, insert a new slide with the Title Only layout	
3 In the title placeholder, enter **Website Launch Team**	You'll be adding a small hierarchy chart that shows who is in charge of what while people work to get the Gourmet Collections brand of spices started up.
4 Click the **Insert** tab	If necessary.
In the Illustrations group, click **SmartArt**	To open the Choose a SmartArt Graphic dialog box. There are several types of SmartArt graphics you can create. On this slide, you'll be adding a hierarchy (an organization chart).
5 In the left pane, select **Hierarchy**	To display the various hierarchy options.
Select the **Horizontal Organization** diagram type	
Click **OK**	
6 Observe the SmartArt object	(As shown in Exhibit 6-5.) The SmartArt Tools tabs appear—Design and Format. To the left of the object is a Text Pane you can use to add text to the chart.
7 In the Text Pane, verify that the insertion point appears next to the first item	
8 Enter **Kathy Sinclair, President**	Kathy will head up this project.

⚠ *If the Text Pane doesn't appear, have students click Text Pane in the Create Graphic group.*

Objective 3.4.1

Type your text here   ⌧

• |
   ↳ [Text]
• [Text]
• [Text]

The text you enter here will be added to the first box in the hierarchy.

9	Click the next bullet	To place the insertion point in it.
	Add the text as shown	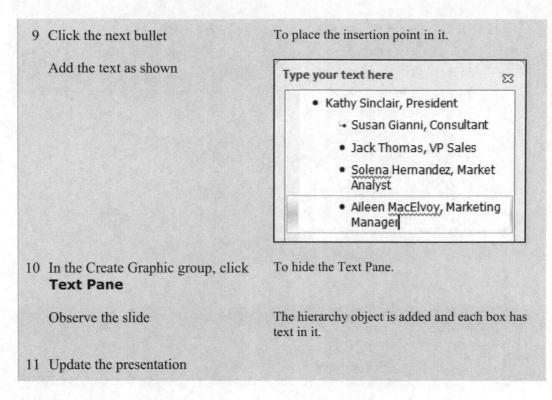
10	In the Create Graphic group, click **Text Pane**	To hide the Text Pane.
	Observe the slide	The hierarchy object is added and each box has text in it.
11	Update the presentation	

Modifying diagrams

Explanation

After you've inserted a diagram and added text to it, you can modify it by using the SmartArt Tools | Design and Format tabs.

Changing the layout

Objective 3.4.3

The SmartArt Tools | Design tab has the tools you need to quickly change the layout of an object, apply Quick Styles, add shapes, and move shapes around. For example, to add a shape to a SmartArt graphic, click Add Shape in the Create Graphic group and select an option. You can remove a shape from a SmartArt graphic by selecting the shape and pressing Delete.

To format a SmartArt object by applying a Quick Style, select a style from the SmartArt Styles group.

You can change a graphic's theme colors by selecting an option from the Change Colors list in the SmartArt Styles group. You can also change the graphic's colors and apply effects by selecting options from the SmartArt Styles group.

Formatting the object

The SmartArt Tools | Format tab has five groups—Shapes, Shape Styles, WordArt Styles, Arrange, and Size. To use these options, select a box or multiple boxes in the chart. Then, in the Shapes group, you can change the shape and increase or decrease the size. In the WordArt Styles group, you can change the text colors and text outline formatting. To use the WordArt styles, select text in a box and then apply the desired style.

Flipping SmartArt graphics

Objective 3.4.4

You can flip a SmartArt graphic to reverse its orientation. To flip a graphic, click the SmartArt Tools | Design tab, and in the Create Graphics group, click Right to Left. Click the same button again to return the graphic to its original orientation.

Do it! **C-2: Modifying a hierarchy chart**

Here's how	Here's why
1 Click the **Format** tab	(Under SmartArt Tools.) You'll increase the size of each box, apply a new style, and modify the formatting.
2 Select all five boxes in the hierarchy	Click an edge of the first box, press Ctrl, and click any part of a second box. Press Ctrl and click the remaining boxes.
Objective 3.4.7 3 In the Shapes group, click **Larger** twice	To increase the size of each box.
4 Click the **Design** tab	Under SmartArt Tools.
Objective 3.4.3 5 In the Layouts group, click the More button	To display the Layouts gallery.
Click the **Organization Chart** layout	To apply a new layout to the hierarchy object.
Objective 3.4.7 6 Drag the right-middle sizing handle to the right	(The middle sizing handle, not a corner.) To increase the size of the chart.
7 Display the Text Pane	Click the Text Pane button.
8 Select the **Susan Gianni** box	(Click the edge of the box.) Susan Gianni is a consultant to the project, reporting directly to Kathy Sinclair. While Kathy will be heading up the project, she wants Susan's daily communication to be with Jack Thomas.
Objective 3.4.4 In the Create Graphic group, click **Move Down** once	To move the assistant position down one place in the Text Pane.
Objective 3.4.9 9 In the Create Graphic group, click **Demote**	To move the assistant box below Jack Thomas's box.
10 Hide the Text Pane	Click the Text Pane button.
11 Deselect the box and select the entire object	Click the edge of the object frame.
Objective 3.4.2 In the SmartArt Styles group, display the gallery	Click the More button.
Under 3D, click the **Polished** style	To change the style.

	12	In the SmartArt Styles group, click **Change Colors**	To display the Change Colors gallery.
		Under Accent 3, click the **Gradient Loop – Accent 3** theme	
Objective 3.4.1	13	Select the **Aileen MacElvoy** box	You'll add a box under it.
		In the Create Graphic group, click the **Add Shape** arrow	To display a menu.
		Choose **Add Shape Below**	To add a position that reports to Aileen MacElvoy.
	14	Type **Matt Smith, Senior Web Designer**	To add the name and title to the box.
Objective 3.4.4	15	In the Create Graphic group, click **Right to Left**	To flip the chart.
	16	Deselect the object	
	17	Update and close the presentation	

Unit summary: Using tables and charts

Topic A   In this topic, you added a **table** to a slide. Next, you modified and formatted the table.

Topic B   In this topic, you created a **chart** on a slide. Then you changed the chart's formatting.

Topic C   In this topic, you added a **SmartArt hierarchy chart** to a slide. Then you modified the chart by formatting it and adding boxes.

Independent practice activity

In this activity, you'll create a table, add text, modify it, and apply formatting. Then you'll create a hierarchy chart, add text, and apply formatting to it.

The files for this activity are in Student Data folder **Unit 6\Unit summary**.

1   Create a new, blank presentation with a Title and Content layout slide.

2   Type **Sales (in Dollars)** in the title placeholder.

3   Add a 6-column, 5-row table to the slide.

4   Complete the table as shown in Exhibit 6-6.

5   Delete the last row and last column.

6   Resize the table and move it to the center of the slide. Apply the formatting of your choice, and compare the table to the one shown in Exhibit 6-7.

7   Add another slide that uses the Title and Content layout.

8   Type **The Project Team** in the title placeholder.

9   Insert a SmartArt hierarchy chart and add the text shown in Exhibit 6-8. (*Hint:* Press Tab to indent an item, or press Shift+Tab to remove an indent.)

10 Delete the assistant position.

11 Apply the formatting of your choice and compare your chart to Exhibit 6-9.

12 Save the presentation as **My sales** and close it.

	1st Qtr	2nd Qtr	3rd Qtr	4th Qtr	
Cumin	30	45	45	30	
Thyme	50	80	80	60	
Oregano	85	60	60	75	

Exhibit 6-6: The Sales table data for Step 4

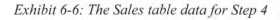

	1st Qtr	2nd Qtr	3rd Qtr	4th Qtr
Cumin	30	45	45	30
Thyme	50	80	80	60
Oregano	85	60	60	75

Exhibit 6-7: The Sales table after Step 6

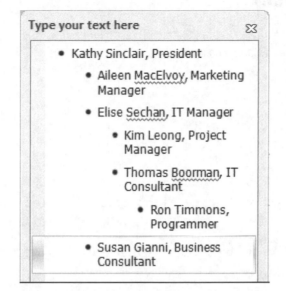

Exhibit 6-8: The chart text for Step 9

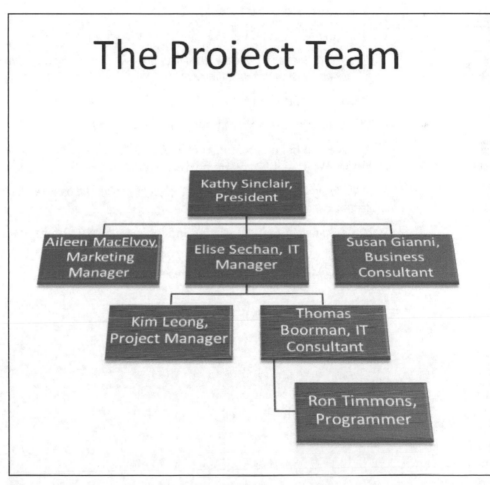

Exhibit 6-9: The organization chart after Step 10

Review questions

1 What is a table cell?

   The intersection of a row and a column.

2 How many ways are there to add a table to a slide?

   A One

   B Two

   C Three

   D More than three

3 True or false? When you add a table to a slide, the Table Tools tabs appear.

   True

4 What keyboard keys do you use to move from one cell to another in a table?

   Press Tab or use the arrow keys.

5 When the insertion point is in the last cell of the last row and you press Tab, what happens?

   A new row is added to the table.

6 How do you select an entire row in a table with just one click?

   Just outside the table (on either the left or right side), point to a row. When the pointer changes to a black arrow, click to select the row.

7 What is a chart used for?

   Charts are used to graphically represent numerical data.

8 You've just begun creating a chart by clicking the Chart button in the Illustration group. What would you do next?

   In the Insert Chart dialog box, select a chart type in the left pane. In the right pane, select the specific chart you want to create. Click OK.

9 Which tabs contain the groups and tools you use to modify and format a SmartArt object?

   The SmartArt Tools | Design and Format tabs.

Unit 7

Modifying presentations

Unit time: 75 minutes

Complete this unit, and you'll know how to:

A Modify a presentation by using a template.

B Make global changes in a presentation by using Master Slide view.

C Add visual appeal to a slide show by using transitions and timings.

D Prepare for a slide show by adding speaker notes.

E Set up a slide show for a speaker and a kiosk.

Topic A: Templates and themes

This topic covers the following Microsoft Office Specialist exam objective for PowerPoint 2010.

#	Objective
2.4	**Format slides**
	2.4.1 Format sections
	2.4.2 Modify themes

Using templates

Explanation

When creating a single slide show, you usually start with a blank presentation, add slides, type content, insert images, and then format the slides with theme colors and fonts. But if you want to create multiple presentations with a consistent style, you should use a template to create them.

A template combines slide layouts, theme colors, theme fonts, custom effects, backgrounds, slide masters, and title masters into a file that you can use to create presentations with a consistent format and style. For example, a company that wants all sales presentations to have the same professional look and feel would create a PowerPoint template for all sales reps to use.

PowerPoint comes with a variety of professionally designed templates, and more are available from Office.com.

To create a presentation based on a template stored on your computer:

1   Click the File tab and then click New to display the Available Templates and Themes page, shown in Exhibit 7-1. The templates and themes are divided into two sections. The top section contains the templates stored on your computer, and the bottom section provides access to templates and themes available at Office.com.

2   Under Home, select Sample Templates to access the templates stored on your computer.

3   Select a template. A preview is displayed in the top-right corner of the window.

4   Under the preview, click Create.

Exhibit 7-1: The Available Templates and Themes page

If you don't find a suitable template on your computer, you can download one from Office.com. Here's how:

1   On the File tab, click New.

2   Under Office.com Templates, navigate to the desired template:

 a   Click a folder or icon that represents the desired presentation category. Depending on the folder or icon you've clicked, you are presented with either additional folders or templates to choose from.

 b   Continue to click folders until the desired templates are displayed.

3   Select a template. A preview is displayed in the top-right corner of the window.

4   Under the preview, click Download.

You can also perform a search for Office.com templates. On the Available Templates and Themes page, type your search terms in the "Search Office.com for templates" box and press Enter. Then select a template from the search results and click Download.

Sections

Objective 2.4.1

Some presentations require a large number of slides, which can be cumbersome. To deal with this, PowerPoint 2010 includes a new Sections feature that enables you to group slides into categories. For example, let's say you have a presentation with 20 slides that are logically grouped into 6 categories. Using sections, you can group the presentation into:

- Introduction (two slides)
- Point 1 (four slides)
- Point 2 (five slides)
- Point 3 (four slides)
- Point 4 (three slides)
- Conclusion (two slides)

Adding and naming sections

You'll work with sections in either Normal view or Slide Sorter view. To add a section, point to the space between two slides, right-click, and choose Add Section. The new section will be untitled. To name it, right-click it and choose Rename section. In the Rename section dialog box, type a section name and click OK.

Moving sections

To move a section in either Normal view or Slide Sorter view, drag the section to the new location. This method can get awkward when you're working in a large presentation. Another way to move a section is to right-click the section name and choose either Move Section Up or Move Section Down.

Formatting sections

When you click a section name, the section and all slides associated with it are selected. This is a convenient way to select multiple slides at once so you can then change them simultaneously. For example, you can apply a new slide layout, reset the slide layout, apply a new theme, edit the current theme, or apply slide transitions.

Collapsing and expanding sections

When you create a section and add slides to it, it is expanded by default, meaning that all of the slides are visible. To collapse a section, click the triangle to the left of the section name. When you collapse a section, the slides are not visible on the Slide tab in Normal view or in Slide Sorter view; however, they can be printed and viewed in Slide Show view and Reading View. To expand a section, click the triangle to the left of its name.

Deleting sections

There are three options when you delete a section. Right-click the section and choose one of the commands listed in the following table.

Command	Description
Remove Section	Deletes the section. The slides in the deleted section remain and are included in the section above it.
Remove Section & Slides	Deletes the section and the slides in it.
Remove All Sections	Deletes all sections in the presentation but leaves the slides.

You can also delete a single section by selecting it and pressing Delete. This method removes the section, but the slides remain.

Do it!

A-1: Creating a presentation based on a template

Here's how	Here's why
1 On the File tab, click **New**	To display the available templates and themes, as shown in Exhibit 7-1.
2 Under Office.com Templates, click **Presentations**	To display the various presentation template folders at Office.com. If you don't have an Internet connection, skip this step and the next.
Click **Training**	To view the training presentation templates available at Office.com.
3 Under Available Templates and Themes, observe the navigation bar	Available Templates and Themes ← → ⌂ Home ▸ Presentations ▸ Training You can click the Back, Forward, Home, and folder-names icons to navigate through the template and theme options.
Click **Home**	← → ⌂ Home ▸ To navigate back to the top-level view of the available templates and themes, as shown in Exhibit 7-1.
4 Under Home, click **Sample templates**	To view the templates available on your computer.
Select **Project Status Report**	A preview of the presentation is displayed in the top-right corner of the window.
Click **Create**	(Under the preview.) To open the template as a presentation file.

Students need an Internet connection to perform this step.

Have students experiment with the navigation tools.

If this template isn't available, tell students to select a different one.

5 View the presentation in Reading view	On the status bar, click the Reading View button to play the slide show from the current slide. Navigate through all of the slides and observe them. At the end of the presentation, return to Normal view.

Objective 2.4.1

6 On the Slides tab, observe the sections	(Scroll down.) The 11 slides are divided into six sections.
On the Slides tab, select Slide 10	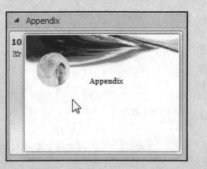 There are two slides in the Appendix section.

7   Point to the Collapse icon, as shown

Click once	To hide the two slides in the Appendix section. The icon changes from Collapse to Expand.

8   Point to the Expand icon, as shown

Click once	To display the Appendix section.
9 Right-click the **Appendix** section	To display the shortcut menu. You can use it to rename a section, collapse or expand all sections, move them up or down in the slide order, remove a section, remove a section and its slides, or remove all sections.
Choose **Remove Section**	Slides 10 and 11 are now part of the Next Steps and Action Items section.
10 Right-click the **Next Steps and Action Items** section and choose **Remove Section & Slides**	To delete the section and slides 8 through 11.

11	Switch to Slide Sorter view	On the status bar, click the Slide Sorter button.
	Zoom out and observe the slides	So that all seven slides are visible at the same time. There are four remaining sections, and they are used to organize the slides.
12	View Slide 1 in Normal view	Double-click slide 1.
13	Replace the slide title text with **Outlander Spices Quarterly Report**	You'll use this template to create a presentation.
	Delete the remaining text on the slide	Select the placeholder that contains "Presenter Name" and Presentation Date" and press Delete.
14	Delete the **Status Update** section and the slides in it	Right-click the section and choose Remove Section & Slides.
15	Delete the **Timeline** section	Right-click the section and choose Remove Section. The Project Overview section now has slides 2 through 5 in it.
16	Delete the **Project Overview** section and the slides in it	Only slide 1 remains.
17	Insert a new slide with the Title and Content layout	(Click the New Slide arrow and choose Title and Content.) The new slide has the same design template applied to it.
18	Save the presentation as **My presentation**	In Student Data folder Unit 7\Topic A.
	Close the presentation	

Point out that the sections are not visible in Reading or Slide Show view. Sections are used only for organizing slides.

Using themes

Explanation

When you create a presentation based on a template, you give your slides a professional look and feel. Applying themes is another way to quickly provide a professional appearance.

Objective 2.4.2

To apply a design theme to a presentation:

1 Click the Design tab.

2 In the Themes group, shown in Exhibit 7-2, point to a theme to see the Live Preview applied to the selected slide. Or click the More button to display the Themes gallery, and point to a theme to see the Live Preview.

3 Click a theme to apply it.

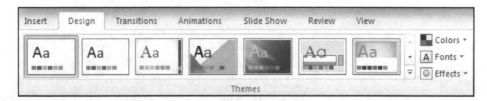

Exhibit 7-2: The Themes group on the Design tab

Using multiple themes in a single presentation

You can apply a theme to an entire presentation or to specific slides. You can apply multiple themes within a single presentation. Here's how:

1 In Slide Sorter view or Normal view, select the slides to which you want to apply a different design theme.

Objective 2.4.2

2 Click the Design tab.

3 In the Themes group, right-click the desired theme and choose Apply to Selected Slides.

Do it!

A-2:   Changing the design themes

The files for this activity are in Student Data folder **Unit 7\Topic A**.

Objective 2.4.2

Here's how	Here's why
1 Open Website launch1	From the current topic folder.
Save the presentation as **My website launch1**	
2 Click the **Design** tab	
3 In the Themes group, click the More button	To display the Themes gallery. Themes are shown in alphabetical order.
Click the **Waveform** theme	To apply it to the presentation.
4 Go to slide 2 and observe the title	The title on this slide was previously formatted individually, and it still displays that custom formatting. You'll set this slide to use only the formatting specified by the current theme.

5 Click the **Home** tab	
In the Slides group, click **Reset**	To apply the current theme's formatting to the entire slide, removing the custom formatting that was applied to the title.
6 Observe each slide in the presentation	Each slide has the same design theme applied.
7 Switch to Slide Sorter view	
8 Select the first slide	(If necessary.) You'll apply a different design template to the first slide.
9 Click the **Design** tab	
In the Themes group, point to a theme	Point to any theme in the group, but don't display the gallery.
Right-click any theme	To display a shortcut menu.
Choose **Apply to Selected Slides**	To apply this theme to only the title slide.
10 Observe the slide	The title slide has a theme that is different from the other slides in the presentation.
11 Press (CTRL) + (Z)	To undo the theme change.
Switch to Normal view	
12 Update and close the presentation	

Topic B: Slide masters

This topic covers the following Microsoft Office Specialist exam objectives for PowerPoint 2010.

#	Objective
2.4	**Format slides**
	2.4.4 Apply formatting to a slide
	2.4.5 Set up slide footers
2.5	**Enter and format text**
	2.5.2 Change text formats
	2.5.3 Change the formatting of bulleted and numbered lists
3.1	**Manipulate graphical elements**
	3.1.2 Position graphical elements
7.2	**Share a presentation**
	7.2.3 Create handouts (send to Microsoft Word)

Working with slide masters

Explanation

All PowerPoint presentations have a *slide master* that controls text characteristics, background color, and certain special effects, such as shadowing and bullet styles. If you change the formatting in the slide master, the formatting for the entire presentation will be affected.

Elements of a slide master

To display the slide master, click the View tab and then click Slide Master. A Slide Master tab appears on the Ribbon.

In Slide Master view, there are two panes, as shown in Exhibit 7-3. In the left pane, there is one slide master with eleven slide layouts indented under it; the first slide layout is selected.

When you change the slide master, the changes are applied to all of the indented slide layouts below it. When you make a change directly on one of the specific layout masters, the change is applied to that layout only.

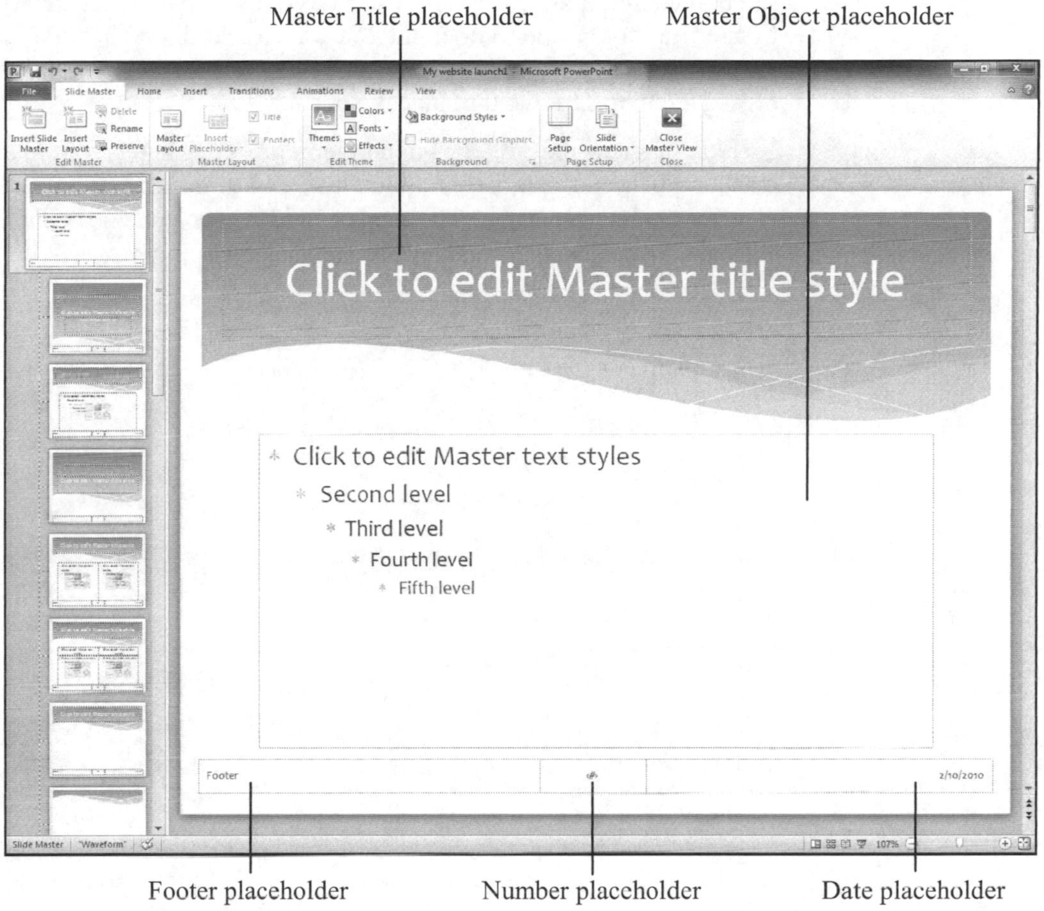

Master Title placeholder   Master Object placeholder

Footer placeholder   Number placeholder   Date placeholder

Exhibit 7-3: Slide Master view with the slide master selected

In the right pane, the selected slide master is displayed, along with the various placeholders it contains. The following table describes the placeholders available on the slide master (the first slide).

Placeholder	Description
Master Title	Controls the font, size, color, style, and alignment of the slide title text.
Master Object	Controls the font, size, color, style, and alignment of the slide text, such as bulleted lists.
Number	Controls the font, size, color, style, and alignment of the slide number placeholder.
Footer	Controls the font, size, color, style, and alignment of the slide footer placeholder.
Date	Controls the font, size, color, style, and alignment of the date placeholder.

Slide numbers, footers, and the date are not displayed in a presentation by default.

To hide or show the Number, Footer, Date, and other placeholders on the slide master, select the slide master. In the Master Layout group on the Slide Master tab, click the Master Layout button to open the Master Layout dialog box. Clear or check the desired placeholders and click OK. In addition, you can select any individual placeholder and press Delete to remove that placeholder.

To hide or show the Title or Footer elements on a slide layout master, select the desired master. Then, in the Master Layout group, clear or check Title or Footers. Once a title or footer placeholder has been deleted or hidden, you can check Title or Footers in the Master Layout group to display the elements again.

Do it!

B-1: Examining the elements of a slide master

The files for this activity are in Student Data folder **Unit 7\Topic B**.

Here's how	Here's why
1 Open Website launch2	From the current topic folder.
Save the presentation as **My website launch2**	
2 Click the **View** tab	
Click **Slide Master**	In the Master Views group.
3 In the left pane, select the first slide	To display the primary slide master, as shown in Exhibit 7-3. This view is also called Master view.
4 Observe the Master Title placeholder	It controls the formatting of the title placeholder on the slide.
5 Observe the Master Object placeholder	It controls the formatting of the slide text.
6 Observe the Date placeholder	It controls the formatting of the date and time.
7 Observe the Footer placeholder	It controls the formatting of the footer. You'll enter the footer text next.
8 Click the Footer placeholder	To place the insertion point.
Type **Outlander Spices**	Although you specified the footer text, by default, the footer won't appear on the presentation slides. You'll add the footer to your slides in the next activity.
9 Observe the Number placeholder	It controls the formatting of the slide numbers.
10 In the left pane, point to the first slide and read the ScreenTip	
	It tells you that this slide master is being used by slides 1 through 6.
11 Observe the slides in the left pane	Slide 1 is selected and there are multiple indented slides under it. The indented slides correspond to the available slide layouts.

Header and footer elements

Explanation

Even when the footer elements appear on the slide master, they will not be displayed on the slides in your presentation by default. To display footer elements on your presentation slides:

Objective 2.4.5

1 Click the Insert tab.

2 In the Text group, click Header & Footer to open the Header and Footer dialog box, shown in Exhibit 7-4.

3 Under Include on slide, check or clear Date and time, Slide number, and Footer, as needed.

4 Click Apply to display the checked items on the current slide, or click Apply to All to apply them to all slides in the presentation.

You can also use the Header and Footer dialog box to display headers and footers on notes pages and handouts pages. To do so, click the Notes and Handouts tab, specify the content you want, and click Apply to All.

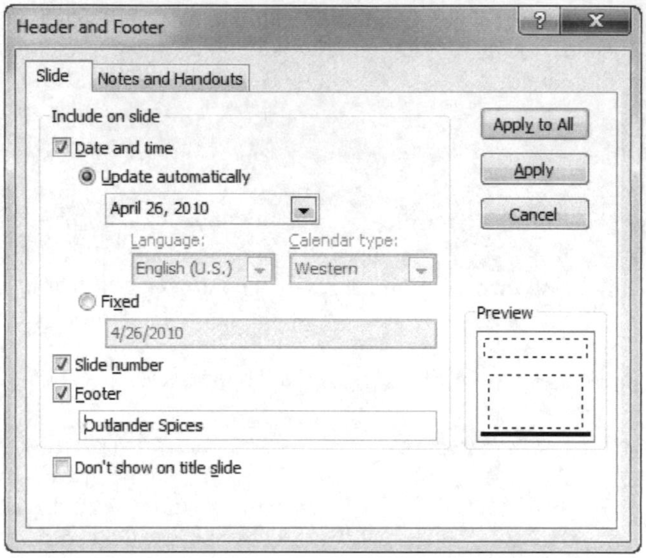

Exhibit 7-4: The Header and Footer dialog box

B-2: Displaying header and footer elements

Here's how	Here's why
1 Click the **Insert** tab	You'll indicate that you want the footer elements to appear on the slides in your presentation.
2 Click **Header & Footer**	To open the Header and Footer dialog box.
3 Check **Date & Time**	To display the date on each slide. You'll specify that the date be updated automatically. You'll also choose a different date format.
Verify that **Update automatically** is selected	
Under Update automatically, display the list and select the indicated option	The specific date shown will be different, but be sure to choose the format shown.
4 Check **Slide number**	To display the slide number on each slide.
5 Check **Footer**	To activate the Footer box and place the insertion point in it. The footer text you entered on the slide master appears in the Footer box.
6 Click **Apply to All**	To apply these Header and Footer settings to all slides.
7 Click **Header & Footer**	To open the Header and Footer dialog box.
8 Click the **Notes and Handouts** tab	No header or footer has been specified for the notes and handouts pages. You'll do that later in this topic.
Click **Cancel**	To close the dialog box.

Graphical elements

Explanation

Objective 3.1.2

Any graphical elements you add to a slide master will also appear on all slides based on that master. While viewing the slide master, click the Insert tab and draw shapes or insert a picture or clip art just as you'd add those elements to a slide.

Do it!

B-3: Adding a logo to a slide master

The files for this activity are in Student Data folder **Unit 7\Topic B**.

Objective 3.1.2

Here's how	Here's why
1 Click the **Insert** tab	(If necessary.) You'll insert a logo that will appear on all slides.
2 Click **Picture**	(In the Images group.) To open the Insert Picture dialog box.
3 Select **Outlander Spices logo**	In the current topic folder.
Click **Insert**	The logo appears in the center of the slide master.
4 Drag the logo to the top-right corner of the slide master	
5 Observe the master slide layouts	(The indented slides.) The image is applied to five layouts—only the ones with a title placeholder.
6 Click the **Slide Master** tab	
7 Click **Close Master View**	(In the Close group.) To return to Normal view.
8 View each slide	The slide logo appears on slides 2 through 5 but not on the first slide. The footer elements appear on all six slides. To remove the logo, you must return to Master view.
9 Return to Master view	On the View tab, click Slide Master.
10 In the left pane, select the first slide	This is the slide where you placed the logo (not one of the indented slide layouts).
11 Click the logo	To select it.
Press ⬚DELETE⬚	To delete the logo.

Changing the font and font size on a slide master

Explanation

The slide master controls how the slides in a presentation are formatted. The slide master contains placeholders for title, text, and background items. You can emphasize the title or some of the bullet text by changing the font, size, or color in the slide master.

To change the slide format in a presentation:

Objective 2.5.2

1   Open the slide master and select the Master Title placeholder.
2   Change the font, font size, or color as needed.
3   Select the Master Object placeholder.
4   Change the font, font size, or color as needed.
5   Switch to Normal view.
6   Update the presentation.

Do it!

Objective 2.5.2

B-4: Changing the default font

Here's how	Here's why
1 Click an edge of the Master Title placeholder	
2 Click the **Home** tab	
3 From the Font list, select **Arial Narrow**	To change the title font.
Observe the Master Title placeholder	The font has changed.
4 Click an edge of the Master Object placeholder, as shown	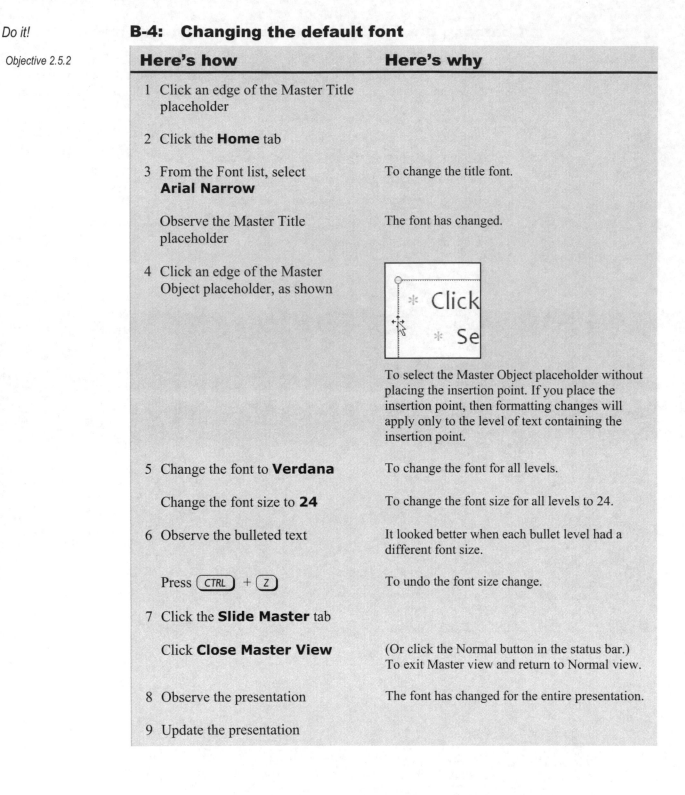
	To select the Master Object placeholder without placing the insertion point. If you place the insertion point, then formatting changes will apply only to the level of text containing the insertion point.
5 Change the font to **Verdana**	To change the font for all levels.
Change the font size to **24**	To change the font size for all levels to 24.
6 Observe the bulleted text	It looked better when each bullet level had a different font size.
Press CTRL + Z	To undo the font size change.
7 Click the **Slide Master** tab	
Click **Close Master View**	(Or click the Normal button in the status bar.) To exit Master view and return to Normal view.
8 Observe the presentation	The font has changed for the entire presentation.
9 Update the presentation	

Modifying bullets on a slide master

Explanation

You can format the Master Object placeholder in a variety of ways. For example, you can change the text formatting, the default bullets, and the line spacing.

To modify the default bullets:

Objective 2.5.3

1 In Master view, select the Master Object placeholder and place the insertion point in the bullet level you want to modify.

2 Click the Home tab.

3 In the Paragraph group, click the Bullets arrow and select a bullet style.

4 To modify other bullet levels, place the insertion point in the desired bullet level and repeat step 3.

5 Switch to Normal view.

B-5: Modifying the default bullets

Here's how	Here's why
1 Go to the first slide	If necessary.
2 Switch to Master view	(Click the View tab and click Slide Master.) You'll modify the bullets.
3 In the left pane, select the slide master	Not one of the indented slide layout masters.
4 In the Master Object placeholder, place the insertion point in the first line of bulleted text	You'll format the text.
5 Click the **Home** tab	
In the Paragraph group, click the Bullets arrow	To display the Bullets gallery.
Select **Star Bullets**, as shown	
6 Observe the Master Object placeholder	The bullet style for the first level has changed.
7 Place the insertion point in the third level of bulleted text	
8 In the Bullets gallery, click **Filled Round Bullets**, as shown	
9 Return to Normal view	
Observe the third slide	The bullets for both the first and third levels have changed.
10 Update the presentation	

Inserting slide masters

Explanation

You can have multiple slide masters in a presentation. To add a new slide master:

1 Switch to Master view.
2 On the Slide Master tab, click Insert Slide Master to insert a new slide master. A new slide master and the eleven indented slide layouts are added to the left pane.
3 Format the slide master as needed.
4 Switch to Normal view.

Preserving slide masters

PowerPoint automatically deletes a slide master when it's not used by any of the slides. To prevent this, you need to preserve a slide master. By default, a new slide master is preserved when you insert it by using the Insert Slide Master button in the Edit Master group.

Slide master themes

As you view the slide master, the Slide Master tab is selected in the Ribbon by default. You can apply a different theme to the slide master by clicking Themes in the Edit Theme group and selecting a new theme. If you right-click a theme in the Themes gallery, you can use the shortcut menu to apply the theme to the selected master or to create a new slide master using that theme.

Do it!

B-6:   Inserting a new slide master

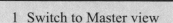

Here's how	Here's why
1 Switch to Master view	
2 In the left pane, click the first slide	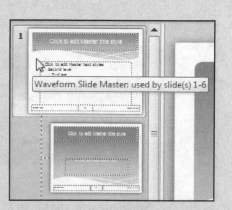 This is the current slide master, which is used by all slides in the presentation.
3 In the Edit Master group, click **Insert Slide Master**	To insert a new slide master.
Observe the left pane and the selected slide	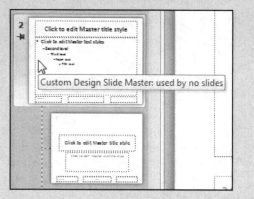 This is the new slide master you just inserted. It has a custom design and isn't being used by any slides.
4 Point as shown	This thumbtack icon indicates that the slide master is preserved.
In the left pane, scroll up	To observe the first slide master; notice that it is not preserved (no icon appears next to it). Therefore, if you apply a different master to all of your slides, this master will be deleted automatically.

5 Scroll down and select the second master slide

Select the middle Footer placeholder

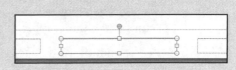

(The center text placeholder at the bottom.) You'll enter footer text here.

Type **Outlander Spices**

6 In the Edit Theme group, click **Themes**

To display a gallery. The theme for the custom master you just inserted is selected.

Click the icon for the Angles theme

You'll add this design theme to the presentation. Notice that doing this adds another master to the presentation. If this presentation contained only one master, then the new theme would apply to that master.

7 Select the third master's first slide

(In the left pane.) You might need to scroll to view the third master's first slide.

Observe the left pane

There are three masters now, each with eleven indented slides. Only the second master is preserved.

8 In the Edit Master group, click **Preserve**

(Or right-click the master and choose Preserve Master.) To preserve the third master. The thumbtack icon appears next to it to indicate that the master is preserved now.

9 Update the presentation

Slide master backgrounds

Explanation

You can apply a color, gradient, pattern, or graphic to the background of a slide master to add visual interest to your slides. When you add a graphic to a slide background, you can stretch the graphic to fill all or part of each slide, or you can tile it on the slide.

Objective 2.4.4

To format the slide background:

1 Display Master view.

2 Select the desired slide master.

3 In the Background group, click Background Styles, and then do either of the following:

- Select a style.

- Choose Format Background to open the Format Background dialog box. Select the desired fill type, specify settings for the fill type you selected, and click Close.

Do it!

B-7:   Adding slide master backgrounds

The files for this activity are in Student Data folder **Unit 7\Topic B**.

Objective 2.4.4

Here's how	Here's why
1 Select the second master slide	(Not one of the indented slide layout masters.) This master has a blank background. You'll apply a colored background.
2 Click **Background Styles**	(In the Background group.) To display the Background Styles gallery.
3 Select the icon for Style 6	
	To apply the style. Next, you'll add a graphic to the slide background.
4 Click **Background Styles** and choose **Format Background...**	To open the Format Background dialog box with the Fill tab active. You can use these settings to apply a solid fill, a gradient fill, or a picture or texture fill.
5 Under Fill, select **Picture or texture fill**	You can insert a texture by using the Texture list, or you can insert a picture by using the File button, Clipboard button, or Clip Art button.
6 Under Insert from, click **Clip Art**	To open the Select Picture dialog box.
In the Search text box, type **frames**	
Click **Go**	To display the relevant clip art.

7 Click as shown

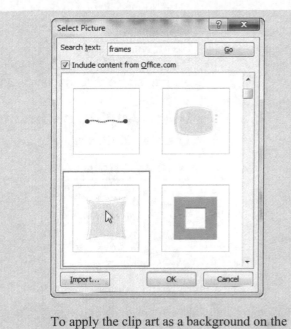

Click **OK**

To apply the clip art as a background on the second slide master.

8 Drag the Transparency slider to **50%**

To apply transparency to the slide so that it appears lighter.

9 Click **Close**

Slide master placeholders

Explanation

If you want to add another placeholder to a slide master, select a master layout, click Insert Placeholder in the Master Layout group, and choose the type of placeholder you want to add. You can then drag to draw the placeholder.

Do it!

B-8: Adding a placeholder to a slide master

The files for this activity are in Student Data folder **Unit 7\Topic B**.

Here's how	Here's why
1 Select the second master's Section Header layout	Section Header Layout: used by no slides
	You'll use this layout to create a section header slide before each new section of a presentation. You want to display a different image on each section header slide, so you'll add a picture placeholder to the slide master.
2 Click the **Insert Placeholder** arrow	(On the Slide Master tab, in the Master Layout group.) To display the Insert Placeholder list.
3 Choose **Picture**	The pointer changes to a crosshair.
4 Drag as shown	• Picture Click to edit Master text styles CLICK TO EDIT MASTER TITLE STYLE
	To create a picture placeholder centered above the text placeholders.
5 Return to Normal view	
6 Update the presentation	

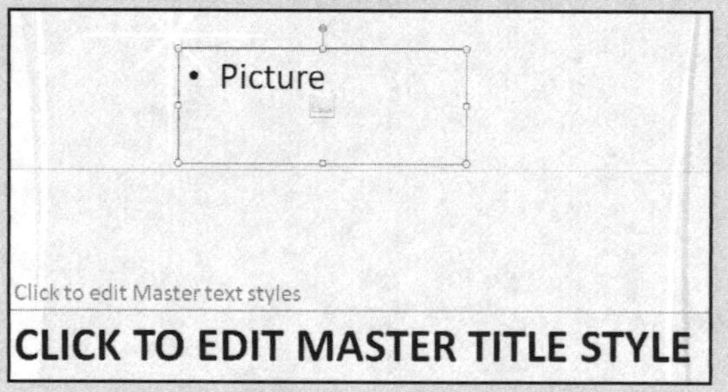

Applying multiple slide masters

Explanation

After you've added multiple slide masters to a presentation, you can use them to add slides to the presentation. In Normal view, click the Home tab. In the Slides group, click the New Slide arrow to display a gallery of layouts provided by the slide masters. Select a layout to apply it to a new slide.

In addition, you can apply any master to existing slides. A theme for each master appears in the Themes group on the Design tab. You can select slides, right-click the theme for a master, and choose Apply to Selected Slides to apply the master to the selected slides. To apply a master to all slides, just click the theme for that master.

Deleting slide masters

You can delete slide masters that are no longer necessary. When you delete a slide master, all of its slide layouts are also deleted automatically.

To delete a slide master:

1   In Master view, select the slide master that you want to delete.
2   Do any of the following:
    - Click the Delete button in the Edit Master group.
    - Right-click to display a shortcut menu and choose Delete Master.
    - Press Delete.

B-9: Using multiple slide masters

Here's how	Here's why
1 In the Slides group, click the **New Slide** arrow	To display the gallery of slide layouts.
Scroll down in the gallery	The first group of layouts corresponds to the first master. The next set is the Custom Design template, and the last set is the Angles master.
Under Custom Design, select **Section Header**	To add a new slide with the Section Header slide layout. This slide uses the Custom Design master. It also includes the picture placeholder you added to the Section Header layout master.
2 Delete the slide	In the left pane, right-click the slide and choose Delete.
3 Switch to Master view	
Observe the left pane	It shows three masters.
Point to each master and view the description	
4 Select the third master	
In the Edit Master group, click **Delete**	To delete the selected master.
5 Observe the left pane	Only two masters are left.
6 Close the Master view	
7 Update the presentation	

TIPS *Tell students they can also press Delete.*

The handout master and notes master

Explanation

Objective 7.2.3

In addition to working with slide masters, you can view and customize the masters for the handouts and notes pages that you can print from your presentation. To view the handout master or the notes master, click the View tab and click the Handout Master button or the Notes Master button. Each button adds a corresponding tab to the Ribbon.

You can click Background Styles and select a Quick Style to apply a background color or gradient to the handout master or notes master. After you customize either master, click Close Master View to return to the presentation.

Do it!

Objective 7.2.3

B-10: Customizing the handout master

Here's how	Here's why
1 Click the **View** tab	
2 Click **Handout Master**	(In the Master Views group.) To view the handout master and add a Handout Master tab to the Ribbon.. You can print from one to nine slides per handout page.
3 Click **Background Styles**	(In the Background group.) To display a gallery.
Select the background style of your choice	To apply a background style to the handout master. When you print slide handouts, they'll use the background style you specified.
4 Return to Normal view	Click Close Master View.
5 Update and close the presentation	

Topic C: Transitions and timings

This topic covers the following Microsoft Office Specialist exam objectives for PowerPoint 2010.

#	Objective
5.4	**Apply and modify transitions between slides**
5.4.1	Modify a transition effect
5.4.2	Add a sound to a transition
5.4.3	Modify the transition's duration
5.4.4	Set up manual or automatically timed advance options
8.2	**Set up a slide show**
8.2.2	Play narrations
8.2.4	Use timings
8.3	**Set presentation timing**
8.3.1	Rehearse timings
8.3.2	Keep timings
8.3.3	Adjust a slide's timing
8.4	**Record a presentation**
8.4.1	Starting recording from the beginning of a slide show
8.4.2	Starting recording from the current slide of the slide show

Working with transitions

Explanation

Transitions are special effects that appear during a slide show when it moves from one slide to another. You can specify a single transition for the entire presentation or specify individual transitions for each slide. You can choose from a variety of transitions and vary their speed. A good use of transition effects is to indicate a new section of a presentation or to emphasize a certain slide.

You can also set timings for your presentation so that you can run the slide show without using your mouse or keyboard to display the next slide. Instead, the slides will be displayed automatically at specified time intervals.

Transition effects for individual slides

Each slide can have a different theme and different text styles. In the same manner, you can apply different transition effects to each slide by using the Transition To This Slide group. You can set transition effects for a slide in Normal view or Slide Sorter view.

To set a transition effect for an individual slide:

1 Select the slide.
2 Click the Transitions tab. It contains the Transition To This Slide group, shown in Exhibit 7-5.
3 Point to one of the transitions, or click the More button to display the gallery and point to a transition, to see the Live Preview. Click a transition to apply it.

Exhibit 7-5: The Transition To This Slide group on the Transitions tab

After you apply a transition to a slide, you can preview it by clicking the transition icon that appears on each slide in Slide Sorter view.

Do it!

C-1: Setting transitions for individual slides

The files for this activity are in Student Data folder **Unit 7\Topic C**.

Here's how	Here's why
1 Open Website Launch3	From the current topic folder.
Save the presentation as **My website launch3**	
2 Switch to Slide Sorter view	
Select the first slide	(If necessary.) You'll apply a transition to this slide.
3 Click the **Transitions** tab	
Observe the Transition To This Slide group	(Shown in Exhibit 7-5.) No transition is applied to this slide yet. On the right side of the group, you'll find the Transition Sound list, the Transition Speed list, and the Apply to All button.
4 In the Transition To This Slide group, click **Uncover**, as shown	
	To apply this transition to the first slide and see a preview of the transition.
Observe the first slide	
	Under the bottom-left corner of the slide is an icon indicating that the slide has a transition effect applied to it.
5 Click **Effect Options**	(In the Transition to This Slide group.) To display a menu.
Choose **From Left**	To specify that the slide will uncover from the left.

Depending on their screen resolution, students may need to scroll through the list or open the gallery.

Objective 5.4.3

6 In the Duration list, select **1.00**

Sound:	[No Sound] ▾
Duration:	01.00 ▴▾
Apply To All	
	Timing

In the Timing group.

   Enter **1.5**

Sound:	[No Sound] ▾
Duration:	01.50 ▴▾
Apply To All	
	Timing

To change the transition speed.

7 Select slide 2

   Apply the **Uncover** transition   In the Transition To This Slide group.

   Click **Effect Options** and
   choose **From Left**

   Change the Duration to **1.5**   In the Duration list, select "1.00" and enter
                                           "1.5".

8 On slide 3, apply the **Uncover**
   transition

   Click **Effect Options** and
   choose **From Left**

   Change the Duration to **1.5**

9 Select slide 1

10 Run the presentation in Reading   (Click the Reading View button in the status
   view   bar.) You'll see the transition as the first slide is
                                            displayed.

   Click the mouse six times   To advance through the presentation. Notice the
                                            transition effects you've applied. When you
                                            advance from slide 3 to slide 4, there is no
                                            transition effect.

11 Return to Slide Sorter view

12 Update the presentation

Applying transition effects to the entire presentation

Explanation

To apply the same transition effect to the entire presentation:

1 Display the presentation in Slide Sorter view.

2 In the Transition To This Slide group, select a transition, apply a transition sound, and change the duration speed as needed. Or verify that the slide with the transition effect(s) is selected.

3 In the Timing group, click Apply To All.

Applying transition effects to selected slides

Sometimes you might want to set transition effects for only some of the slides in your presentation. Here's how:

1 Switch to Slide Sorter or Normal view.

2 Select the slides that will have the transition effects applied to them.

3 In the Transition To This Slide group and the Timing group, specify the transition effects.

Do it!

C-2: Setting a transition for the entire presentation

Here's how	Here's why
1 Select the first slide	In Slide Sorter view.
2 Display the Transition gallery and click **Gallery**, as shown	
	(In the Transition To This Slide group.) To apply the transition effect to the first slide.
Observe the Transition To This Slide group	The effects that are displayed for quick access have changed. They include the Gallery effect and those similar to it.
Objective 5.4.4 3 Click **Apply To All**	In the Transition To This Slide group.
4 Point as shown	
	On any slide.
Click once	To preview the transition effect.
5 Run the presentation in Reading view	Click the mouse to advance slides. You'll view the transition effects for the entire presentation.
Press ESC	To end the slide show.
Objectives 5.4.1, 5.4.4 6 Select slides 2, 4, and 6	In Slide Sorter view, click slide 2; then press Ctrl and click slides 4 and 6.
Click **Effect Options** and choose **From Left**	To change the direction the slides will transition from.
7 Run the presentation in Reading view	(From the first slide.) To view the alternating transition effects.
8 Update the presentation	

Setting timings for a slide show

Explanation

You can set timings manually for each slide and then run the slide show to review the timings, or you can record timings automatically as you rehearse the presentation. Timings are useful when you want the audience to spend more time reading a specific slide. You can also use recorded timings for running a slide show in a kiosk or as a continuous background show at a convention or in a store.

To manually set the timing for a slide show:

Objectives 5.4.4, 8.3.3

1 In the Timing group on the Transitions tab, clear On Mouse Click.
2 Check After.
3 In the box next to After, enter the desired number of seconds.
4 Click Apply to All.

Adding sound to a transition

Objective 5.4.2

Also in the Timing group is the Sound list. Use this tool to have a sound play when the transition effect plays. To add a sound to a transition:

1 Display the slide in either Normal view or Slide Sorter view.
2 Apply the transition effect of your choice and set the timing, if necessary.
3 Display the Sound list and select the desired sound.
4 If you want the sound to continue playing until another sound plays, display the Sound list again and select Loop Until Next Sound.

C-3: Adding timings to a slide show

Here's how	Here's why
1 Select the first slide	In Slide Sorter view.
2 In the Timing group, clear **On Mouse Click**	You'll set up the presentation so that it will advance to the next slide without requiring a mouse click. Instead, PowerPoint will do it automatically after a specific period of time.
Check **After**	The After box shows 00:00.
3 Next to After, click the up-arrow four times	
	Advance Slide
	☐ On Mouse Click
	☑ After: 00:04.00
	To set the timing to four seconds between slides.
4 Click **Apply to All**	(In the Transition To This Slide group.) To apply the transition effect to all slides in the presentation.
5 Observe the slides	
	Redesign Website
	Outlander Spices
	Princely Potatoes
	⭐ 00:04 2
	Under each slide, you'll see the transition icon along with a timing indicator. Note that the Effect Options transition on slides 2, 4, and 6 was replaced when you clicked Apply To All.
6 Run the presentation in Reading view	The slides appear automatically after an interval of four seconds.
7 Update the presentation	

Rehearsing slide show timings

Explanation

You can use the Rehearse Timings feature to fine-tune your pace before you give a presentation. You can either set the timings for your slides before you rehearse, or set them automatically while you rehearse. You can use the buttons on the Rehearsal toolbar to pause between slides, restart a slide, and advance to the next slide. PowerPoint keeps track of how long each slide appears and sets the timing accordingly. When you finish your rehearsal, you can accept the timings, or you can try again.

Objectives 5.4.4, 8.3.1

To rehearse timings:

1 Click the Slide Show tab. In the Set Up group, click Rehearse Timings to switch to Slide Show view and display the Rehearsal toolbar, as shown in Exhibit 7-6.

2 Click the Next button on the Rehearsal toolbar to move through your presentation.

3 Click Yes to record the timings.

4 Press F5 to view the slide show.

Exhibit 7-6: The Rehearsal toolbar on a slide

Adding narration

Objective 8.3.1

In addition to giving your presentation live, you can record a slide show along with all of the narration, transitions, animations, and laser pointer actions that go with it. You can then share the presentation or save it as a video file for others to use.

Recording a slide show

To record your slide show, you must first connect a microphone to your computer and set it up. When the microphone is working, you are ready to start:

1   On the Slide Show tab, in the Set Up group, click the Record Slide Show arrow and choose either Start Recording from the Beginning or Start Recording from Current Slide. The Record Slide Show dialog box opens.

2   Check both "Slide and animation timings" and "Narrations and laser pointer."

3   Click Start Recording to switch to Slide Show view and display the Rehearsal toolbar, shown in Exhibit 7-6.

4   Click the Next button on the Rehearsal toolbar to move through your presentation.

When you are finished with the last slide, the presentation is displayed in Slide Sorter view, the transition timings are automatically saved, and each slide shows a sound icon.

Using a laser pointer

To turn your mouse into a laser pointer while running a presentation:

1   Run the presentation in Reading view or Slide Show view.

2   Press and hold Ctrl. At this point, the mouse pointer is hidden.

3   Click the left mouse button to display the laser pointer. Point to the slide content that you want to draw the audience's attention to.

4   Release the mouse button and the Ctrl key.

To change the color of the laser pointer:

1   In the Slide Show tab's Set Up group, click Set Up Slide Show.

2   In the Set Up Show dialog box, display the Laser pointer color list and select the desired color.

3   Click OK.

Playing narrations

To preview a narration, in Normal view, point to a sound icon and click the Play button.

To play the narrations and laser pointer movements when you run the slide show, you'll need to check Play Narrations, located in the Set Up group on the Slide Show tab, and then play the slide show.

Removing timings and narration

After you've recorded the slide show, you can remove the timings and narration by doing the following:

1   On the Slide Show tab, in the Set Up group, click the Record Slide Show arrow to display a menu.

2   Choose one of the following:
* Clear Timings on Current Slide
* Clear Timings on All Slides
* Clear Narration on Current Slide
* Clear Narration on All Slides

C-4: Rehearsing timings

The files for this activity are in Student Data folder **Unit 7\Topic C**.

Here's how	Here's why
1 Click the **Slide Show** tab	
Observe the Set Up group	It contains the Set Up Slide Show, Hide Slide, Rehearse Timings, and Record Slide Show buttons and the Play Narrations, Use Timings, and Show Media Controls checkboxes.
2 Click **Rehearse Timings**	The Slide Show starts and the Rehearsal toolbar is displayed.
Observe the screen	The first slide is displayed in Slide Show view with the Rehearsal toolbar in the top-left corner. PowerPoint has started recording the amount of time this slide is displayed.
3 Press ⌐SPACEBAR⌐	(Or click the Next button on the Rehearsal toolbar.) To move to the next slide. The Slide Time box returns to zero and starts counting again.
4 Every few seconds, move to the next slide	(Until the end of the presentation.) You'll see a message box.
Observe the message box	It displays the total time for the slide show.

Objectives 5.4.4, 8.4.1, 8.3.1

Verify that students are in Slide Sorter view.

Tell students that the total time for the slide show will probably differ for each student.

Microsoft PowerPoint

ⓘ The total time for the slide show was 0:00:27. Do you want to keep the new slide timings to use when you view the slide show?

[Yes] [No]

5 Click **Yes**	To record the new slide timings and return to Slide Sorter view.
Observe the window	The timing indicators display the new slide timings.
6 Press ⌐F5⌐	To run the slide show.
View the presentation	The slides appear automatically at the specified intervals.
7 Return to Slide Sorter view	
8 Update and close the presentation	

Objective 8.3.2

Tell students that the time for each slide might differ for each student.

Objectives 8.2.2, 8.2.4

Topic D: Speaker notes

This topic covers the following Microsoft Office Specialist exam objective for PowerPoint 2010.

#	Objective
2.4	**Format slides**
	2.4.5 Set up slide footers

Working with speaker notes

Explanation

In addition to the primary slide content, you can add speaker notes to your slides for the speaker to use as a reference. You can also add headers and footers to the speaker notes pages.

Adding speaker notes

Each slide can have corresponding notes to help the presenter remember key points in a presentation. Every slide in a presentation has a notes page, which contains a slide image and space for speaker notes. The presenter can use the speaker notes as a reference tool and can print them to distribute to the audience. The speaker notes don't appear on screen during the slide show.

To add speaker notes to a slide:

1   Display the slide to which you want to add notes.

2   Click the View tab and click Notes Page.

3   Click the notes placeholder to place the insertion point.

4   Enter the text.

You can also add speaker notes by typing in the Notes pane, which might appear below the Slides pane in Normal view. You can use the PowerPoint Options dialog box to specify whether the Notes pane appears for presentations when you open them. Here's how:

1   Click the File tab and click Options to open the PowerPoint Options dialog box.

2   Select the Advanced tab.

3   Under Display, select an option from the "Open all documents using this view" list. Click OK.

D-1: Adding speaker notes

The files for this activity are in Student Data folder **Unit 7\Topic D**.

Here's how	Here's why
1 Open Website Launch4	From the current topic folder.
Save the presentation as **My website launch4**	
2 Go to the first slide	If necessary.
3 Click the **View** tab	
Click **Notes Page**	In the Presentation Views group.
4 Under the slide, click the notes placeholder	

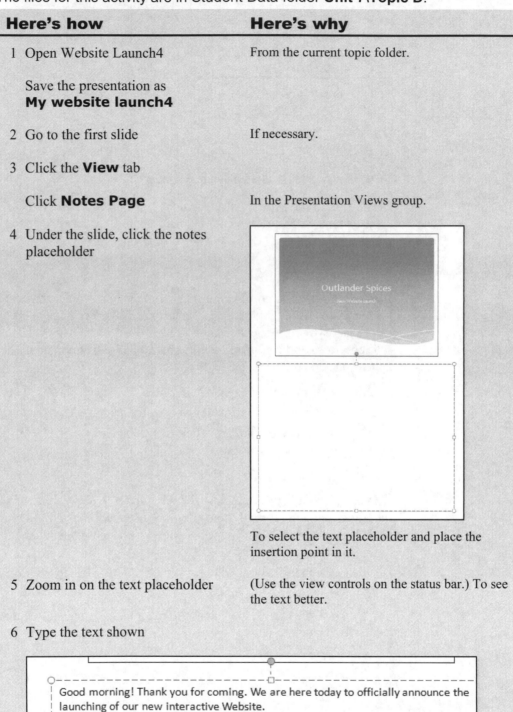

To select the text placeholder and place the insertion point in it.

5 Zoom in on the text placeholder	(Use the view controls on the status bar.) To see the text better.
6 Type the text shown	

Good morning! Thank you for coming. We are here today to officially announce the launching of our new interactive Website.

7	Go to the last slide	(Scroll down.) You'll see a slide titled "GC Transition Team."
	In the text placeholder, type the text shown	

If you're running short on time, you can have students type something shorter.

Kathy Sinclair is heading up the Website Launch Team because we are expecting this venture to generate some good press coverage.

8	Switch to Normal view	Slide 6 is selected.
9	Update the presentation	

Adding headers and footers to notes pages

Explanation

You can add headers and footers to your presentation's notes pages. A header is the text that appears at the top of each page in Notes Page view, and a footer is text that appears at the bottom of each page. You might want to include information such as the project name and company name in headers and footers.

To add headers and footers to notes pages:

Objective 2.4.5

1 On the Insert tab, click Header & Footer to open the Header and Footer dialog box.
2 Click the Notes and Handouts tab, shown in Exhibit 7-7.
3 Check Header.
4 In the Header box, enter the text you want to display in the header.
5 Check Footer.
6 In the Footer box, enter the text you want to display in the footer.
7 Click Apply to All.

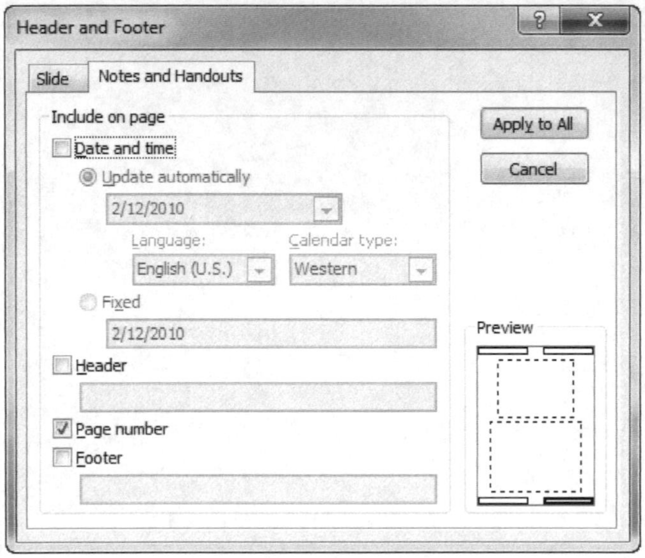

Exhibit 7-7: The Notes and Handouts tab in the Header and Footer dialog box

Do it!

Objective 2.4.5

D-2:   Adding headers and footers to notes pages

Here's how	Here's why
1 Open the Header and Footer dialog box	On the Insert tab, in the Text group, click Header & Footer.
2 Click the **Notes and Handouts** tab	To display the options shown in Exhibit 7-7.
3 Under Include on page, check **Date and Time**	Update automatically is selected, so the current date will always be displayed on the slides.
4 Verify that **Page number** is checked	
5 Check **Header**	To display the header.
Under Header, enter **Website Launch Meeting**	
6 Check **Footer**	To display the footer.
Under Footer, enter **Presentation for Sales Reps**	
7 Click **Apply to All**	To apply the new settings to all notes in the presentation.
8 Display Notes Page view	Click the View tab and click Notes Page.
Fit the slide to the current view	(If necessary.) On the status bar, click the "Fit slide to current window" button.
9 Observe the notes page	You'll see the footer in the lower-left corner of the page and the header in the upper-left corner. The page number is at the bottom of the page, and the date is at the top.
10 Switch to Normal view	
11 Update and close the presentation	

Topic E: Slide shows

This topic covers the following Microsoft Office Specialist exam objectives for PowerPoint 2010.

#	Objective
8.1	**Apply presentation tools**
	8.1.1　Add pen and highlighter annotations
	8.1.2　Change the ink color
	8.1.3　Erase an annotation
	8.1.4　Discard annotations upon closing
	8.1.5　Retain annotations upon closing
8.2	**Set up slide shows**
	8.2.1　Set up a slide show
	8.2.3　Set up Presenter view

Preparing for delivery

Explanation

PowerPoint provides multiple options for running a presentation. You can set up slide shows for different audiences and situations. The presentation might need to be run on a kiosk, at a trade show, or in a location where no one can constantly monitor the slide show. For such situations, you can use the various options in the Set Up Show dialog box.

Slide shows for speakers

Objectives 8.1.1–8.1.5

When creating a presentation to accompany a speech, you can set up the presentation so that the speaker can talk while advancing slides automatically or manually. Whether the presentation advances automatically or manually, the speaker can take control of the presentation to pause it, move to any slide, or even draw on the current slide.

During the presentation, if the presenter moves the mouse, several slide show controls appear in the bottom-left corner of the current slide, as shown in Exhibit 7-8. The presenter can:

- Click the arrow buttons to manually move backward or forward in the presentation.

- Click the Pen icon to display a menu including Pen and Highlighter tools you can use for drawing on slides during a presentation. The menu also includes options for erasing ink you've drawn on the slide, changing the ink color, and switching back to an arrow pointer. When you end the slide show, you can choose to discard or keep your pen markings.

- Click the Menu icon to display options for navigating the slide show.

Exhibit 7-8: Slide show controls

Objective 8.2.1

To set up a slide show for a speaker, click the Slide Show tab. In the Set Up group, click Set Up Slide Show to open the Set Up Show dialog box, shown in Exhibit 7-9. Under Show type, select "Presented by a speaker (full screen)" and other options as needed. For example, under Show options, you can indicate whether you want the presentation to loop continuously, to be presented without any narration recorded with the presentation, and to be presented without animation effects. After specifying options, click OK.

Exhibit 7-9: The Set Up Show dialog box

Presenter view

Objective 8.2.3

Connecting external monitors to computers is beyond the scope of this course.

⚠ *Warn students that they should verify that their computer works with the external monitor and experiment with Presenter view before trying to use it in front of an audience.*

When giving a presentation in front of an audience, you'll often run the presentation on your laptop, and the laptop will also be connected to a projector or a large monitor. This setup will enable you and your audience to see the presentation at the same time.

Connecting your laptop to an external monitor or a projector involves a number of factors. It is recommended that you experiment with the setup at least a day before your scheduled presentation to give yourself time to resolve any problems, read your laptop's instruction manual, or consult your system administrator.

While you're experimenting with the external monitor setup, take some time to familiarize yourself with Presenter view. Using this tool allows your audience to see the presentation on the external monitor while you view your presentation, alongside your speaker notes, on your laptop.

To deliver your presentation in Presenter view:

1 Verify that your laptop (primary monitor) is connected to the desired external monitor (secondary monitor) and that both monitors are displaying your desktop.

2 Open the presentation in PowerPoint 2010.

3 On the Slide Show tab, in the Monitors group, check Use Presenter View. If the external monitor isn't set up correctly, an error message will appear and you'll be prompted to adjust the display settings.

4 In the Set Up group, click Set Up Slide Show to open the Set Up Show dialog box, shown in Exhibit 7-9.

5 Under Multiple monitors, select the monitor on which the audience will view the slide show and check Show Presenter View. Click OK.

6 In the Start Slide Show group, click From Beginning.

The slide show begins for both you and your audience. On your laptop, you will see the slide show, your notes in large type, thumbnails of each slide in your presentation, the slide show tools, and a status bar that displays the slide number, the elapsed time of your presentation, and the current time.

Adjusting the monitor resolution

By default, PowerPoint displays your presentation in the resolution set by Windows 7. If you are showing a large presentation or your computer is running slowly, you can reduce the resolution to increase performance. To do so, display the Resolution list (on the Slide Show tab in the Monitors group), and select the desired resolution, as shown in Exhibit 7-10. The lower the resolution, the faster the presentation will run.

There can be some unexpected consequences, though. Changing the resolution might cause the slide content to shift or cause images to be displayed differently than intended. If this happens, select a higher resolution or the Use Current Resolution option.

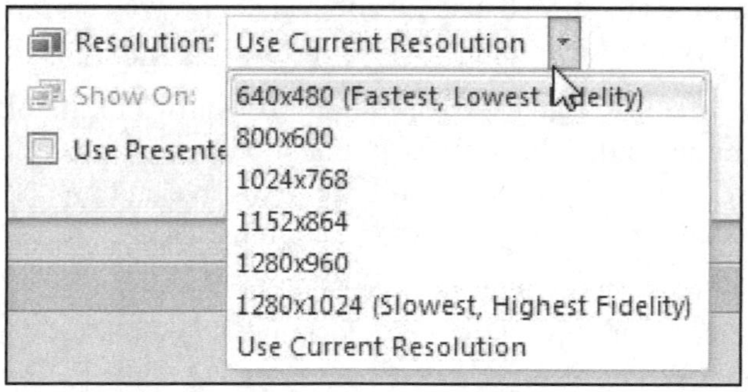

Exhibit 7-10: The Resolution list

Do it!

E-1: Setting up and running a slide show for a speaker

The files for this activity are in Student Data folder **Unit 7\Topic E**.

Here's how	Here's why
1 Open Website Launch5	From the current topic folder.
Save the presentation as **My website launch5**	
2 Display the first slide in Normal view	If necessary.
3 Click the **Slide Show** tab	
In the Set Up group, click **Set Up Slide Show**	To open the Set Up Show dialog box, shown in Exhibit 7-9.
4 Under Show type, verify that **Presented by a speaker (full screen)** is selected	A speaker will present this slide show.
5 Under Show slides, verify that **All** is selected	To show all of the slides. You can also select specific slides to be shown during the slide show.
6 Under Advance slides, select **Manually**	The presenter will manually advance to the next slide.
7 Under Show options, check **Show without narration**	To specify that the slide show will run without including any recorded narration.
Click **OK**	
8 Run the slide show	In Slide Show view.
9 Move the mouse	To display the slide show controls, shown in Exhibit 7-8, in the bottom-left corner of the current slide. The controls are dimmed until you point to them.
10 Click ➡	To move to the next slide.
Click ⬅	To return to the previous slide.
11 Click 🖹	To display the menu.
Choose **Go to Slide**, **4 Projected Online Sales**	To navigate directly to slide 4. You'll use a Pen tool to draw on this slide during the presentation.

Objective 8.2.1

If you have time, you can have students experiment with the pen as well

Objective 8.1.1	12 Click	The Pen icon.
	Choose **Pen**	To select the Pen tool. Your other options include Arrow and Highlighter.
Demonstrate this for students.	13 Drag to draw a circle around the Total value	
Objective 8.1.3	14 Click the **Pen** icon and choose **Erase All Ink on Slide**	To erase the circle you drew.
	15 Click	To display the menu.
	Choose **Go to Slide**, **3 Launch Plan**	To navigate to slide 3.
	16 Click the **Pen** icon and choose **Highlighter**	To select the Highlighter tool.
Objective 8.1.1	17 Drag across the last bulleted item on the slide, as shown	
		To add a yellow highlight.
	18 Click the **Pen** icon and choose **Arrow**	To return to the arrow pointer.
	19 Press ESC	To return to Normal view. An alert box asks you whether you want to keep your ink annotations for the next time you run the slide show.
Objective 8.1.4	Click **Discard**	To remove the highlight you added.
	20 Update the presentation	

Slide shows for kiosks

Explanation

To customize slide shows to run on a kiosk or for a situation such as a convention, you can use the Set Up Show dialog box. While setting up a slide show for a kiosk or booth, you need to consider several things. Will a person be there to monitor the kiosk or booth? Will you use transition effects in the presentation? Should the user be given control of the slide show?

To set up a slide show for a kiosk:

Objective 8.2.1

1 Open the Set Up Show dialog box.

2 Under Show type, select the "Browsed at a kiosk (full screen)" option.

3 Under Show slides, select the range of slides you want to include in the slide show.

4 Under Advance slides, select the options you want for controlling the pace of the presentation.

5 Click OK.

Do it!

Objective 8.2.1

E-2: Setting up a slide show for a kiosk

Here's how	Here's why
1 Go to the first slide	If necessary.
2 Open the Set Up Show dialog box	On the Slide Show tab, click Set Up Slide Show.
3 Under Show type, select **Browsed at a kiosk (full screen)**	Under Show options, the "Loop continuously until 'Esc'" option is checked and is no longer available. The slide show will loop continuously until the Esc button is pressed.
4 Under Advance slides, select **Using timings, if present**	The time settings used in the slide transitions will be used to advance slides.
5 Click **OK**	To accept the changes and close the dialog box.
6 Run the presentation	(In Slide Show view, from the first slide.) After the presentation runs through once, the first slide appears again after the last slide. In addition, moving the mouse does not display the slide show controls that appeared for the speaker presentation.
Press (ESC)	To stop the slide show, or it will run continuously.
7 Update and close the presentation	

Tell students to run the entire presentation and notice that the first slide appears again after the last slide.

Unit summary: Modifying presentations

Topic A   In this topic, you created a presentation based on a **template**. Then you applied a new **design theme** to quickly change the look and feel of the presentation.

Topic B   In this topic, you examined the elements of a **slide master**, changed the default font, modified the default bullets, and applied the changes to your presentation. Next, you inserted a new slide master and learned how to apply multiple slide masters to a presentation.

Topic C   In this topic, you set **transitions** for individual slides and for the entire presentation. Then you added **timings** to a slide show. Finally, you used the Rehearse timings feature to create custom timing for your presentation.

Topic D   In this topic, you added **speaker notes** to individual slides. You also added headers and footers to notes pages.

Topic E   In this topic, you set up a **slide show** for a speaker. Then you set up a slide show for a kiosk.

Independent practice activity

In this activity, you'll apply a new design theme to your presentation, change defaults in Slide Master view, insert a new slide master, and apply it. Then you'll add transition effects, automatic timings, and speaker notes to your presentation. Next, you'll add a footer, set up the slide show for a kiosk, and run the presentation.

The files for this activity are in Student Data folder **Unit 7\Unit summary**.

1 Open Progress to date.

2 Save the presentation as **My progress to date**.

3 Apply a design theme of your choice.

4 On the slide master, change the font of the Master Title placeholder to Arial Black.

5 Change the font of the Master Object placeholder to Arial Narrow.

6 Change the first-level bullet style to a style of your choice.

7 Update the presentation.

8 Add transition effects and automatic timings to all of the slides.

9 Add the speaker note **Mention a few things regarding the final point** to slide 2.

10 Add the footer **Outlander Spices** to the entire presentation. (*Hint:* Use the Text group on the Insert tab.)

11 Set up the slide show for a kiosk, using automatic timings. (*Hint:* Use the Set Up group on the Slide Show tab.)

12 Run the presentation.

13 Update and close the presentation.

Review questions

1 True or false? Templates contain themes, slide masters, and title masters that provide a consistent format for a presentation.

   True

2 List the steps you use to create a presentation based on a template.

   a *Click the File tab and click New.*

   b *Click Sample templates to access the templates stored on your computer, or navigate through the folders under Office.com Templates.*

   c *If you selected a template stored on your computer, click Create. If you selected a template from Office.com, click Download.*

3 How can you apply a theme to an entire presentation or to selected slides?

   Click the Design tab, display the Themes gallery, and click a theme to apply it to the entire presentation. To apply a theme to only selected slides, select the slides; then right-click a theme and choose Apply to Selected Slides.

4 How do you display the slide master?

   Click the View tab and click Slide Master.

5 How can you change the default format settings on the slide master?

   Display Slide Master view, select the placeholder or text, and then change the formatting.

6 What are transitions?

   Transitions are special effects that appear during a slide show when it moves from one slide to another.

7 What happens when you apply timings to a presentation?

   When you run the slide show, it will automatically advance from one slide to the next until the presentation is complete. Each slide appears for the specified amount of time.

8 List the steps to set up a slide show to run as a kiosk.

   a *On the Slide Show tab, click Set Up Slide Show to open the Set Up Show dialog box.*

   b *Select "Browsed at a kiosk (full screen)."*

   c *Select the range of slides you want to include in the slide show.*

   d *Select the options you want for controlling the pace of the presentation.*

   e *Click OK.*

Unit 8

Proofing and delivering presentations

Unit time: 45 minutes

Complete this unit, and you'll know how to:

A Proof a presentation by using the Spell Check and AutoCorrect features, and use the Thesaurus.

B Preview and run a presentation, and hide selected slides to customize a presentation for a specific audience.

C Print an entire presentation, a range of slides, an individual slide, handouts, notes pages, and the outline.

Topic A: Proofing presentations

This topic covers the following Microsoft Office Specialist exam objectives for PowerPoint 2010.

#	Objective
1.4	**Configure PowerPoint file options**
	1.4.1 Use PowerPoint Proofing
6.2	**Apply proofing tools**
	6.2.1 Use Spelling and Thesaurus features

Working with Spelling, AutoCorrect, and Thesaurus

Explanation

After you finish creating a presentation, you need to ensure that it does not contain any mistakes. You do this by using the proofing tools, such as the spelling checker. You can also use AutoCorrect to correct common mistakes and style inconsistencies as you type. And you can use the Thesaurus to look up a word's synonyms.

Correcting misspelled words

Objective 6.2.1

When you misspell a word, it will be underlined in red by default. You can correct the spelling by using the Spelling dialog box, shown in Exhibit 8-1, or by right-clicking the misspelled word to display a shortcut menu and choosing the correct word.

To open the Spelling dialog box, click the Review tab, and in the Proofing group, click Spelling. You can also press F7. You can check spelling in Normal and Slide Sorter views.

Exhibit 8-1: The Spelling dialog box

Do it!

A-1: Checking the spelling in a presentation

The files for this activity are in Student Data folder **Unit 8\Topic A**.

Objective 6.2.1

Here's how	Here's why
1 Open New product kickoff meeting1	
Save the presentation as **My new product kickoff meeting1**	

Tell students they will be using three methods to start the spelling checker in this activity.

2 Click the **Review** tab

   In the Proofing group, click **Spelling** — To open the Spelling dialog box.

3 Observe the application window — You'll see the fourth slide. This is the first slide with incorrect spelling. The incorrectly spelled words are underlined in red, and the first incorrectly spelled word is highlighted.

   Observe the Spelling dialog box — It contains options to correct the spelling, as shown in Exhibit 8-1.

4 Click **Change** — In the Spelling dialog box. The misspelled word "Asembled" changes to "Assembled." Now, the text "mangement" is selected.

5 Click **Change** — To enter the correct spelling of "management." The next word, "Prelimnary," is selected.

   Click **Change** — To correct the spelling to "Preliminary."

   Click **Close** — To close the dialog box. You'll use a different technique to correct the next misspelled word.

6 On the fifth slide, right-click **Devloping** and choose **Developing**

   To correct the misspelled word.

7 Press ⟨F7⟩ — To open the Spelling dialog box. You'll continue to check the spelling. The misspelled word "kickof" is selected.

   Click **Change** — To correct the spelling of "Kickoff." A message box states that the spelling check is complete.

   Click **OK**

8 Deselect the text

9 Update the presentation

The AutoCorrect feature

Explanation

AutoCorrect automatically corrects any typing mistakes that you make, as long as the mistakes are included in the AutoCorrect list. You can use the AutoCorrect dialog box, shown in Exhibit 8-2, to add any words that you frequently misspell.

Objective 1.4.1

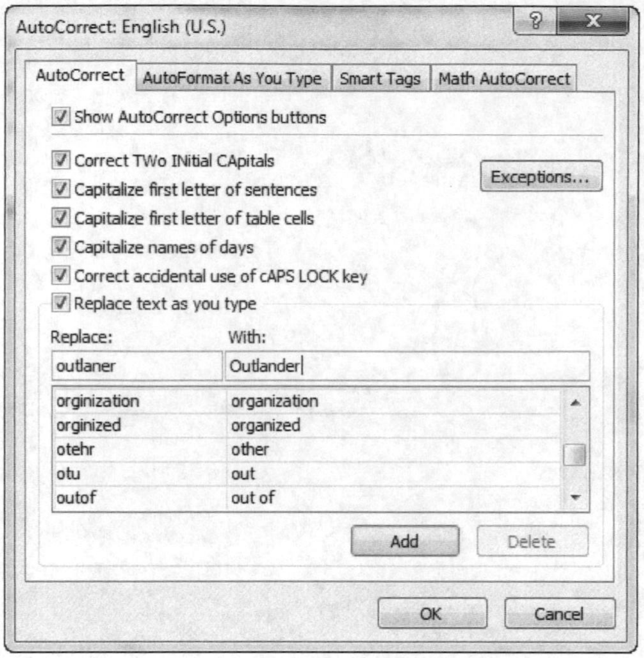

Exhibit 8-2: The AutoCorrect: English (U.S.) dialog box

Do it!

A-2:   Using AutoCorrect

Here's how	Here's why
1 Click the **File** tab	To display Backstage view.
At the bottom of the left pane, click **Options**	To open the PowerPoint Options dialog box.
2 In the left pane, click **Proofing**	To display the proofing options in the right pane.
Under AutoCorrect options, click **AutoCorrect Options**	To open the AutoCorrect dialog box.
3 Observe the dialog box	The insertion point appears in the Replace box. By default, all of the checkboxes are checked.
4 In the Replace box, enter **outlaner**	To specify a word you often mistype.
In the With box, enter **Outlander**	To specify the correct word, as shown in Exhibit 8-2.
Click **Add**	To add the word to the AutoCorrect list.
5 Click **OK**	To close the AutoCorrect dialog box.
6 Click **OK**	To close the PowerPoint Options dialog box.
7 Place the insertion point after **event**	(The last word in the fifth bullet on slide 5.) To add text here.
Press (↵ ENTER)	
8 Type **outlaner**	
Press (SPACEBAR)	The incorrect spelling is immediately corrected.
Type **Spices' new cookbook**	To complete the bullet item.
9 Update the presentation	

Ask students to scroll through the list.

Tell students they need to click the With box so the insertion point appears.

The Thesaurus

Explanation

Objective 6.2.1

If you find yourself looking for just the right word to use or you want to know the general meaning of a word, you can use the Thesaurus feature. On the Review tab, in the Proofing group, click Thesaurus to open the Research pane with a list of synonyms. By reading through the list, you can get a general sense of the meaning of the word. You can also use one of the synonyms to replace the selected word.

Do it!

Objective 6.2.1

A-3: Using the Thesaurus

Make sure students select the word only, not the space after it.

TIPS *Tell students they can also press Shift+F7.*

Here's how	Here's why
1 Go to the second slide	
2 Drag to select the word **inventory**	You'll replace this word with its synonym. Make sure you don't select the space after the word.
3 Click **Thesaurus**	(In the Proofing group.) To display the Research task pane.
4 Click as shown	Point to "stock" to display the arrow; then click the arrow.
Choose **Insert**	The word "inventory" is replaced by "stock."
5 Close the task pane	Click the Close button.
6 Update and close the presentation	

Topic B: Running presentations

Explanation

After a presentation is complete, you are ready to show it to your audience. Before you do so, however, it's a good idea to preview it to ensure that the slide order is correct and that you want to include all of the slides for this particular audience.

Previewing and running presentations in Slide Show view

In Slide Sorter view, you can typically see the entire presentation at once to get a rough preview. In Slide Show view, there are five techniques you can use to run the presentation, and the following table describes them.

Item	Description
From Beginning button	Plays the slide show starting with the first slide, no matter what slide is selected. This button is in the Start Slide Show group on the Slide Show tab.
From Current Slide button	Plays the slide show starting with the selected slide, not from the first slide. This is in the Start Slide Show group on the Slide Show tab.
Slide Show button	Plays the slide show starting with the selected slide, not from the first slide. This button is in the status bar.
F5 key	Plays the slide show starting with the first slide, no matter what slide is selected.

Reading view

When you need to preview a presentation, another option is to use PowerPoint's new Reading view. Slide Show view is intended to be used with a projector or a large screen and with an entire audience watching. Sometimes, though, a presentation needs to be viewed by an audience of one or by multiple people all watching it on their own computers. In this instance, Reading view is a better option.

To display a presentation in Reading view:

- To start the presentation at the current slide, click the Reading View button on the status bar.

- To start the slide show on the first slide, click the Reading View button on the View tab.

Reading view acts just like Slide Show view, but it also displays the PowerPoint status bar, with simple controls on it, and the Windows taskbar, as shown in Exhibit 8-3.

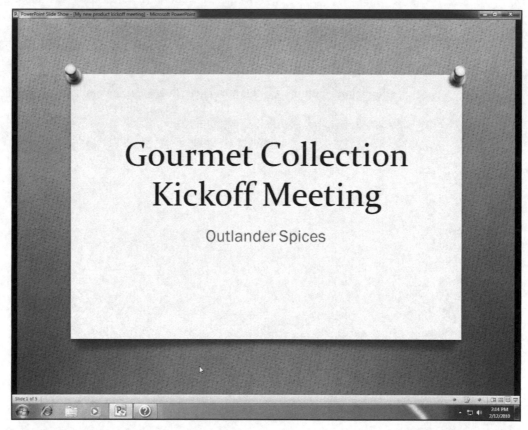

Exhibit 8-3: Reading View

Do it!

B-1:   Previewing and running a presentation

The files for this activity are in Student Data folder **Unit 8\Topic B**.

Here's how	Here's why
1 Open New product kickoff meeting2	In the current topic folder.
Save the presentation as **My new product kickoff meeting2**	
2 Switch to Slide Sorter view	If necessary.
3 Select the fourth slide	
4 Click 🖵	To switch to Slide Show view. The slide show begins from the fourth slide.
5 Move through the slides until you reach the end of the presentation Press (ESC)	
6 Observe the window	The presentation is in Slide Sorter view, and the fifth slide is selected.
7 Click 📖	(On the status bar.) To switch to Reading view. The slide show begins from the current slide (the fifth slide).
8 On the status bar, click the **Previous** icon	 To view the fourth slide.
9 Click **Previous** again	To view the third slide.

Tell students that they can press Ctrl and click, or press Page Up, to view a previous slide.

10 On the status bar, click the **Menu** icon, as shown

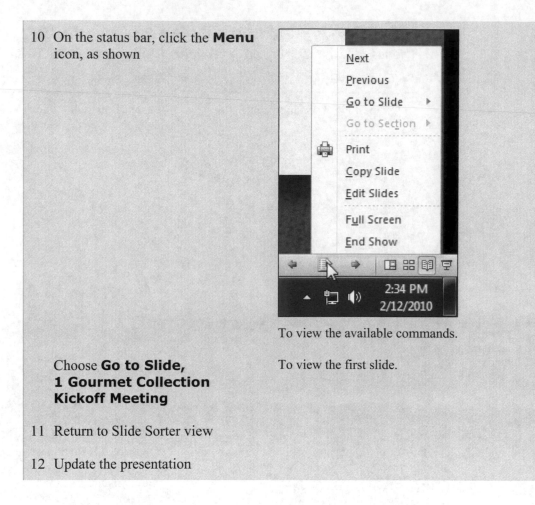

To view the available commands.

Choose **Go to Slide, 1 Gourmet Collection Kickoff Meeting**

To view the first slide.

11 Return to Slide Sorter view

12 Update the presentation

Hiding and unhiding slides

Explanation

When you create a presentation, you might want to use it for more than one audience. In that case, you might want to include some slides for one audience that are not included for another audience. You can hide individual slides so they aren't displayed in Slide Show or Reading view.

To hide a slide, select it and click the Slide Show tab. Then, in the Set Up group, click Hide Slide. The Hide Slide button works as a toggle. When you want to show a hidden slide again, you select that slide and click Hide Slide. Hidden slides remain visible in both Normal and Slide Sorter views but won't appear during a slide show.

Do it!

B-2: Hiding and unhiding a slide

Here's how	Here's why
1 Select the last slide	(In Slide Sorter view.) You'll hide this slide.
2 Click the **Slide Show** tab	
In the Set Up group, click **Hide Slide**	
3 Observe the slide	

Outstanding issues

◊ Building new Web site
◊ Identifying new markets
◊ Developing a production schedule
◊ Sales rollout plan
◊ Schedule kickoff event
◊ Outlander Spices' new cookbook

A box appears around the slide number, and a diagonal line appears over the slide number.

4 Select the first slide	
5 Run the presentation	In Slide Show view.
Move through the presentation	The "Outstanding issues" slide does not appear in the slide show.
6 Select the fifth slide	
Click **Hide Slide**	To unhide the slide.
7 Update and close the presentation	

If time allows, have students repeat this step in Reading view.

Topic C: Printing presentations

This topic covers the following Microsoft Office Specialist exam objectives for PowerPoint 2010.

#	Objective
2.2	**Apply slide size and orientation settings**
	2.2.1 Set up a custom size
	2.2.2 Change the orientation
7.3	**Print a presentation**
	7.3.1 Adjust print settings

Previewing slides in black and white

Explanation

Objective 7.3.1

By default, PowerPoint creates presentations in color. If you want to print the presentation in black and white, you might want to preview it to ensure that the colors have appropriate contrast when converted to black and white.

To preview a presentation in black and white, click the View tab and click Pure Black and White. To preview a presentation in gray, click Grayscale.

Do it!

Objective 7.3.1

C-1: Previewing a presentation in black and white

The files for this activity are in Student Data folder **Unit 8\Topic C**.

Here's how	Here's why
1 Open New product kickoff meeting3	
Save the presentation as **My new product kickoff meeting3**	
2 Switch to Normal view	If necessary.
Click the **View** tab	
3 Click **Black and White**	In the Color/Grayscale group.
4 Observe the slides	All colors have changed to black and white.
Observe the Ribbon	The Black And White tab is selected and it contains two groups. The Change Selected Object group has 10 options, and White is selected.
5 Click **Grayscale**	(In the Change Selected group.) The background is now visible on the slides.
Experiment with the options in the Change Selected Object group	Click each button to observe its effects on the slides.
6 Click **Back To Color View**	(In the Close group.) To display the slides in color.
7 Update the presentation	

Tell students they can double-click a slide in Slide Sorter view to display it in Normal view.

Changing the page setup

Explanation

You can print slides in a variety of formats, but the presentation's page setup determines the size and orientation of the printed output. In PowerPoint, *size* refers to the size of the slide on a printed page, and *orientation* refers to whether the pages are set up as portrait (tall) or landscape (wide). The default settings for any new presentation are for an on-screen slide show with landscape orientation. The slide numbering begins with 1. Handouts, outlines, and notes print in portrait orientation by default. You can change these settings.

Objectives 2.2.1, 2.2.2

To change the page setup for slides:

1 Click the Design tab.

2 In the Page Setup group, click Page Setup to open the Page Setup dialog box.

3 From the "Slides sized for" list, select the desired format.

4 Select an orientation (Portrait or Landscape) for the slides and the other components of the presentation.

5 Click OK.

You can change the orientation by clicking Slide Orientation in the Page Setup group and choosing Portrait or Landscape.

Slide size format options

The following table describes some of the size format options in the Page Setup dialog box.

Format	Description
On-screen Show (4:3)	The default setting; used when designing a presentation that will be shown on screen. The slides are sized smaller than a standard sheet of paper. The "4:3" refers to the aspect ratio of your monitor; this is the standard ratio for older monitors and TV sets.
On-screen Show (16:9)	Used when designing a presentation that will be shown on a screen that uses the 16:9 standard (the international standard format of HDTV and most wide-screen TVs).
On-screen Show (16:10)	Used when designing a presentation that will be shown on a screen that uses the 16:10 standard. (This aspect ratio is appropriate for displaying two full pages of text side by side.)
Letter Paper (8.5×11 in)	Prints the presentation on standard U.S. letter stock (8.5" × 11").
Ledger Paper (11×17 in)	Prints the presentation on standard U.S. ledger stock (11" × 17").
A3 Paper (297×420 mm)	Prints the presentation on an international letter stock (297 mm × 420 mm).
A4 Paper (210×297 mm)	Prints the presentation on an international letter stock (210 mm × 297 mm).
B4 (ISO) Paper (250×353 mm)	Prints the presentation on an international letter stock (250 mm × 353 mm).
B5 (ISO) Paper (176×250 mm)	Prints the presentation on an international letter stock (176 mm × 250 mm).
35mm Slides	Adapts the presentation for 35mm slides. (This setting is smaller than the default setting.)
Overhead	Prints your slides on overhead transparency stock (8.5" × 11").
Banner	Adjusts the slide size to create an 8" × 1" banner when printed.
Custom	Used to accommodate special sizing needs.

Objective 2.2.1

C-2: Modifying the page setup

Here's how	Here's why
1 Click the **Design** tab	
2 In the Page Setup group, click **Slide Orientation**	To display the menu.
Choose **Portrait**	To change the page orientation.
3 Click **Slide Orientation** and choose **Landscape**	To return the page orientation to its default setting.
4 In the Page Setup group, click **Page Setup**	To open the Page Setup dialog box.
5 From the "Slides sized for" list, select **On-screen Show (16:9)**	
6 Under Slides, select **Portrait**	Notice that the width and height boxes change automatically.
7 Verify that the "Number slides from" box reads **1**	To apply the page setup from slide 1 onwards.
8 Click **OK**	To close the Page Setup dialog box. The change in page setup is reflected in the slide.
9 Press (CTRL) + (Z)	To undo the last step and restore the default page setup.

Objective 2.2.2 (beside step 3)

Objective 2.2.1 (beside step 5)

Printing presentations

Explanation

Objective 7.3.1

When you click the File tab and then click Print, the print options are displayed, as shown in Exhibit 8-4. You can specify the printer you'll use, the range of slides you'll print, the number of copies, and so on.

If you're using a black-and-white printer to create overhead transparencies, you should preview the slides in black and white before printing. You can then make any necessary adjustments before printing your presentation directly on overhead transparency stock.

Tell students that the Printer name might be different depending on the printer that's connected to their PCs.

Exhibit 8-4: The Print options

C-3: Printing a presentation

Here's how	Here's why
1 Click the **File** tab and then click **Print**	To display the print options, as shown in Exhibit 8-4.
2 Observe the lists under Settings	You'll click the arrow for each list to observe the options.
Display the first list	Use this list to specify whether you're printing all slides, the current slide, or a range of slides. Under this list is the Slides box; use it to specify which slides you want to print.
Display the second list	Use this list to set the Print layout or the Handouts layout. You can also check Frame Slides, Scale to Fit Paper, or High Quality to apply those options.
3 Display the third list	When printing multiple copies of the presentation, use this list to specify whether the pages should be collated.
Display the fourth list	Use this list to print the presentation in Color, Grayscale, or Pure Black and White.
4 Under Settings in the fourth list, select **Grayscale**	The preview on the right changes from color to grayscale.
5 Under the preview, click **Next Page** four times	 To preview each slide.
6 Observe the Copies options	You can print multiple copies of a presentation.
7 Under Printer, click **Printer Properties**	To open the Properties dialog box for your specific printer.
Close the dialog box	

8 Under Settings, click
   Edit Header & Footer

   To open the Header and Footer dialog box. You can edit these settings here.

   Close the dialog box

⚠ Tell students that this step will not work unless students' computers are connected to a printer.

9 Click **Print**

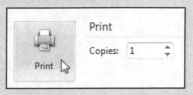

To print the presentation. If your computer isn't connected to a printer, click the Home tab.

10 Update the presentation

Printing individual slides

Explanation

You can also print an individual slide from a presentation. To do so:

Objective 7.3.1

1 Select the slide you want to print.

2 On the File tab, click Print (or press Ctrl+P) to display the print options.

3 Under Settings in the first list, select Print Current Slide.

4 Click Print.

You can also specify the number of copies of that slide that you want to print.

Do it!

C-4: Printing an individual slide

Objective 7.3.1

Here's how	Here's why
1 Select the first slide	If necessary.
2 Display the print options	Press Ctrl+P.
3 Under Settings in the first list, select **Print Current Slide**	You'll print only the first slide.
4 Under the preview, click **Next Page**	You can't because only one slide is selected to print.
5 Click **Print**	To print the slide. If your computer isn't connected to a printer, click the Home tab.
6 Update the presentation	

Print output options

Explanation

Objective 7.3.1

PowerPoint provides various print output options. You can print slides, handouts, speaker notes, or a presentation outline.

Audience handouts

When printing handouts for your presentation, you can print them with one, two, three, four, six, or nine slides per page. When you're deciding how many slides to include per page, consider the readability of the handout. If you include too many slides with text, the handouts might be difficult for your audience to read.

To print audience handouts:

1 Click the File tab and click Print to display the print options.
2 Under Settings in the second list, select one of the handout layouts.
3 (Optional) In the Slides box, enter the desired slide range. For example, you can print the speaker notes for slides 1, 2, 3, 4, and 7 by entering "1–4, 7".
4 Click Print.

Speaker notes

You can print speaker notes for your presentation as well. Each page of speaker notes includes a small version of the associated slide. This will help you keep track of your progress as you deliver your presentation.

To print speaker notes:

1 On the File tab, click Print.
2 Under Settings in the second list, select Notes Pages.
3 (Optional) In the Slides box, enter the desired slide range.
4 Click Print.

Outlines

If you want to print the text from your presentation slides, you can print Outline view; this setting prints the text shown on the Outline tab in Normal view. To do so, press Ctrl | P to display the print options. Under Settings in the second list, select Outline, and then click Print.

C-5: Printing handouts, notes, and the outline

Here's how	Here's why
1 Display the print options	Press Ctrl+P.
2 Under Settings in the first list, select **Print All Slides**	If necessary.
3 Under Settings in the second list, select **6 Slides Horizontal**	To specify that you want to use this layout to print audience handouts of the slides.
Observe the preview	All five slides fit on one page.
4 Under Settings in the second list, select **3 Slides**	To change the handout layout.
Observe the preview	Using this layout, the presentation fits onto two pages. The first page contains three slides, and there are lines for notes to the right of the slides.
5 Under Settings in the second list, select **Notes Pages**	To change from the 3 Slides handout layout to Notes Pages.
Observe the preview	Under the preview, click the Next Page button four times to view each slide.
6 Under Settings in the second list, select **Outline**	To change from Notes Pages to a one-page outline of the entire presentation.
Observe the preview	This is the same layout that is displayed on the Outline tab in Normal view.
7 Click **Print**	To print the outline view. If your computer isn't connected to a printer, click the Home tab.
8 Update and close the presentation	

Unit summary: Proofing and delivering presentations

Topic A   In this topic, you corrected **spelling mistakes** by using the Spell Check feature. Then you customized the AutoCorrect feature. Finally, you used the Thesaurus to replace a word with a synonym.

Topic B   In this topic, you previewed and ran the presentation in **Slide Show view** and **Reading view**. Next, you hid and unhid slides.

Topic C   In this topic, you previewed a presentation in **black and white** and modified the **page setup**. Finally, you learned how to **print** an entire presentation, individual slides, handouts, notes, and the outline.

Independent practice activity

In this activity, you'll check a presentation for spelling mistakes, run the presentation in Slide Show view, and print the slides.

The files for this activity are in Student Data folder **Unit 8\Unit summary**.

1 Open Products.

2 Save the presentation as **My products**.

3 Check the spelling of the entire presentation. (*Hint:* Use the Review tab.)

4 Run the presentation (starting from the first slide) in Reading view.

5 Print the presentation if your computer is connected to a printer. If you don't have access to a printer, view the slides in Print Preview.

6 Print the presentation as a color handout with two slides per page if your computer is connected to a printer. If you don't have access to a printer, preview the handouts and return to the Home tab.

7 Update and close the presentation.

8 Close PowerPoint.

Review questions

1 True or false? When you misspell a word, it will be underlined in green by default.

False; it will have red underlining.

2 Select the correct methods for correcting a spelling mistake. (Choose all that apply.)

A Use the Spelling dialog box.

B Right-click anywhere on the slide and choose the correct word.

C Use the Spelling and Grammar dialog box.

D Right-click the misspelled word and choose the correct word.

3 What does the AutoCorrect feature do?

AutoCorrect automatically corrects any typing mistakes that you make, as long as the mistakes are included in the AutoCorrect list.

4 How do you access the Thesaurus feature?

Select a word; then click the Review tab and click Thesaurus to open the Research pane with a list of synonyms.

5 True or false? When you click the Slide Show button in the status bar, the slide show always starts at the first slide.

False

6 True or false? When you click the Slide Show button on the View tab, the slide show always starts at the selected slide, not the first slide.

False

7 True or false? When you press F5 the slide show starts at the selected slide, not the first slide.

False

8 List the steps you perform to hide a slide.

Select the slide and click the Slide Show tab. In the Set Up group, click Hide Slide.

9 List the steps you perform to print audience handouts.

a Click the File tab and then click Print.

b Under Settings in the second list, select one of the nine handout layouts.

c Click Print .

Course summary

This summary contains information to help you bring the course to a successful conclusion. Using this information, you will be able to:

A Use the summary text to reinforce what students have learned in class.

B Direct students to the next courses in this series (if any), and to any other resources that might help students continue to learn about PowerPoint 2010.

Topic A: Course summary

At the end of the class, use the following summary text to reinforce what students have learned. It is intended not as a script, but rather as a starting point.

Unit summaries

Unit 1

In this unit, students opened a presentation and viewed it as a **slide show**. Then they examined the **PowerPoint environment** and switched among Normal, Slide Sorter, Reading, and Slide Show views. Next, students adjusted magnification in Normal view and used **PowerPoint Help**.

Unit 2

In this unit, students **created** a presentation, added slides, entered text, and edited the text. They **saved** a presentation, updated it, and saved it in a new location. They **moved slides** in both Normal view and Slide Sorter view. Next, they **deleted slides**. Finally, students **inserted slides** from another presentation into the current presentation.

Unit 3

In this unit, students applied **character formatting** to selected text and used the **Format Painter** to copy the formatting. Then, they changed bullet styles and created a numbered **list**. Students also searched for and replaced specific text, and learned how to move and copy text. They used the **Clipboard pane** to copy and paste multiple items. Finally, students applied **paragraph formatting**.

Unit 4

In this unit, students used **drawing tools** to create basic shapes and formatted selected objects. Next, students duplicated, deleted, and moved objects. Then, students resized, rotated, and aligned objects. And finally, students added text to an object, modified text in an object, and worked with text boxes.

Unit 5

In this unit, students added a **WordArt object** to a slide and then modified it by applying different styles. Next, they inserted a **picture** file. They modified the picture and grouped images together. Finally, students inserted and modified a **clip art** image.

Unit 6

In this unit, students added a **table** to a slide, and modified and formatted the table. They also created and modified a **chart**. Next, they added a **SmartArt hierarchy chart** to a slide, formatted it, and added boxes to it.

Unit 7

In this unit, students created a presentation based on a **template** and then changed its appearance by applying a new **design theme**. Next, they examined the elements of a **slide master**, changed the default font and bullets, and applied the changes to the current presentation. Students also inserted a new slide master and applied multiple slide masters to a presentation. Then, they set **transitions** for individual slides and for the entire presentation. Next, they added **timings** to a slide show. Students used the Rehearse Timings feature to create custom timing, added **speaker notes** to individual slides, added footers to slides, and added headers and footers to **notes pages**. Finally, students set up a **slide show** for a speaker and for a kiosk.

Unit 8

In this unit, students **corrected spelling mistakes** by using the Spell Check feature, customized the AutoCorrect feature, and used the Thesaurus to replace a word with a synonym. Then, they previewed and **ran the presentation** in Slide Show view, hid and unhid slides, and previewed a presentation in black and white. They also modified the **page setup**. Finally, they learned how to **print** an entire presentation, individual slides, handouts, and notes.

Topic B: Continued learning after class

Point out to your students that it is impossible to learn how to use any software effectively in a single day. To get the most out of this class, students should begin working with PowerPoint to perform real tasks as soon as possible. We also offer resources for continued learning.

Next courses in this series

This is the first course in this series. The next course in this series is:

- *PowerPoint 2010: Advanced, MOS Edition*
    - Customize PowerPoint
    - Work with clip art, video and audio clips, animations, and photo albums
    - Customize SmartArt graphics, tables, and charts
    - Add action buttons and equations, and create custom slide shows
    - Distribute a presentation
    - Integrate slide content with content from other Office applications

Other resources

For more information, visit www.axzopress.com.

Glossary

AutoCorrect

A feature that automatically corrects typing mistakes you make if the mistakes are included in the AutoCorrect list.

Backstage view

The view displayed when you click the File tab to display options that were previously available on the File menu in older versions of PowerPoint.

Cell

The smallest part of a table. It is defined by the intersection of a row and a column.

Character formatting

Any formatting that you can apply to individual characters (examples are font, font size, and typestyle).

Chart

A graphical representation of numerical data. PowerPoint includes several chart types and various formatting options you can use to modify them.

Clipboard

A temporary storage area that holds the text or object you have cut or copied until you specify where to place it in a document. The Windows Clipboard can hold only one selection at a time and is cleared when you shut down your computer.

Grid

A set of intersecting lines that appear on a slide.

Guide

A pair of horizontal and vertical nonprinting lines that intersect in the middle of the slide but can be moved.

Live Preview

A feature that temporarily applies the setting or format you are pointing to in a list or gallery so you can see what the result will be. For example, moving the pointer over each font in the Font list causes any selected text on the current slide to appear in that font temporarily.

Mini toolbar

A floating palette that appears immediately after you select text on a slide. The Mini toolbar contains some of the formatting options available in the Font and Paragraph groups.

Normal view

The default view, which you'll usually work in as you create slides. It contains two tabs (Slides and Outline) on the left and a Slide pane on the right.

Paragraph formatting

Any formatting that can be applied only to whole paragraphs (examples are text alignment, line spacing, and bulleted and numbered lists).

Quick Access toolbar

A toolbar that contains icons for frequently used commands (by default, Save, Undo, and Repeat/Redo). Can be customized to include the commands you specify.

Reading view

A new view in PowerPoint 2010 that provides a full-screen view of your presentation, as in Slide Show view, but with the PowerPoint status bar and the Windows taskbar still visible.

Ribbon

A panel that contains PowerPoint's primary tools and commands, divided among tabs named File, Home, Insert, Design, Transitions, Animations, Slide Show, Review, and View, as well as several contextual tabs.

Slide Show view

Provides a full-screen view of your presentation. Any special effects you add, such as transitions and timings, are visible during the slide show.

Slide Sorter view

Provides a miniature view of all slides in a presentation. You can change the order of slides in this view.

Transitions

Special effects that appear during a slide show when it moves from one slide to another. You can specify a single transition for the entire presentation, or specify individual transitions for each slide.

Index